A CHARLTON STANDARD CAT

WADE WHIMSICAL COLLECTABLES

SEVENTH EDITION

By

PAT MURRAY

PUBLISHER

W. K. CROSS

The Charlton Press

TORONTO, ONTARIO • PALM HARBOR, FLORIDA

PRODUCTION

Editor	Jean Dale
Graphic Technician	Davina Rowan
Colour Technician	Marina Tsourkis
Photography	Gordon Murray
Cover Illustration	Betty Boop

ACKNOWLEDGMENTS

The Charlton Press wishes to thank those who have assisted with the seventh edition of the *Wade Whimsical Collectables* – A Charlton Standard Catalogue.

Special Thanks

To my husband Gordon for his help and encouragement, and his time devoted to taking thousands of photographs for the Charlton Library of Wade Catalogues.

Also to the George Wade Pottery and staff for providing information on the manufacture of Wade porcelain. Many thanks to The Official International Wade Collectors Club, and to Jenny Wright the Club Manager.

Contributors to the Seventh Edition

The Publisher and the Author would like to thank the following collectors and dealers for their assistance in supplying photographs, measurements, and backstamp details:

Mary Ashby and Alan Clark, U.K.; Helen Barker, UK; Alice Bedlington, Australia; Elizabeth Bowden, UK; Gerry Bullock, USA; Lisa Burlingham, USA; Craig Burns, New Zealand; Sue Burt, UK; C&S Collectables Direct (David Chown and Russell Schooley); John Commons, UK; Tess Contois, USA; Father David Cox, USA; Ellen Dart, UK; Joyce and David Divelbiss, USA; Terry Dove, UK; Steve and Heather Dubblue, USA; May Eden, USA; Sandy Elphick, UK; Catherine Evans, UK; Chris Fogden, USA; Val Freeman, UK; Jean-Pierre Gauthier, New Zealand; Yvette Godstone, USA; Gerry Gordner, USA; May Graham, USA; Betty and Dennis Hannigan, USA; Liz Harper, UK; Vince Harvey, UK; David Hawkes, UK; Jean and Rachel Higham, UK; Sue Horbury, USA; Howard Houk, USA; Jane Hucknell, UK; Ian Humphries, UK; Scott and Janet Ickles, USA; Andrew Key (Key Kollectables), UK; Jolene Jackson, USA; Linda Jannis, USA; Caroline Jarvis, UK; Linda Jessop, UK; Peg and Fred Johnson, USA; Dennis Johnston and family, USA; Trudi Kane, USA; Pat and Gerry Keenan, USA; Esther and Gene Kramer, USA; Dave Lee, author of the Wade Dynasty, UK; Wendy and Derek Lucas, Australia; Linda Lyon, UK; Jim Lyttle, N. Ireland; Barbara Mabey, Canada; JoAnne and Don Mandryk, Canada; Mary Marquez, USA; Chris Martin, USA; Reva and Michael Matthews, USA; James McCraig, UK; Sherry McGill, USA; Karen McKenna, UK; Ed and Kathy Morgan, USA; Judi and Brian Morris, USA; Rose Muniz, USA; Tony Murphy, UK; Daniel Murray, Canada; Sydney Jaques, Canada; Jan and Gene Myszkowski, USA; Molly and Peter Newman, USA; Michael and Sue Norton, UK; Alan O'Flaherty, Ireland; Patty O'Meara, USA; Sarah, Teresa and Santos Perez, USA; Joanne Postlethwaite, UK; Dan Reddan, USA; Margaret Remihana, New Zealand; Ginny Reynolds, USA; David Rigg, Redco Foods, USA; Janet and Brian Robertson, New Zealand; Bob and Marge Rolls, USA Ed and Beverly Rucker, USA; Diane Self, USA; Judy Shoper, USA; Caroline Smith, USA; Ed and Nancy Smoller, USA; Evette Stables, UK; Saxon Stoof, Canada; Steven Swales, UK; Sue Swan, UK; Sheila Swetland, USA; Michelle Tenty, UK; Charly Thornkins, Canada; Fay Thompson, Canada; Derek, Kim and Del Watson, UK; Sandra and Bob Wright, USA; Mary and Steve Yager, USA

And many thanks to all those who have helped with information and photographs for this book and preferred to remain anonymous.

A SPECIAL NOTE TO COLLECTORS

We welcome and appreciate any comments or suggestions in regard to the Wade Whimsical Collectables. If you would like to participate in pricing, please contact Jean Dale at the Charlton Press. To provide new information or corrections, please write to Pat Murray, 1944 Innisfil Beach Road, Innisfil, Ontario L9S 4B9, Canada.

The Charlton Press

Editorial Office
P.O. Box 820, Station Willowdale B
North York, Ontario M2K 2R1, Canada
Telephone: (416) 488-1418   Fax: (416) 488-4656
Telephone: (800) 442-6042   Fax: (800) 442-1542
www.charltonpress.com   e-mail: chpress@charltonpress.com

PRICING AND THE INTERNET

Over the past thirty years we have gathered pricing information from auctions, dealer submissions, direct mail catalogues and newsletters, all contributed prices on one of two levels, wholesale or retail. We at the Charlton Press consider auctions basically a dealer affair, while price lists, naturally retail. To equate both prices, we needed to adjust the auction results upward, by a margin of 30% to 40%, allowing for dealer markups, before comparing and looking for a consensus on a retail price.

The marketplace has changed, the Internet and on-line auctions are growing at such a rate that all other pricing sources we used are being completely overwhelmed by the sheer weight of the items being offered.

Below is a table to illustrate this growth. On the left under categories is a list of English brands that have produced collectables for the past hundred years. Across the top from left to right are four dates starting with January 4, 2001 and ending with December 9, 2003, below each date is the number of items offered for sale at that instant on a major Internet on-line auction.

Items for sale at a point in time from 2001 to 2003.

Category	Jan. 4th 2001	Jan. 4th 2002	Jan. 4th 2003	Dec. 9th 2003
Wade	3,150	3,450	4,250	5,500
Beswick	600	1,000	1,400	1,950
Coalport	300	525	800	1,450
Moorcroft	250	300	400	525
Royal Doulton	3,500	3,700	5,700	8,200
Royal Worcester	600	800	1,150	1,850
Total items	**8,400**	**9,775**	**13,700**	**19,475**

At that moment in time during December 9, 2003, under the Wade category 5,500 individual items were up for sale. For the six brands the total approached 19,500 items.

Comparing the totals of 8,400 for January 2001 with 19,475 for December 2003 we are witnessing a growth of more than 130% in the four-year period, carrying the calculations forward to a yearly level, we first, must assume that items are added at a rate equal to the number expiring. The assumption does have flaws, for all days are not equal, due to ebb and flow of the items. However, assuming all is equal, Wade over a period of a year had 2,007,500 items listed (5,500 x 365) an extremely large number when equated to the Land Auctions that may not exceed 10% of that number for all auction categories.

The impact the Internet will have on collectables has yet to be appreciated by collectors and dealers alike. All the old avenues such as fairs, shows, dealer stores, retail outlets, direct mail houses and auction rooms are being forced to change due to the extreme pressure of this marketing venue. Margins have come under pressure, wholesale and retail prices are starting to blend, and competition for the Collectors' budget will intensify. However, through it all one point remains, a price guide is just that, a guide, the final say is between the buyer and the seller.

CONTENTS

**Printed in Canada
in the Province of Ontario**

HOW TO USE THIS CATALOGUE

THE PURPOSE

As with the other catalogues in Charlton's Wade reference and pricing library, this publication has been designed to serve two specific purposes: first to furnish the collectors with accurate and detailed listings that will provide the essential information needed to build a rich and rewarding collection; second, to provide collectors and dealers with an indication of the current market prices on Wade Whimsical Collectables.

THE LISTINGS

This guide is divided into three main sections. The first section includes models produced for and by the Wade product line (for example *Wade Whimsies*), which are listed alphabetically. The second section focuses on models produced for fairs, events, and membership exclusives, and is listed chronologically. The third section includes models produced by Wade under commission for other corporations. These are listed alphabetically according to the issuing company.

STYLES AND VERSIONS

STYLES: A change in style occurs when a major element of the design is altered or modified as a result of a deliberate mould change. An example of this is *Snow White and the Seven Dwarfs*, 1938 (style one) and *Snow White and the Seven Dwarfs*, 1982-1984 (style two).

VERSIONS: Versions are modifications in a minor style element of the figures, such as the open- and closed-eared rabbits in the Red Rose Tea series. A version could also indicate a change in colourways, for example, the variety of hat colours of the *Lucky Leprechauns*.

TECHNICAL INFORMATION

The whimsical Wades in this book were produced in the George Wade Pottery, the Wade Heath Pottery and in the Wade Ireland Pottery between the 1930s and 2002, For each model, the name of its series, the year of production, the model's name, its size (the height first, then the width in millimeters), the colours and its present value are presented. All known backstamps of the models are listed above the tables. If the figures can be found with a variety of backstamps, then each backstamp is followed, in a parenthesis, by the model numbers applicable to it. For a few listings, only approximate dates of issue are given, as they could not be confirmed by Wade. When known, the year the model was discontinued and its original issue price is also given.

FURTHER READING

Pre-War and More Wades, 1st Edition, 1991, by Pat Murray

Whimsical Wades, 1st Edition, 1986, by Pat Murray

The Charlton Standard Catalogue of Wade, Volume One: General Issues, 3rd Edition, 1999, by Pat Murray

The Charlton Standard Catalogue of Wade, Volume Two: Decorative Wares, 3rd Edition, 2002, by Pat Murray

The Charlton Standard Catalogue of Wade, Volume Three: Tableware, 1998, by Pat Murray

The Charlton Standard Catalogue of Wade, Volume Four: Liquor Containers, 3rd Edition, 1999, by Pat Murray

The Wade Collector's Handbook, 1997, by Robert Prescott-Walker

The Wade Dynasty, 1996, by Dave Lee

The World of Wade, 1988, by Ian Warner with Mike Posgay

The World of Wade Book 2, 1994, by Ian Warner and Mike Posgay

The World of Wade Price Trends, 1996, by Ian Warner and Mike Posgay

CLUBS AND NEWSLETTERS

The Official International Wade Collectors Club, run by Wade Ceramics, was founded in 1994. Members receive an annual Wade membership model upon joining and the opportunity to purchase club limited edition models. The full-colour quarterly *Wade's World* magazine has information on new and old Wade models, dates and locations of Wade shows and exhibitions, and much more. To join the club, write to: The Official International Wade Collectors Club, Royal Works, Westport Road, Burslem, Stoke-on-Trent, ST6 4AP, Staffordshire, England.

The Wade Watch, a quarterly six-page newsletter, is published by Wade Watch, Ltd. For more information, please contact: Wade Watch, Ltd., 8199 Pierson Court, Arvada, CO, 80005, USA or www.wadewatch.com.

INTRODUCTION

WHIMSICAL WADES

By the early 1950s, the Wade Potteries had filled the demand to replace industrial ceramics damaged in the war, and there was not sufficient work to keep the employees busy. This was when Sir George Wade decided to produce his now world-famous miniature animals—the *First Whimsies* — which he referred to as his "pocket money toys." They first appeared in spring 1954 at the British Industries Fair. The miniatures were intended for school children, but they soon attracted the attention of adults and became very collectable.

George Wade's policy was to limit the number of whimsical models produced, so they would not flood the market and lose their appeal. Models of the early 1950s were produced in sets, usually of five, and most sets were in production for only a year or two, some for as little as a few months. Whenever a large industrial order was received, the whole pottery would revert to the production of industrial wares, leaving some sets or series unfinished. Perhaps the pottery intended to go back to unfinished series, but because of slow sales, high production costs, copyright laws, or a new interest by the public, they were never completed.

In some of these cases there were only a few thousand models made, usually as a test run, and therefore they were not issued for nationwide sale. To recoup production costs, some models may have been sold only in one area of the United Kingdom.

In 1958 the three English Wade Potteries were restructured under the name Wade Potteries Ltd., later renamed Wade PLC. Wade (Ulster) Ltd. was renamed Wade Ireland Ltd. in 1966.

Sir George Wade died in 1986 at age 95, to be followed a year later by the untimely death of his son Tony. With their passing, 120 years of Wade family involvement in ceramics came to an end.

In 1989 Wade PLC was taken over by Beauford PLC and renamed Wade Ceramics Ltd., which is still in production today. Wade Ireland was renamed Seagoe Ceramics and continued to manufacture domestic table wares until 1993, when it reverted back to the production of industrial ceramics.

THE PRODUCTION PROCESS

The Wade Pottery manufactures a particularly hard porcelain body which has been used in many different products. It consists of a mixture of ball clays, china clay, flint, feldspar, talc, etc., some ingredients imported from Sweden, Norway and Egypt. These materials are mixed in large vats of water, producing a thick sludge or "slip." The slip is passed into a filter to extract most of the water, leaving large flat "bats" of porcelain clay, approximately two feet square and three inches thick. The clay bats are dried and then ground into dust ready for the forming process. Paraffin is added to the dust to assist in bonding and as a lubricant to remove the formed pieces from the steel moulds.

Once pressed into the required shape, the clay articles are dried, then all the press marks are removed by sponging and "fettling," which is scraping off the surplus clay by hand, using a sharp blade. From the early 1960s, a new method of fettling was used, whereby the base of the model was rubbed back and forth on a material similar to emery paper. This resulted in a lined or ribbed base, which is the best method of identifying the majority of post-1960 Wade figures.

One or more ceramic colours are applied to the clay model, which is then sprayed with a clear glaze that, when fired, allows the colours underneath to show through. This process is known as underglaze decoration. On-glaze decoration is also used by Wade, which includes enamelling, gilding and transfer printing, and is done after the article has been glazed and fired.

Some whimsical Wades are hollow, usually because they were prototype models that were discarded or removed from the pottery by workers. Other models may be found in different colour glazes than the originals, due to one or more of the following reasons:

1. The first colour glaze was laid down for a test run, but when the models came out of the kiln at the end of the firing period (sometimes as long as three days), it was either too light or too dark. This occurred in the case of the black *English Whimsies* "Zebra," which was so dark when it emerged after its run through the kiln that the striped pattern could not be clearly seen. The colour glaze was then changed to beige.

2. When the model was shown to the client he did not like the initial colour, so another was chosen.

3. Some models were reissued in different colour glazes for use in promotions for Red Rose Tea and for Tom Smith Christmas crackers.

WADE MODELLERS, 1954-1994

Listed below are the modellers who helped to create whimsical Wade figures. The year that each modeller started working at Wade is given and, if known, the year he or she left.

After leaving Wade, many modellers went on to work for Royal Doulton, Szeiler, Sylvac, Dilsford Studio and other well-known British potteries. This accounts for the great number of other collectable models that bear a distinctive and characteristic likeness to Wade models.

Jessica Van Hallen, 1930
  Snow White set, 1938

Robert Barlow, Late 1930s
  Tinker, Tailor, Soldier, Sailor
  Comic Duck Family

Nancy Great-Rex, Late 1930s-Early 1940s
  Butcher, Baker and Candlestick Maker

William K. Harper, 1954-1963
  First Whimsies
  Bernie and Pooh
  Hat Box models
  Drum Box series
  Minikins series
  Noddy set
  Tortoise Family
  TV Pets
  Shamrock Cottage
  Irish Comical Pig
  Pink Elephant
  Flying Birds
  Disney Blow Ups

Leslie McKinnon, 1959-1961
  The British Character set
  Happy Families series

Paul Zalman, 1961
  Mabel Lucie Attwell models

Ken Holmes, 1975 to the present
  Dinosaur Collection
  Burglar and Policeman series
  Children and Pets

Alan Maslankowski, 1975
  Snow White set, 1982

MODEL BOXES, 1954-1995

Most collectors have seen or purchased Wade models in their original boxes. In order to catch the eye of a collector, early Wade boxes were made to be just as colourful, appealing and decorative as their contents.

When Wade models were issued in the 1950s, their appeal to collectors was not as avid as it is today; as a result, few boxes from the 1950s were kept by the original purchasers. Models in their boxes can command a higher price than a model alone, and depending on the age and condition of the box, the price of the model may increase by 30 to 50 percent.

In the 1970s the rising cost of paper and the fact that Wade produced an established collector's product caused the company to produce less appealing containers. But by the 1980s, the boxes again became colourful and eye-catching, although they had lost the old-world charm of the boxes of the 1950s.

Box designs and colours can vary depending on the year of issue and the length of the production run. Some popular models that were reissued two or more times can be found in two, and at times three, different box sizes and colours (as in the *Happy Families* series, which were issued and reissued in three different box designs).

WADE MARKS, 1930s-1998

Wade Heath Ltd. and George Wade and Son Ltd. not only shared their pottery moulds, they also shared the Wade trademark during the late 1940s and into the 1950s. This makes it difficult to distinguish which pottery a particular model came from. As a general guide for those models produced in both potteries, the Wade Heath postwar novelty models have a green or greenish brown "Wade England" mark on their bases, and the postwar George Wade figures have a black or blue "Wade England" transfer on their bases.

Later, with the addition of Wade Ireland, it became even more difficult to determine the origin of a model. The potteries had a habit of helping each other out in order to speed up production. These figures all had the mark of the originating pottery on their bases and were packed in boxes from that pottery, even though they may have been made in another location.

A good example of this practice is the 1977 *Bisto Kids* set. During one of our conversations, Tony Wade told me that, although they were marked "Wade Staffordshire" on their bases, these models were in fact produced in the Wade Ireland Pottery. The George Wade Pottery had another large order to complete, so Wade Ireland took over.

Similarly, some of the 1950s *First Whimsies* are believed to have been produced by Wade Ireland, although none of the models have a Wade Ireland mark, and the entire series of ten sets was packed in Wade England boxes.

Many small open-caste models (models with no bases and standing on thin legs) do not have enough space on them for a Wade label or an ink stamp. They were originally issued in boxes with "Wade England" clearly marked on the box or packet front. Once removed from their container, however, these models are hard to identify without the aid of Wade collector books (the *First Whimsies* is a good example of this).

Larger, more solid-based models were marked with a Wade ink stamp or with a black and gold label on their bases. But over the years the label or the ink stamp can wear off or be washed off by previous owners, leaving them unmarked.

Wade Heath

Ink Stamps

1. Black ink stamp "Flaxman Ware Hand Made Pottery by Wadeheath England," 1935-1937.
2. Black ink stamp "Flaxman Wade Heath England," 1937-1938.

3. Black ink stamp "Flaxman Wade Heath," 1937-1938.
4. Black ink stamp "Wadeheath Ware England," 1935-1937.
5. Green-brown ink stamp "Wade England," late 1940s-early 1950s.
6. Green ink stamp "Wade England [name of model]," late 1940s-early 1950s.

7. Black ink stamp "Wadeheath by permission Walt Disney England," 1937-1938.
8. Black ink stamp "Wade" and red ink stamp "Made in England," 1938.
9. Black ink stamp "Wade England," late 1940s-early 1950s.

WADE

Hand-painted Marks

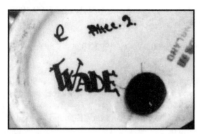

1. Black hand painted "Wade Alice 2," with black ink stamp "Made in England," 1930s.
2. Black hand painted "Wade Alice 7" and red ink stamp of leaping deer, 1930s.
3. Black hand painted "Hiawatha Wade England," 1937.

Ink Stamps

4. Black ink stamp "Wade England," late 1940s.
5. Black ink stamp "Wade Made in England," 1955.
6. Brown ink stamp "Wade England," with brown cricket in large C. Only seen on some of the *Happy Families* models.

Transfer Prints

7. Small black transfer "Wade England [name of model]," 1950s.
8. Large black transfer "Wade England [name of model]," 1950s.
9a. Black transfer "Wade Snippet No. 1 Mayflower Carried 102 Pilgrims to North America 1620-Real Porcelain-Made In England," 1956.
9b. Black transfer "Wade Snippet No. 2 Santa Maria Flag ship of Columbus 1492-Real Porcelain-Made In England," 1956.
9c. Black transfer "Wade Snippet No. 3 Revenge Flag ship of Sir Richard Grenville 1591-Real Porcelain-Made In England," 1956.
9d. Black transfer "Wade Snippet No. 4 Hansel-Real Porcelain-Made in England," 1957.

9e. Black transfer "Wade Snippet No. 5 Gretel-Real Porcelain-Made in England," 1957
9f. Black transfer "Wade Snippet No. 6 Gingy-Real Porcelain-Made in England," 1957.
10. Blue transfer "Wade England," 1956-1957.
11. Black transfer "Wade Porcelain England," 1961.
12. Black transfer "Wade Porcelain Copyright Walt Disney Productions Made in England," 1961.

13. Brown transfer "Wade Made in England," 1962.
14. Brown transfer "Copyright RHM Foods Ltd. & Applied Creativity, Wade Staffordshire," 1977.

15. Black transfer "Wade Made in England," 1978-1987.
16. Black transfer "Walt Disney Productions" in an oval shape, with "Wade England" in centre, 1981-1987.
17. Black transfer "Wade Porcelain England S/F [1-6]," 1984-1986.
18. Red transfer "Wade Made in England," 1985, 1994.
19. Black transfer "Harrods Knightsbridge," 1991-1994.
20. Black transfer "Wade Limited Editions Modelled by Ken Holmes [includes model name, series number and limited edition number]," 1993-1994.

21. Black transfer "Arthur Hare [Holly Hedgehog] © C&S Collectables Wade England," 1993-1995.
22. Black transfer "Wade," enclosed in an outline of the Isle of Wight and numbered, 1994.
23. Black transfer "[Limited edition number] © H/B Inc, Scooby-Doo, Limited edition of 2,000, Wade England, G&G Collectables," 1994.

24. Black transfer "1994 [1995] Mirror Group Newspapers Ltd © C&S Collectables Wade England," 1994-1995.

Impressed Marks

25. Impressed "Wade Porcelain Made in England," 1958.

Embossed Marks

26. Small embossed "Wade," 1954-1983.

27. Embossed "'Whimtrays' Wade Porcelain Made in England," 1958-1965.

28. Embossed "Wade Porcelain Made in England," 1958-1984.
29. Embossed "Wade Porcelain - Mabel Lucie Attwell © Made in England," 1959-1961.
30. Embossed "Angel Dish Wade Porcelain Made in England," 1963.
31. Embossed "Robertson," 1963-1965.
32. Embossed "Wade England," 1965-1994.

33. Large embossed "Wade Made in England," 1975-1984.

34. Embossed "Mianco [year of issue] Wade England" on rim of base,
    1989-1995.
35. Embossed "Wade England 1990 [1991]," 1990-1991.
36. Embossed "Wade England 1991" on rim of base and ink stamp "GSG," 1991.
37. Large embossed "Wade," 1993-1994.

Labels

38. Small black and gold label "Wade England," 1954-1959.
39. Black and gold label "Genuine Wade Porcelain Made in England," 1959-1965.
40. Large black and gold label "Wade England," early 1970s-1981.
41. Black and gold label "Walt Disney Productions Wade England," 1981-1985.

WADE IRELAND

Ink Stamps

1. Black ink stamp "'Pogo' Copyright, Walt Kelly, Made in Ireland 1959," 1959.
2. Black ink stamp "Made in Ireland," 1974-1985.
3. Purple ink stamp "Made in Ireland," 1974-1985.

Transfer Prints

4. Green transfer "Shamrock Pottery Made in Ireland," 1953-1956.

Impressed Marks

5. Impressed "Shamrock Pottery Made in Ireland," 1953-1956.

6. Impressed "Irish Porcelain Made in Ireland by Wade Co. Armagh," with shamrock, early 1950s.
7. Impressed "Made in Ireland," early 1970s.

Embossed Marks

8. Embossed "Irish Porcelain, Made in Ireland," with a shamrock leaf, 1953-1956.
9. Embossed "Shamrock Pottery Made in Ireland," 1959.
10. Embossed "Wade Porcelain Made in Ireland," 1970s-1980s.
11. Embossed "Made in Ireland, Porcelain Wade, Eire Tir-Adheanta,"

    1980-1988.
12. Embossed "Wade Ireland," 1984-1987.

COMIC ANIMALS AND BIRDS

COMIC ANIMALS AND BIRDS

From the late 1940s to the 1950s, the Wade Heath Royal Victoria Pottery and the George Wade Pottery produced a large series of animal and bird models, some described as comic or novelty. Because the two Potteries produced the same models using the same moulds and both used the "Wade England" mark, it is hard to tell which models were made in which pottery. But it is believed that models stamped "Wade England" in green, brown or black were produced in the Royal Victoria Pottery before 1953, and those models transfer printed with a black or blue "Wade England" mark were produced in the George Wade Pottery in the early to mid- 1950s. The *Comic Families* models have been found with creamy beige background glazes and dark coloured clothing and are also found in white with pastel blue and grey colours.

During this period whenever Sir George Wade would come across surplus models, he would say, "Stick'em on something." The figures would be sent to the Wade Heath Pottery, where they were joined onto surplus bramble-ware mustard pots (minus their lids) or basket-ware eggcups, then mounted on a moulded leaf-shaped base to make a novelty bowl. The finished product was then recoloured and called a "Posy Bowl."

For ease of reference, the models are listed in alphabetical order, not in order of issue.

DONKEYS

Circa 1948-1952

The *Comic Donkeys* set is a pair of comic figures, one happy and one sad, which were produced in the Wade Pottery between the late 1940s and the early 1950s. The original price was 2/6d each.

A model of Cheerful Charlie with the words "Cheerful Charlie" hand written on his body and "Montreal" hand written on his ears has been found and is possibly a souvenir model exported to Montreal, Quebec, Canada. For other models with similar hand written souvenir place names please see "Staffordshire House Gifts."

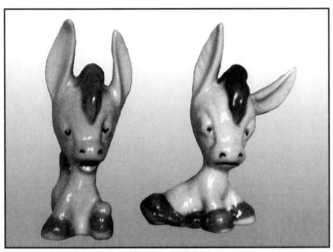

Cheerful Charlie and Doleful Dan

Cheerful Charlie "Montreal"

Backstamp: Black ink stamp "Wade England"

No.	Name	Description	Size	U.S. $	Can. $	U.K. £
1a	Cheerful Charlie	Beige; coffee mane, tail, hooves	110 x 55	275.00	360.00	180.00
1b	Cheerful Charlie	Pink; coffee mane, tail, hooves; black lettering Montreal	110 x 55	275.00	360.00	180.00
2	Doleful Dan	Beige; coffee mane, tail, hooves	110 x 55	275.00	360.00	180.00

Donkey Derivatives
Cheerful Charlie and Doleful Dan Salt and Pepper, Circa 1948

Doleful Dan and Cheerful Charlie

Backstamp: Green-brown ink stamp "Wade England"

No.	Name	Description	Size	U.S. $	Can. $	U.K. £
1a	Cheerful Charlie	Pink; beige mane, tail, hooves	110 x 55	185.00	240.00	120.00
1b	Cheerful Charlie	Pink; grey mane, tail, hooves	110 x 55	185.00	240.00	120.00
2	Cheerful Charlie	Pink; grey mane, tail, hooves	110 x 55	185.00	240.00	120.00

Cheerful Charlie and Doleful Dan Egg-cup / Posy Bowl, Circa 1948

Cheerful Charlie Posy Bowl

Doleful Dan Posy Bowl

Backstamp: Green-brown ink stamp "Wade England"

No.	Name	Description	Size	U.S. $	Can. $	U.K. £
1a	Cheerful Charlie	Blue egg-cup posy bowl	105 x 105	125.00	160.00	80.00
1b	Cheerful Charlie	Cream egg-cup posy bowl	105 x 105	125.00	160.00	80.00
1c	Cheerful Charlie	Multicoloured egg-cup posy bowl	105 x 105	125.00	160.00	80.00
2a	Doleful Dan	Blue egg-cup posy bowl	105 x 105	125.00	160.00	80.00
2b	Doleful Dan	Green egg-cup posy bowl	105 x 105	125.00	160.00	80.00
2c	Doleful Dan	Multicoloured egg-cup posy bowl	105 x 105	150.00	195.00	100.00

DUCK FAMILY

1950s

The *Comic Duck Family* was designed by Robert Barlow. The original price for "Mr. Duck" and "Mrs. Duck" was 2/6d each. "Dack" and "Dilly" each sold for 1/6d.

The Comic Duck Father and Mother are also found marked "Szeiler." Joseph Szeiler worked for the Wade pottery in the early 1950s. Before leaving to start his own pottery, 'Studio Szeiler,' he was given permission by Sir George and Anthony Wade to 'borrow' some of the discontinued Wade moulds to produce models for a limited time, providing these were clearly marked with a Szeiler backstamp. For other Wade/Szeiler models see "Cheerful Charlie and Doleful Dan," "Comic Rabbit," and the "Kissing Bunnies."

Duck Family

Backstamp: A. Unmarked (1a, 2)
B. Black transfer print "Wade England" (1b, 1c, 2, 3, 4)

No.	Name	Description	Size	U.S. $	Can. $	U.K. £
1a	Mr. Duck	White; beige beak, tail, feet; blue cap, tie; small eyes	70 x 38	200.00	260.00	130.00
1b	Mr. Duck	White; yellow beak, feet; orange-red cap; small eyes	70 x 38	200.00	260.00	130.00
2	Mrs. Duck	White; yellow beak, feet; bonnet; small eyes	70 x 37	200.00	260.00	130.00
3	Dack	White; yellow beak, feet; blue cap; small eyes	40 x 28	200.00	260.00	130.00
4	Dilly	White; yellow beak, feet; orange tam; small eyes	40 x 27	200.00	260.00	130.00

FROG FAMILY
STYLE ONE
Circa 1948-1952

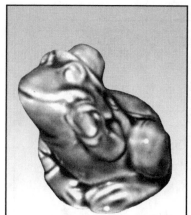

Mr. Frog

Mrs. Frog

Boy Frog

Backstamp: Black ink stamp "Wade England"

No.	Name	Description	Size	U.S. $	Can. $	U.K. £
1	Mr. Frog	Dark green; bowler hat; cigar	40 x 58	200.00	260.00	130.00
2	Mrs. Frog	Dark green; bonnet; umbrella	40 x 58	200.00	260.00	130.00
3	Boy Frog	Dark green; football	28 x 38	200.00	260.00	130.00
4	Girl Frog	Dark green; bunch of flowers	28 x 38	200.00	260.00	130.00

PENGUIN FAMILY

Circa 1948-1955

The *Comic Penguin Family* was produced in pastels and in dark colours. Before the 1950s these models were stamped "Wade England" and afterwards were printed with a "Wade England" mark. "Mr. Penguin" and "Mrs. Penguin" are also found as salt and pepper pots. The original price of "Mr. Penguin" and "Mrs. Penguin" was 2/6d each. "Benny" and "Penny" each sold for 1/6d.

Mrs. Penguin, Benny and Mr. Penguin

Penny

Backstamp: **A.** Black ink stamp "Wade England" (1b, 3)
B. Black transfer "Wade England" (1a, 4)
C. Unmarked (2, 5)

No.	Name	Description	Size	U.S. $	Can. $	U.K. £
1a	Mr. Penguin	White/grey; pale blue cap, scarf; black umbrella	90 x 40	225.00	280.00	140.00
1b	Mr. Penguin	White; blue cap, scarf; black umbrella	90 x 40	225.00	280.00	140.00
2	Mr. Penguin	Black/white; dark blue cap, scarf; yellow beak, hands, feet	65 x 40	225.00	280.00	140.00
3	Mrs. Penguin	White/grey penguin, shawl; black bag	85 x 40	225.00	280.00	140.00
4	Benny	White/grey; blue tam; black book	55 x 25	225.00	280.00	140.00
5	Penny	White/grey; blue bonnet; black penguin doll	50 x 25	225.00	280.00	140.00

Penguin Family Derivatives
Circa 1948

Salt and Pepper Pots

Backstamp: **A.** Black ink stamp "Wade England" (1, 2)
B. Black transfer "Wade England" (1, 2)
C. Unmarked (3, 4, 5)

No.	Name	Description	Size	U.S. $	Can. $	U.K. £
1	Mr. Penguin Pepper Pot	Black/white; maroon cap, scarf, umbrella	90 x 40	140.00	175.00	86.00
2	Mr. Penguin Pepper Pot	Black/white; blue cap, scarf	65 x 40	140.00	175.00	86.00
3	Mr. Penguin Pepper Pot	Pale green	75 x 40	140.00	175.00	86.00
4	Mrs. Penguin Salt Pot	Black/white; maroon shawl, handbag	85 x 40	140.00	175.00	86.00
5	Mrs. Penguin Salt Pot	Pale green	65 x 40	140.00	175.00	86.00

PIG FAMILY

"Mr. Pig" and "Mrs. Pig" were produced in cream with dark coloured clothing. As no evidence of the "Boy Pig" and "Girl Pig" have been found, it is believed these models may be prototypes and never put into production.

Photograph not available
at press time

Backstamp: Black ink stamp "Wade England"

No.	Name	Description	Size	U.S. $	Can. $	U.K. £
1	Mr. Pig	Cream; maroon tie, jacket	90 x 32	180.00	160.00	80.00
2	Mrs. Pig	Cream; dark yellow hat	80 x 30	180.00	160.00	80.00
3	Boy Pig	Unknown	Unknown		Rare	
4	Girl Pig	Unknown	Unknown		Rare	

Pig Family Derivatives

Circa 1948

The "Mr. Pig Salt Pot" and "Mrs. Pig Pepper Pot" were issued as a cruet set, both standing on an oval tray. The ink stamp on these models is a type used before the 1950s.

Salt and Pepper Pots

Backstamp: Black ink stamp "Wade England"

No.	Name	Description	Size	U.S. $	Can. $	U.K. £
1	Mr. Pig Salt Pot	Cream; maroon tie, jacket	90 x 32	130.00	160.00	80.00
2	Mrs. Pig Pepper Pot	Cream; dark yellow hat	90 x 32	130.00	160.00	80.00
—	Set (2) with Tray		90 x 32	290.00	360.00	180.00

Note: The model of Mr. Pig illustrated has damaged feet.

RABBIT FAMILY

Circa 1948-1955

Before the 1950s these models were produced in cream with dark coloured clothing; in the 1950s they were made in white with pastel markings. The original prices were 2/6d each for "Mr. Rabbit" and for "Mrs. Rabbit" and 1/6d each for "Fluff" and for "Puff."

Rabbit Family   Mr Rabbit (1a)

Backstamp: A. Black ink stamp "Wade England" (1a, 2a, 3a, 4a)
B. Black transfer "Wade England" (1c, 2b, 3b, 4b)
C. Unmarked (1b, 1d)

No.	Name	Description	Size	U.S. $	Can. $	U.K. £
1a	Mr. Rabbit	Cream; dark green jacket	90 x 40	200.00	250.00	125.00
1b	Mr. Rabbit	Cream; dark yellow jacket	90 x 40	200.00	250.00	125.00
1c	Mr. Rabbit	Cream; black jacket	90 x 40	200.00	250.00	125.00
1d	Mr. Rabbit	White; blue jacket	90 x 40	200.00	250.00	125.00
1e	Mr. Rabbit	Bright yellow all over	90 x 40	200.00	250.00	125.00
2a	Mrs. Rabbit	Cream; maroon bonnet; yellow basket	90 x 40	200.00	250.00	125.00
2b	Mrs. Rabbit	White; grey ear tips; blue bonnet, basket	90 x 40	200.00	250.00	125.00
3a	Fluff	Cream; dark blue shawl	40 x 30	185.00	230.00	115.00
3b	Fluff	White; grey ear tips; blue/grey shawl	40 x 30	185.00	230.00	115.00
4a	Puff	Cream; dark yellow jacket	40 x 30	185.00	230.00	115.00
4b	Puff	White; grey ear tips; blue jacket	40 x 30	185.00	230.00	115.00

Rabbit Family Derivatives

Circa 1948

The "Mr. Rabbit Salt Pot" and "Mrs. Rabbit Pepper Pot" were issued as a cruet set, both standing on an oval tray.

Salt and Pepper Pots

Backstamp: Black ink stamp "Wade England"

No.	Name	Description	Size	U.S. $	Can. $	U.K. £
1	Mr. Rabbit Salt Pot	Cream; black hat; yellow jacket	90 x 40	130.00	160.00	80.00
2	Mrs. Rabbit Pepper Pot	Cream; maroon hat; yellow ribbon	90 x 40	130.00	160.00	80.00
—	Set (2) with Tray			290.00	300.00	180.00

RABBIT (LITTLE LAUGHING BUNNY)

Circa 1948-1952

This model is a miniature version of the *Laughing Rabbit* produced by Wade Heath, 1937-1939, in Flaxman ware glazes (see Novelty Animals). There are a number of variations in the size of the "Little Laughing Bunny," due to the die being retooled when worn. The colour of the grey models is also not consistent because the models were decorated in two different potteries. The original price was 1/-.

A poem by one of the Wade Heath figure casters in a spring 1954 *Jolly Potter* magazine refers to the "Comic Rabbit" as the "Little Laughing Bunny."

A "Comic Rabbit" with grey body, brown arms and feet has been found with a John Szeiler backstamp. Joseph Szeiler worked for the Wade pottery in the early 1950s. Before leaving to start his own pottery, 'Studio Szeiler,' he was given permission by Sir George and Anthony Wade to 'borrow' some of the discontinued Wade moulds to produce models for a limited time, providing these were clearly marked with a Szeiler backstamp. For other Wade/Szeiler models see "Cheerful Charlie and Doleful Dan," "Mr. and Ms. Duck," and the "Kissing Bunnies."

Little Laughing Bunnies

Backstamp: **A.** Black ink stamp "Wade England" (1a, 1b, 1c)
B. Black transfer print "Wade England" (1d)
C. Blue transfer print "Wade England" (1d)
D. Brown ink stamp (1e, 1f, 1g, 1h, 1i, 1j)

No.	Description	Size	U.S. $	Can. $	U.K. £
1a	Beige; red mouth; black eyes; white stomach	65 x 40	75.00	95.00	48.00
1b	Dark grey; red mouth	63 x 40	75.00	95.00	48.00
1c	Dark grey; red mouth; black eyes	63 x 40	75.00	95.00	48.00
1d	Pale grey; brown ears, mouth; black eyes	63 x 38	75.00	95.00	48.00
1e	Pale grey; brown ears, mouth; red eyes	63 x 38	75.00	95.00	48.00
1f	Pale grey; brown striped ears; red mouth; black eyes	63 x 40	75.00	95.00	48.00
1g	Pale grey; red mouth; black eyes	63 x 40	75.00	95.00	48.00
1h	Pink; red mouth; black eyes	70 x 38	75.00	95.00	48.00
1i	White; brown ears, toes	63 x 38	75.00	95.00	48.00
1j	White; brown striped ears; red mouth; black eyes	65 x 40	75.00	95.00	48.00

Rabbit Derivatives

Ashtrays, Circa 1948

This Art Deco shaped ashtray is similar in shape to a model produced by Sylvac in the late 1940s which would have an impressed "Sylvac" and a design No 1532 on the base. Although the illustrated model does not have a Wade mark, it has a registered design number 827631 on the base.

Art Deco Ashtray

S-Shaped Ashtray

Backstamp: **A.** Ink stamp "Regd 827631 Made in England"
B. Green-brown ink stamp "Wade England"

No.	Description	Size	U.S. $	Can. $	U.K. £
1a	Beige rabbit; grey Art Deco ashtray	92 x 92	132.00	160.00	80.00
1b	Grey rabbit; speckled blue Art Deco ashtray	92 x 92	132.00	160.00	80.00
2a	Dark grey rabbit; yellow S-shaped ashtray	110 x 110	132.00	160.00	80.00
2b	Dark grey rabbit; marbled blue S-shaped ashtray	110 x 110	132.00	160.00	80.00

Mustard Pot, Circa 1948

Rabbit Mustard Pot

Rabbit Mustard Pot (1d)

Backstamp: Green-brown ink stamp "Wade England"

No.	Description	Size	U.S. $	Can. $	U.K. £
1a	Blue; bramble-ware mustard pot	85 x 80	140.00	175.00	85.00
1b	Green; bramble-ware mustard pot	85 x 80	140.00	175.00	85.00
1c	Yellow; bramble-ware mustard pot	85 x 80	140.00	175.00	85.00
1d	Grey/white rabbit; multicoloured mustard pot	85 x 80	140.00	175.00	85.00

HAPPY FAMILIES

HAPPY FAMILIES

Circa 1961-1987

The *Happy Families* series was first issued from 1961 to 1965 and consisted of a mother animal and her two babies. The original five sets were sold in boxes with "Happy Families" printed in large letters in different colours on the front.

The first three *Happy Families* were the *Hippo Family* (3/11d), the *Tiger Family* (4/6d) and the *Giraffe Family* (4/11d). They were modelled by Leslie McKinnon and issued in the autumn and winter of 1961. They proved to be so popular that in spring 1962, Wade issued two more families, the *Rabbit Family* and the *Mouse Family*. In 1978 four sets were reissued using the original moulds. *The Tiger Family* (which is the most sought after set) was not considered suitable for reissue. The only way to distinguish the reissued models from the earlier models is by a slight variation in colour. By 1984 four more families had been added — the *Frog Family*, *Pig Family*, *Elephant Family* and *Owl Family*. In spring 1987, the last year of the series, the *Dog Family* and *Cat Family* joined the series, making a total of eleven sets issued from 1961 to 1987.

The firsts sets were issued in two-tone, end opening boxes of blue and green, and lilac and navy, with large lettering "Happy Families" in alternate colours. The second series were issued in white and blue, top opening boxes, with giraffes, rabbits, mice and hippos printed on them. The boxes were changed again in 1984 to white with pastel-coloured jungle scenes.

At some time during the late 1980s, Wade sold off its remaining stock of *Happy Families* to Tesco Stores, a British discount company. The Tesco Stores box had a rigid cellophane top, front and sides; the base and back were cardboard. There is no reference to Wade on these boxes.

For "Mother" models in different colourways see "Pocket Pals" (page 178). See also Cricket Design Incorporated, page 296.

Cat Family

Dog Family

CAT FAMILY
1987

Backstamp: Black transfer "Wade Made in England"

No.	Name	Description	Size	U.S. $	Can. $	U.K. £
1	Mother	Grey/white; blue eyes; pink ear tips	45 x 35	45.00	55.00	28.00
2	Kitten, lying	Grey/white; blue eyes; pink ears	30 x 35	25.00	30.00	15.00
3	Kitten, seated	Grey/white; blue eyes; pink ears	30 x 20	25.00	30.00	15.00
—	3 pce set	Boxed	—	90.00	110.00	55.00

DOG FAMILY
1987

Backstamp: A. Black transfer "Wade Made in England" (1-3)
               B. Unmarked (1-3)

No.	Name	Description	Size	U.S. $	Can. $	U.K. £
1	Mother	Brown; white face, chest	55 x 35	45.00	55.00	28.00
2	Puppy, lying	Brown; white face, chest	30 x 40	25.00	30.00	15.00
3	Puppy, standing	Brown; white face, chest	30 x 35	25.00	30.00	15.00
—	3 pce set	Boxed	—	90.00	110.00	55.00

Elephant Family

Frog Family

ELEPHANT FAMILY
1984-1987

Backstamp: Black transfer "Wade Made in England"

No.	Name	Description	Size	U.S. $	Can. $	U.K. £
1a	Mother	Blue; pink ears, mouth	35 x 70	45.00	55.00	28.00
1b	Mother	Grey; pink ears, mouth	35 x 70	45.00	55.00	28.00
2a	Baby, trunk down	Blue; pink ears, mouth	25 x 55	25.00	30.00	15.00
2b	Baby, trunk down	Grey; pink ears, mouth	25 x 55	25.00	30.00	15.00
3a	Baby, trunk up	Blue; pink ears, mouth	45 x 22	25.00	30.00	15.00
3b	Baby, trunk up	Grey; pink ears, mouth	45 x 22	25.00	30.00	15.00
—	3 pce set	Boxed	—	90.00	110.00	55.00

FROG FAMILY
STYLE TWO
1984-1987

Backstamp: A. Black transfer "Wade Made in England" (1-3)
B. Red transfer "Wade Made in England" (1-3)

No.	Name	Description	Size	U.S. $	Can. $	U.K. £
1a	Mother	Brown; red-brown spots	25 x 45	45.00	55.00	28.00
1b	Mother	Dark brown	25 x 45	45.00	55.00	28.00
2	Baby, singing	Brown; red-brown spots	25 x 25	25.00	30.00	15.00
3	Baby, smiling	Brown; red-brown spot	20 x 30	25.00	30.00	15.00
—	3 pce set	Boxed	—	90.00	110.00	55.00

Giraffe Family   Hippo Family

GIRAFFE FAMILY
FIRST ISSUE, 1961-1965

Except for a slight variation in eyelid and horn colour, the original and reissued models are hard to distinguish from each other.

Backstamp: **A.** Brown ink stamp "Wade England" with cricket (1-3)
B. Black and gold label Genuine "Wade Porcelain Made in England" (1-3)
C. Unmarked (1-3)

No.	Name	Description	Size	U.S. $	Can. $	U.K. £
1	Mother	Beige; light blue eyelids; light grey horns	60 x 45	50.00	60.00	30.00
2	Baby, awake	Beige; light blue eyelids; light grey horns	40 x 28	30.00	40.00	20.00
3	Baby, sleeping	Beige; light blue eyelids; light grey horns	15 x 30	30.00	40.00	20.00
—	3 pce set	Boxed	—	100.00	120.00	60.00

SECOND ISSUE, 1978-1987

Backstamp: **A.** Black transfer "Wade Made in England" (1-3)
B. Brown transfer "Wade Made in England" (1-3)
C. Unmarked (1-3)

No.	Name	Description	Size	U.S. $	Can. $	U.K. £
1	Mother	Beige; turquoise eyelids; dark grey horns	60 x 45	45.00	55.00	28.00
2	Baby, awake	Beige; turquoise eyelids; dark grey horns	40 x 28	25.00	30.00	15.00
3	Baby, sleeping	Beige; turquoise eyelids; dark grey horns	15 x 30	25.00	30.00	15.00
—	3 pce set	Boxed	—	90.00	110.00	55.00

HIPPO FAMILY
FIRST ISSUE, 1961-1965

Backstamp: Unknown

No.	Name	Description	Size	U.S. $	Can. $	U.K. £
1	Mother	Dark blue/brown eyes	35 x 50	50.00	60.00	30.00
2	Baby, asleep	Eyes shut	20 x 25	30.00	40.00	20.00
3	Baby, awake	Dark blue/brown eyes	28 x 25	30.00	40.00	20.00
—	3 pce set	Boxed	—	100.00	120.00	60.00

SECOND ISSUE, 1978-1987

Backstamp: Black transfer "Wade Made in England"

No.	Name	Description	Size	U.S. $	Can. $	U.K. £
1	Mother	Smoky blue; blue tear; brown eyes	35 x 50	45.00	55.00	28.00
2	Baby, asleep	Smoky blue; blue tear; brown eyes	20 x 25	25.00	30.00	15.00
3	Baby, awake	Smoky blue; blue tear; brown eyes	28 x 25	25.00	30.00	15.00
—	3 pce set	Boxed	—	90.00	110.00	55.00

MOUSE FAMILY

FIRST ISSUE, 1962-1965

The *Mouse Family* was issued in spring 1962 and reissued from 1978 to 1984. The original models have yellow tails, compared with the pink tails of the later figures.

Backstamp: **A.** Brown ink stamp "Wade Made in England" (1-3)
B. Unmarked (1-3)

No.	Name	Description	Size	U.S. $	Can. $	U.K. £
1	Mother	White; pink ears; yellow tail	50 x 28	60.00	75.00	37.00
2	Baby, eyes closed	White; pink ears, nose; yellow tail	28 x 28	40.00	75.00	25.00
3	Baby, eyes open	White; blue eyes; pink ears, nose; yellow tail	25 x 30	40.00	75.00	25.00
—	3 pce set	Boxed	—	120.00	150.00	75.00

SECOND ISSUE, 1978-1987

Backstamp: **A.** Black transfer "Wade Made in England" (1-3)
B. Unmarked (1-3)

No.	Name	Description	Size	U.S. $	Can. $	U.K. £
1a	Mother	White; brown mouth; grey patch; pink ears, tail	50 x 28	45.00	55.00	28.00
1b	Mother	White; pink mouth; grey patch; pink ears, tail	50 x 28	45.00	55.00	28.00
2a	Baby, eyes closed	White; brown mouth; grey patch; pink ears, tail	28 x 28	25.00	30.00	15.00
2b	Baby, eyes closed	White; pink mouth, grey patch; pink ears, tail	28 x 28	25.00	30.00	15.00
3a	Baby, eyes open	White; brown mouth; grey patch; pink ears, tail	25 x 30	25.00	30.00	15.00
3b	Baby, eyes open	White; pink mouth; grey patch; pink ears, tail	25 x 30	25.00	30.00	15.00
—	3 pce set	Boxed	—	90.00	110.00	55.00

OWL FAMILY,
1984-1987

Backstamp: A. Black transfer "Wade Made in England" (1-3)
B. Red transfer "Wade Made in England" (1-3)

No.	Name	Description	Size	U.S. $	Can. $	U.K. £
1	Mother	Cream; beige head, back, wings	40 x 40	45.00	55.00	28.00
2	Baby, wings closed	Cream; beige head, back, wings	25 x 20	25.00	30.00	15.00
3	Baby, wings open	Cream; beige head, back, wings	25 x 32	25.00	30.00	15.00
—	3 pce set	Boxed	—	90.00	110.00	55.00

PIG FAMILY
1984-1987

Backstamp: A. Black transfer "Wade Made in England" (1-3)
B. Red transfer "Wade Made in England" (1-3)

No.	Name	Description	Size	U.S. $	Can. $	U.K. £
1a	Mother	Pink; black eyes; red mouth	28 x 65	45.00	55.00	28.00
1b	Mother	Reddish pink; white face; black eyes; red mouth	28 x 65	45.00	55.00	28.00
2	Baby, asleep	Pink; blue eyelids	15 x 45	25.00	30.00	15.00
3a	Baby, awake	Pink; black eyes; red mouth	18 x 40	25.00	30.00	15.00
3b	Baby, awake	Reddish pink; white face; black eyes; red mouth	18 x 40	25.00	30.00	15.00
—	3 pce set	Boxed	—	90.00	110.00	55.00

RABBIT FAMILY
FIRST ISSUE, 1963-1965

Backstamp: A. Black and gold label "Genuine Wade Porcelain Made in England" (1-3)
B. Unmarked (1-3)

No.	Name	Description	Size	U.S. $	Can. $	U.K. £
1	Mother	White; turquoise patches	55 x 30	60.00	75.00	37.00
2	Baby, seated	White; turquoise patches	34 x 28	40.00	50.00	25.00
3	Baby, standing	White; turquoise patches	30 x 35	40.00	50.00	25.00
—	3 pce set	Boxed	—	120.00	150.00	75.00

SECOND ISSUE, 1978-1984

Backstamp: A. Black transfer "Wade made in England" (1-3)
B. Unmarked (1-3)

No.	Name	Description	Size	U.S. $	Can. $	U.K. £
1	Mother	White; blue patches	55 x 30	45.00	55.00	28.00
2	Baby, seated	White; blue patches	34 x 28	25.00	30.00	15.00
3	Baby, standing	White; blue patches	30 x 35	25.00	30.00	15.00
—	3 pce set	Boxed	—	90.00	110.00	55.00

TIGER FAMILY
1961-1965

This set was not reissued, so it is rare and highly sought after.

Backstamp: Unmarked

No.	Name	Description	Size	U.S. $	Can. $	U.K. £
1	Mother	Beige; brown stripes; green eyes; red tongue	40 x 40	110.00	135.00	70.00
2	Baby, asleep	Beige; brown stripes; green eyes; red tongue	10 x 30	80.00	100.00	50.00
3	Baby, awake	Beige; brown stripes; green eyes; red tongue	10 x 30	80.00	100.00	50.00
—	3 pce set	Boxed	—	240.00	300.00	150.00

LEPRECHAUNS AND PIXIES

LEPRECHAUNS AND PIXIES

BABY PIXIE

Circa 1978-1980s

The *Baby Pixie* models can be found free standing, on a circular pin tray or on a shamrock leaf dish. Some pin trays have a 1950s mark on the base, which means they may have been old stock reissued with pixies on them to create new products.

Baby Pixie

Backstamp: **A.** Black ink stamp "Made in Ireland" (1)
  B. Embossed "Made in Ireland, Porcelain Wade, Eire Tir-Adheanta" (2,)
  C. Impressed "Irish Porcelain Made in Ireland Co. Armagh"

No.	Name	Description	Size	U.S. $	Can. $	U.K. £
1	Baby Pixie	Blue suit, cap, boots	35 x 10	25.00	30.00	15.00

Baby Pixie Derivatives

Baby Pixie on Shamrock Leaf Dish

No.	Name	Description	Size	U.S. $	Can. $	U.K. £
1	Baby Pixie Pin Tray	Blue suit; blue-green tray	40 x 75	25.00	30.00	15.00
2a	Baby Pixie Shamrock Leaf Dish	Blue suit; blue-grey dish	40 x 75	25.00	30.00	15.00
2b	Baby Pixie Shamrock Leaf Dish	Blue suit; brown dish	40 x 75	25.00	30.00	15.00

LARGE LEPRECHAUNS

1974-1985

Large Leprechaun

Large Leprechaun Derivative
on Connemara Marble Base

Large Leprechaun Derivative
on Simulated Marble Base

Backstamp: Unmarked

No.	Description	Size	U.S. $	Can. $	U.K. £
1a	Bright blue all over	70 x 30	35.00	40.00	20.00
1b	Brown all over	70 x 30	35.00	40.00	20.00
1c	Green hat; dark brown jacket; beige trousers	70 x 30	40.00	60.00	30.00
1d	Grey-green	70 x 30	35.00	40.00	20.00
1e	Turquoise blue	70 x 30	35.00	40.00	20.00
1f	Yellow hat; green jacket; beige trousers	70 x 30	40.00	60.00	30.00

Large Leprechaun Derivatives

Marble Bases

1974-1987

These Large Leprechaun models were mounted on genuine Connemara Marble plinths, or simulated marble plinths which are either greenish-grey, mottled green, slate-grey or light brown in colour. The models were not attached to the plinths by Wade Ireland, but were sold to other companies who mounted them in various combinations of Leprechaun and base for the tourist trade.

The model mounted on a square block of Connemara marble is the original 1974 model. The circular resin base is designed to simulate Connemara marble.

Leprechaun and Pin Tray

Backstamp: A. Gold label "Real Connemara Marble Made in Ireland"
 B. Gold label "Lucky Irish Leprechaun Made in Ireland"
 C. Unmarked

No.	Description	Size	U.S. $	Can. $	U.K. £
1	Dark grey-green; gold label; square base	90 x 55	60.00	75.00	37.00
2	Dark grey-green; mottled grey circular resin base	85	35.00	45.00	22.00
3.	Dark grey-green leprechaun and pin tray	75 x 110	35.00	45.00	22.00

Money Boxes

1987

In 1987 Wade issued three money boxes based on the earlier "Fawn," "Disney Kennel" and "Noddy Toadstool Cottage" money boxes. Because the original moulds were worn, Wade made new moulds, which produced larger, heavier and less delicate-looking models than the originals. New colours were also used. The "Large Leprechaun" was used on the "Toadstool Cottage." The money boxes were sold in plain, unmarked boxes. For other money boxes see *Whimsie-land* and Miscellaneous Models (pages 61, 136 and 158).

Toadstool Cottage Money Box

Backstamp: Unmarked

No.	Name	Description	Size	U.S. $	Can. $	U.K. £
1	Toadstool Cottage	Brown roof, door and shirt; green hat	140 x 155	65.00	80.00	40.00

LARRY AND LESTER, THE LEPRECHAUN TWINS
1974-1985

Backstamp: Black ink stamp "Made in Ireland"

No.	Name	Description	Size	U.S. $	Can. $	U.K. £
1	Larry	Green hat; purple jacket; brown leggings	100 x 60	70.00	85.00	43.00
2	Lester	Yellow hat; green jacket; red leggings	100 x 60	70.00	85.00	43.00

Larry and Lester Derivatives

Bookends
1974-1985

The leprechaun twins were added to a heavy porcelain, L-shaped base to form a pair of bookends.

Larry and Lester Bookends

Backstamp: Purple ink stamp "Made in Ireland"

No.	Description	Size	U.S. $	Can. $	U.K. £
1	Larry on one base; Lester on the other; dark green bookends	115 x 75	200.00	250.00	125.00

LEPRECHAUN ON TOADSTOOL WITH CROCK O'GOLD

Circa 1975

This model is of a smiling leprechaun sitting on top of a toadstool with his hands resting on top of a crock o'gold.

Backstamp: Black ink stamp "Made in Ireland"

No.	Description	Size	U.S. $	Can. $	U.K. £
1a	Grey/brown	125	55.00	70.00	35.00
1b	Grey/brown leprechaun; blue toadstool	145	65.00	80.00	40.00

LUCKY FAIRY FOLK

1956-1986

Lucky Fairy Folk, produced by Wade (Ulster) Ltd., is a set of three models sitting on the backs of a rabbit and a pig and on top of an acorn. Each figure was sold separately in a cylindrical-shaped acetate packet, with a multicoloured string handle. On the end of the string was a black foil label, which read "Made in Ireland by Wade Co. Armagh" in gold lettering. The models themselves are not marked, so once removed from the packet, there is no indication of which pottery they were from. On the first issue "Leprechaun on Pig" the colour of the face is beige-brown and the snout and toes on the pig was originally grey and was then changed to beige.

FIRST VERSION: BROWN FACES

1956-Circa 1960s

Leprechaun on Pig, Pixie on Rabbit, Pixie on Acorn   Original Packaging

Backstamp: Unmarked

No.	Name	Description	Size	U.S. $	Can. $	U.K. £
1a	Leprechaun on Pig	Dark green hat; grey coat; blue trousers; white boots; pig has grey snout and toes	45 x 35	75.00	90.00	45.00
1b	Leprechaun on Pig	Orange hat; blue coat, boots; grey trousers; pig has grey snout and toes	45 x 35	75.00	90.00	45.00
1c	Leprechaun on Pig	Red hat; blue coat; grey trousers; white boots; pig has beige snout and toes	45 x 35	75.00	90.00	45.00
1d	Leprechaun on Pig	Red hat; blue coat, boots; grey trousers; pig has beige snout and toes	45 x 35	75.00	90.00	45.00
1e	Leprechaun on Pig	Yellow hat; blue coat; grey trousers; white boots; pig has beige snout and toes	45 x 35	75.00	90.00	45.00
2a	Pixie on Acorn	Blue hat, boots; white trousers; grey coat	40 x 30	85.00	100.00	50.00
2b	Pixie on Acorn	Dark green hat; white trousers; grey coat	40 x 30	85.00	100.00	50.00
2c	Pixie on Acorn	Orange hat; white trousers; grey coat; blue boots	40 x 30	85.00	100.00	50.00
2d	Pixie on Acorn	Red hat; white trousers; grey coat; blue boots	40 x 30	85.00	100.00	50.00
2e	Pixie on Acorn	Dark yellow hat; white trousers; grey coat; blue boots	40 x 30	85.00	100.00	50.00
2f	Pixie on Acorn	White hat, trousers; grey coat; blue boots	40 x 30	85.00	100.00	50.00
3a	Pixie on Rabbit	Dark green hat; dark blue coat; grey trousers; blue boots; white rabbit	40 x 32	85.00	100.00	50.00
3b	Pixie on Rabbit	Red hat; dark blue coat; grey trousers; blue boots; white rabbit	40 x 32	85.00	100.00	50.00
3c	Pixie on Rabbit	Dark yellow hat; dark blue coat; grey trousers; blue boots; white rabbit	40 x 32	85.00	100.00	50.00

Lucky Fairy Folk Derivative

Butter Dish

1970s

Pixie on Acorn Butter Dish

Backstamp: Embossed "Wade England"

No.	Description	Size	U.S. $	Can. $	U.K. £
1a	Green hat; yellow dish	65 x 80	65.00	90.00	45.00
1b	Yellow hat, dish	65 x 80	65.00	90.00	45.00
1c	Red hat; yellow dish	65 x 80	65.00	90.00	45.00
1d	Blue hat; yellow dish	65 x 80	65.00	90.00	45.00

Pin Tray

c.1960

An unusual find is the *Lucky Fair Folk* "Pixie on a Rabbit" whimtray. This model may have been produced after Wade England discontinued their whimtray series and sent the surplus stock to Wade Ireland.

Pixie on Rabbit Pin Tray

Backstamp: Embossed "Wade Porcelain Made in England"

No.	Description	Size	U.S. $	Can. $	U.K. £
1.	Yellow hat; blue jacket, shoes; grey trousers; white rabbit; yellow tray	60 x 75	100.00	120.00	60.00

SECOND VERSION: LEPRECHAUN ON PIG FLESH COLOURED FACE

1980-1986

Only one of the *Lucky Fair Folk* models was reissued and that was the "Leprechaun On Pig." The difference between the first and second versions is the colour of the Leprechaun's face. The Leprechaun's face is flesh-toned on the second version.

Backstamp: Unmarked

No.	Name	Description	Size	U.S. $	Can. $	U.K. £
1a	Leprechaun on Pig	Green hat; flesh face, hands; blue coat, white boots; grey trousers; pig has light beige snout and toes	45 x 35	48.00	68.00	35.00
1b	Leprechaun on Pig	Red hat; flesh face, hands; blue coat, boots; beige trousers; pig has light beige snout and toes	45 x 35	48.00	68.00	35.00

LUCKY LEPRECHAUNS

1956-1980s

This set of three *Lucky Leprechauns* was first issued in 1956 by Wade (Ulster) Ltd. When the models were originally shipped to retailers, they were packaged in decorative display boxes of 24 models, with hat colours of white, yellow, orange, red, maroon, blue or green. Also included was a porcelain shamrock leaf to use as a price display, see page 40. On it was printed "Lucky Leprechauns Made in Ireland By Wade Co. Armagh 1/11d each." Many of these shamrock plaques have survived and are sought by collectors. The *Lucky Leprechauns* set was reissued in the mid-1960s and again in the 1980s.

FIRST VERSION: BROWN FACES, PAPER LABEL

1956-1959

Originally the models each had a black and gold label on the base. The label is easily washed off and if it is missing it is difficult to tell which version the figure comes from. As a general guide, the 1956-1959 models have brown faces, whereas the faces of later figures are flesh coloured.

Backstamp: A. Black and gold label "Made in Ireland by Wade Co. Armagh" (1-3)
B. Unmarked (1-3)

No.	Name	Description	Size	U.S. $	Can. $	U.K. £
1a	Cobbler	Dark green hat; grey coat; boots; blue trousers	39 x 20	30.00	35.00	18.00
1b	Cobbler	Maroon hat; grey coat, boots; blue trousers	39 x 20	30.00	35.00	18.00
1c	Cobbler	Orange hat; grey coat, boots; blue trousers	39 x 20	30.00	35.00	18.00
1d	Cobbler	Red hat; grey coat, boots; blue trousers	39 x 20	30.00	35.00	18.00
1e	Cobbler	White hat; grey coat, boots; blue trousers	39 x 20	30.00	35.00	18.00
2a	Crock O'Gold	Maroon hat; blue coat; grey trousers; brown boots	34 x 26	30.00	35.00	18.00
2b	Crock O'Gold	Orange hat; blue coat; grey trousers; brown boots	34 x 26	30.00	35.00	18.00
2c	Crock O'Gold	Red hat; blue coat; grey trousers; brown boots	34 x 26	30.00	35.00	18.00
2d	Crock O'Gold	Dark yellow hat; blue coat; grey trousers; brown boot	34 x 26	30.00	35.00	18.00
2e	Crock O'Gold	Yellow hat; green coat; grey trousers; brown boots	34 x 26	30.00	35.00	18.00
3a	Tailor	Blue hat; white coat; blue trousers; grey boot	38 x 31	30.00	35.00	18.00
3b	Tailor	Dark green hat; white coat; blue trousers; grey boot	38 x 31	30.00	35.00	18.00
3c	Tailor	Red hat; white coat; blue trousers; grey boot	38 x 31	30.00	35.00	18.00

Lucky Leprechauns First Version Derivatives

Oak Leaf Dish

1957-1959

The George Wade Pottery's 1957 oak leaf dish was issued with the 1956-1959 "Leprechaun Crock O'Gold" to produce this particular dish. The original selling price was 2/11d.

Backstamp: Embossed "Shamrock Pottery"

No.	Name	Description	Size	U.S. $	Can. $	U.K. £
1a	Crock O'Gold	Maroon hat; blue coat; brown boots; green leaf	40 x 100	25.00	30.00	15.00
1b	Crock O'Gold	Orange hat; blue coat; brown boots; green leaf	40 x 100	25.00	30.00	15.00
1c	Crock O'Gold	Yellow hat; blue coat; brown boots; green leaf	40 x 100	25.00	30.00	15.00
1d	Crock O'Gold	Yellow hat; green coat; white/brown boots; green leaf	40 x 100	32.00	40.00	20.00
2	Tailor	Blue hat and trousers; white coat; grey boot; green leaf	40 x 100	32.00	40.00	20.00

Lucky Leprechauns First Version Derivatives (cont.)

Pintrays
1956-1959

The *Lucky Leprechauns* models used on these pin trays were issued by Wade (Ulster) Ltd. from 1956 to 1959. The pin tray in which the Lucky Leprechaun sits was originally produced as a "pin tray" (plain) and as a "butter pat" (with transfer printed decorations) see *The Charlton Standard Catalogue of Wade Decorative Ware, Vol. 2* and *The Charlton Standard Catalogue of Wade Tableware, Vol. 3*. There are two styles of pin trays: one with a recessed centre (Irish Wade Shape No I.P.619), and an early 1950s backstamp, the second with a flat centre, and 1971-1976 backstamps. The first version *Lucky Leprechauns* are found only on recessed trays.

There are no price differentials between the recessed and flat centre trays or between Version One, Two or Three Leprechauns.

Colour: Blue-green trays
Backstamp: Embossed Circular "Irish Porcelain Made in Ireland" around a central shamrock with letter T (early 1950s)

No.	Name	Description	Size	U.S. $	Can. $	U.K. £
1a	Cobbler	Dark green hat; grey coat, boots; blue trousers	45 x 75	27.00	32.00	16.00
1b	Cobbler	Orange hat; grey coat, boots; blue trousers	45 x 75	27.00	32.00	16.00
1c	Cobbler	Maroon hat; grey coat, boots; blue trousers	45 x 75	27.00	32.00	16.00
1d	Cobbler	White hat; grey coat, boots; blue trousers	45 x 75	27.00	32.00	16.00
2a	Crock O'Gold	Maroon hat; blue coat; grey trousers; brown boots	45 x 75	27.00	32.00	16.00
2b	Crock O'Gold	Orange hat; blue coat; grey trousers; brown boots	45 x 75	27.00	32.00	16.00
2c	Crock O'Gold	Dark yellow hat; blue coat; grey trousers; brown boots	45 x 75	27.00	32.00	16.00
3a	Tailor	Blue hat; white coat; blue trousers; grey boot	45 x 75	27.00	32.00	16.00
3b	Tailor	Dark blue hat; white coat; blue trousers; grey boot	45 x 75	27.00	32.00	16.00
3c	Tailor	Dark green hat; white coat; blue trousers; grey boot	45 x 75	27.00	32.00	16.00
3d	Tailor	Maroon hat; white coat; blue trousers; grey boot	45 x 75	27.00	32.00	16.00

Lucky Leprechauns First Version Derivatives (cont.)

Stone Plinth Souvenir Crock O'Gold Leprechaun
1957-1959

This Crock O'Gold, first version Lucky Leprechaun, with a brown face, is mounted on a thick stone plinth. The plinth has a green and silver shamrock-shaped enamel plaque on the front that reads "Giant's Causeway." This model was not produced by Wade in this form. The porcelain models were purchased by individual companies who applied them to the stone plinths. They were produced in this form for the tourist trade.

Backstamp: None

No.	Name	Description	Size	U.S. $	Can. $	U.K. £
1	Crock O'Gold	Yellow hat; blue jacket; grey trousers; brown boots	65 x 52	35.00	45.00	22.00

SECOND VERSION: FLESH COLOURED FACES, WITHOUT BACKSTAMPS

1960s

This boxed set of three *Lucky Leprechauns* had no labels and were unmarked. Once removed from their box, there is no indication of the year of issue or of the maker. The reissued models have flesh-coloured faces, which distinguish them from the original 1956-1959 version.

Backstamp: Unmarked

No.	Name	Description	Size	U.S. $	Can. $	U.K. £
1a	Cobbler	Green hat; light grey coat, boots; pale blue trousers	39 x 20	20.00	25.00	12.00
1b	Cobbler	Orange hat; light grey coat, boots; pale blue trousers	39 x 20	20.00	25.00	12.00
1c	Cobbler	Red hat; light grey coat, boots; pale blue trousers	39 x 20	20.00	25.00	12.00
1d	Cobbler	Yellow hat; light grey coat, boots; pale blue trousers	39 x 20	20.00	25.00	12.00
2a	Crock O'Gold	Blue hat; pale blue-grey coat; light grey trousers; brown boots with or without brown stripe	34 x 26	20.00	25.00	12.00
2b	Crock O'Gold	Green hat; pale blue-grey coat; light grey trousers; brown boots with or without brown stripe	34 x 26	20.00	25.00	12.00
2c	Crock O'Gold	Red hat; pale blue-grey coat; light grey trousers; brown boots with or without brown stripe	34 x 26	20.00	25.00	12.00
2d	Crock O'Gold	Yellow hat; pale blue-grey coat; light grey trousers; brown boots with or without brown stripe	34 x 26	20.00	25.00	12.00
3a	Tailor	Pale blue hat, trousers; white coat; grey boot	38 x 31	20.00	25.00	12.00
3b	Tailor	Green hat; white coat; pale blue trousers; grey boot	38 x 31	20.00	25.00	12.00
3c	Tailor	Red hat; white coat; pale blue trousers; grey boot	38 x 31	20.00	25.00	12.00
3d	Tailor	Yellow hat; white coat; pale blue trousers; grey boot	38 x 31	20.00	25.00	12.00
—	3 pce set	Boxed		75.00	85.00	38.00

Lucky Leprechaun Second Version Derivatives

Butter Dish

1970s

The George Wade butter dish was first produced from 1955 to 1959, with a model of a squirrel, rabbit (see *The Charlton Standard Catalogue of Wade Decorative Ware, Vol. Two)* or the 1956 *Hat Box* "Jock" on the back rim. In the 1970s, the dish was combined with surplus Irish Wade, *Lucky Leprechauns* to produce novelty butter dishes.

Backstamp: Embossed "Wade England"

No.	Name	Description	Size	U.S. $	Can. $	U.K. £
1a	Cobbler	Blue hat; yellow dish	65 x 80	28.00	38.00	18.00
1b	Cobbler	Green hat; yellow dish	65 x 80	28.00	38.00	18.00
1c	Cobbler	White hat; yellow dish	65 x 80	35.00	45.00	22.00
2a	Tailor	Blue hat; yellow dish	65 x 80	28.00	38.00	18.00
2b	Tailor	Green hat; yellow dish	65 x 80	28.00	38.00	18.00
2c	Tailor	Red hat; yellow dish	65 x 80	28.00	38.00	18.00

Lucky Leprechauns Second Version Derivatives (cont.)

Marble Plinths
Circa 1975-1985

These models were taken from the reissued 1974-1985 *Lucky Leprechauns* set and mounted on a block of Connemara marble. The marble plinths can be found in a variety of shapes: circular, rectangular and square, and the thickness and length can vary. These models were not produced by Wade in this form. The porcelain models were purchased by individual companies, and later applied to marble plinths. They were intended for the tourist trade.

Lucky Leprechauns on Marble Plinths

Backstamp: **A.** Gold label "Lucky Irish Leprechauns, Made in Ireland"
B. Unmarked

No.	Name	Description	Size	U.S. $	Can. $	U.K. £
1	Cobbler	Light brown stool; beige shoe	58 x 52	25.00	35.00	17.00
2a	Crock O'Gold	Blue hat; yellow coins; grey coat, trousers	58 x 52	25.00	35.00	17.00
2b	Crock O'Gold	Red hat; yellow coins; grey coat, trousers	43 x 48	25.00	35.00	17.00
2c	Crock O'Gold	Red hat, yellow coins, grey-blue coat, trousers	45 x 50	25.00	35.00	17.00
2d	Crock O'Gold	Yellow hat, coins; blue coat; beige trousers	58 x 52	25.00	35.00	17.00
2e	Crock O'Gold	Yellow hat, coins; grey coat, trousers	58 x 52	25.00	35.00	17.00
3a	Tailor	Blue hat; grey trousers, shoes	58 x 52	25.00	35.00	17.00
3b	Tailor	Yellow hat; grey trousers, shoes	58 x 52	25.00	35.00	17.00

Simulated Marble Plinths
Circa 1975-1985

Lucky Leprechaun 'Duo of Models' with Irish harp on simulated base 1975-1985

These models were taken from the reissued 1974-1985 *Lucky Leprechauns* set, and mounted on a block of simulated marble (resin). These plinths can be found in a variety of shapes: circular, rectangular or square, and they can be of different lengths and thickness. Some examples can be found with the name of an Irish town on the plinth. These models were not produced by Wade in this form. The porcelain models were purchased by individual companies, and later applied to marble plinths. They were intended for the tourist trade.

Backstamp: **A.** Black or gold label "Lucky Irish Leprechauns, Made in England"
             B. Black or gold label "Irish Leprechauns, Made in Ireland"
             C. Black or gold label "Made in Ireland"

No.	Name	Description	Shape / Size	U.S. $	Can. $	U.K. £
1	Cobbler	Light brown stool; beige shoe	Square/58 x 52	22.00	30.00	15.00
2	Duo of models	Cobbler: red hat; Tailor: blue hat; brass Irish harp	Rect/70 x 115	57.00	70.00	35.00
3a	Trio of models	Cobbler: Red hat; Crock O'Gold: Red hat; Tailor: Blue hat; black lettering "Conway"	Rect./52 x 80	22.00	30.00	15.00
3b	Trio of models	Cobbler: Blue hat; Crock O'Gold: Red hat; Tailor: Blue hat; black lettering "Nenagh"	Rect./52 x 80	35.00	45.00	22.00
4	Trio of models	Cobbler: red hat; Tailor: blue hat; Leprechaun: grey	82 x 79	40.00	60.00	30.00

Pin Trays

The second version of the *Lucky Leprechauns* are found on both styles of trays, recessed and flat centre.

Pin Tray

Colour: Blue-green trays
Backstamp: Embossed Circular "Irish Porcelain Made in Ireland" around a central shamrock with letter T (early 1950s)

No.	Name	Description	Size	U.S. $	Can. $	U.K. £
1a	Cobbler	Dark green hat; grey coat, boots; blue trousers	45 x 75	27.00	35.00	17.00
1b	Cobbler	Maroon hat; grey coat, boots; blue trousers	45 x 75	27.00	35.00	17.00
1c	Cobbler	Orange hat; grey coat, boots; blue trousers	45 x 75	27.00	35.00	17.00
1d	Cobbler	White hat; grey coat, boots; blue trousers	45 x 75	27.00	35.00	17.00
2a	Crock O'Gold	Dark yellow hat; blue coat; grey trousers; brown boots	45 x 75	27.00	35.00	17.00
2b	Crock O'Gold	Maroon hat; blue coat; grey trousers; brown boots	45 x 75	27.00	35.00	17.00
2c	Crock O'Gold	Orange hat; blue coat; grey trousers; brown boots	45 x 75	27.00	35.00	17.00
3a	Tailor	Blue hat; white coat; blue trousers; grey boot	45 x 75	27.00	35.00	17.00
3b	Tailor	Dark green hat; white coat; blue trousers; grey boot	45 x 75	27.00	35.00	17.00
3c	Tailor	Maroon hat; white coat; blue trousers; grey boot	45 x 75	27.00	35.00	17.00

THIRD VERSION: FLESH COLOURED FACES, WITH BACKSTAMP
1971-1976

Backstamp: **A.** Small black ink stamp "Made in Ireland" (1a)
B. Large black ink stamp "Made in Ireland" (1b, 2a, 2b, 3a, 3b, 3c)

No.	Name	Description	Size	U.S. $	Can. $	U.K. £
1a	Cobbler	Red hat; grey coat, boots; pale blue trousers	39 x 20	24.00	30.00	15.00
1b	Cobbler	White hat; dark grey coat, boots; dark blue trousers	39 x 20	24.00	30.00	15.00
2a	Crock O'Gold	Blue hat; blue coat; light grey trousers; brown boots with or without brown stripe	34 x 26	24.00	30.00	15.00
2b	Crock O'Gold	Green hat; blue coat; light grey trousers; brown boots with or without brown stripe	34 x 26	24.00	30.00	15.00
2c	Crock O'Gold	Red hat; blue coat; light grey trousers; brown boots with or without brown stripe	34 x 26	24.00	30.00	15.00
2d	Crock O'Gold	Yellow hat; blue coat; light grey trousers; brown boots with or without brown stripe	34 x 26	24.00	30.00	15.00
3a	Tailor	Blue hat/trousers; white coat; grey boot	38 x 31	24.00	30.00	15.00
3b	Tailor	Yellow hat; white coat; blue trousers; grey boot	38 x 31	24.00	30.00	15.00

Lucky Leprechauns Third Version Derivative

Natural Wood Plinth
1980s

Backstamp: Black ink stamp "A Cottage Series Irish Made Souvenir" with print of a cottage

No.	Name	Description	Size	U.S. $	Can. $	U.K. £
1	Cobbler and Tailor	Cobbler: Red hat; light grey coat; pale blue trousers Tailor: Blue hat; white coat; blue trousers	65 x 115	32.00	45.00	22.00

Lucky Leprechauns Third Version Derivatives (cont.)

Pin Trays

1980s

Backstamp: Embossed circular "Made in Ireland Irish Porcelain Wade Eire Tir A Dheanta" IP 619 with shamrock and crown in centre

No.	Name	Description	Size	U.S. $	Can. $	U.K. £
1a	Cobbler	Green hat; light grey coat, boots; pale blue trousers	45 x 75	24.00	30.00	15.00
1b	Cobbler	Orange hat; light grey coat, boots; pale blue trousers	45 x 75	24.00	30.00	15.00
1c	Cobbler	Red hat; light grey coat, boots; pale blue trousers	45 x 75	24.00	30.00	15.00
1d	Cobbler	Yellow hat; light grey coat, boots; pale blue trousers	45 x 75	24.00	30.00	15.00
2a	Crock O'Gold	Blue hat; pale blue grey coat; light grey trousers; brown boots with or without brown stripe	45 x 75	24.00	30.00	15.00
2b	Crock O'Gold	Green hat; pale blue grey coat; light grey trousers; brown boots with or without brown stripe	45 x 75	24.00	30.00	15.00
2c	Crock O'Gold	Red hat; pale blue grey coat; light grey trousers; brown boots with or without brown stripe	45 x 75	24.00	30.00	15.00
2d	Crock O'Gold	Yellow hat; pale blue grey coat; light grey trousers; brown boots with or without brown stripe	45 x 75	24.00	30.00	15.00
3a	Tailor	Pale blue hat, trousers; white coat; grey boot	45 x 75	24.00	30.00	15.00
3b	Tailor	Green hat; white coat; pale blue trousers; grey boot	45 x 75	24.00	30.00	15.00
3c	Tailor	Red hat; white coat; pale blue trousers; grey boot	45 x 75	24.00	30.00	15.00
3d	Tailor	Yellow hat; white coat; pale blue trousers; grey boot	45 x 75	24.00	30.00	15.00

LUCKY LEPRECHAUN SHAMROCK PLAQUE

1956-1959

This was originally a display plaque for the Lucky Leprechaun models and would have been distributed to the retailer to be displayed with the models and not intended for resale.

Backstamp: None

No.	Description	Size	U.S. $	Can. $	U.K. £
1	White/green; black lettering	100 x 48	180.00	240.00	100.00

SHAMROCK COTTAGE

1956-1984

The *Shamrock Cottage,* which can be found with either a light or dark yellow roof, was a slip cast, hollow model of an Irish cottage, produced by Wade (Ulster) Ltd. It was sold in a box decorated with a shamrock design and labeled "Shamrock Pottery" and "Ireland's own Pottery." The original selling price was 2/6d.

FIRST VERSION: LIGHT BROWN PEAT, GREEN BASE

1956-1961, 1977-Early 1980s

Backstamp: Impressed "Shamrock Pottery Made in Ireland"

No.	Description	Size	U.S. $	Can. $	U.K. £
1	Yellow roof; blue doors, windows; light brown peat; green base	45 x 40	50.00	65.00	32.00

SECOND VERSION: DARK BROWN PEAT, MOTTLED GREEN BASE

1977-1984

This reissued *Shamrock Cottage* is the same as the 1956-1961 model, except that the colour of the base is a mottled green and white and the peat pile at the back of the cottage is a darker shade of brown. It has also been found with names of places of interest printed in black letters on the front rim of the base, the names of the towns being added after the models were sold.

There are variations in the shading of the yellow roofs of the cottages, which changed with each new issue. Donaghadee is a small fishing village 20 miles outside Belfast, it is a popular holiday town famous for Grace Neill's bar, which is the oldest pub in Ireland.

| Plain Cottage (1o) | Bourton-on-the-Water Cottage (1f) |

Backstamp: Impressed "Shamrock Pottery Made in Ireland"

No.	Name	Description	Size	U.S. $	Can. $	U.K. £
1a	Bally Castle	Yellow roof; dark blue doors; dark brown peat; mottled green and white base; black lettering	45 x 40	50.00	65.00	32.00
1b	Belfast	Yellow roof; dark blue doors; dark brown peat; mottled green and white base; black lettering	45 x 40	50.00	65.00	32.00
1c	Bourton-on-the-Water	Yellow roof; dark blue doors; dark brown peat; mottle green and white base; black lettering	45 x 40	50.00	65.00	32.00
1d	Cliftonville	Yellow roof; dark blue doors; dark brown peat; mottled green and white base; black lettering	45 x 40	50.00	65.00	32.00
1e	Conway	Yellow roof; dark blue doors; dark brown peat; mottled green and white base; black lettering	45 x 40	50.00	65.00	32.00
1f	Donaghee	Yellow roof; dark blue doors; dark brown peat; mottled green and white base; black lettering	45 x 40	50.00	65.00	32.00
1g	Giants Causeway	Yellow roof; blue doors; dark brown peat; mottled green and white base; black lettering	45 x 40	50.00	65.00	32.00
1h	Guernsey	Yellow roof; dark blue doors; dark brown peat; mottled green and white base; black lettering	45 x 40	50.00	65.00	32.00
1i	Hawkshead	Yellow roof; dark blue doors; dark brown peat; mottled green and white base; black lettering	45 x 40	50.00	65.00	32.00
1j	Isle of Wight	Yellow roof; dark blue doors; dark brown peat; mottled green and white base; black lettering	45 x 40	50.00	65.00	32.00
1k	Jersey	Yellow roof; dark blue doors; dark brown peat; mottled green and white base; black lettering	45 x 40	50.00	65.00	32.00
1l	Omagh	Yellow roof; dark blue doors; dark brown peat; mottled green and white base; black lettering	45 x 40	50.00	65.00	32.00
1m	Plain Cottage	Yellow roof; blue doors, windows; dark brown peat; mottled green and white base	45 x 40	50.00	65.00	32.00
1n	Shanklin	Yellow roof; dark blue doors; dark brown peat; mottled green and white base; black lettering	45 x 40	50.00	65.00	32.00
1o	Windermere	Yellow roof; blue doors; dark brown peat; mottled green and white base; black lettering	45 x 40	50.00	65.00	32.00

Shamrock Cottage Second Version Derivatives

Shamrock Cottage on Simulated Marble Plinth

This *Shamrock Cottage* is glued onto a simulated resin Connemara marble base. Attached to the base is a gold coloured piece of metal, the top of which is missing the original model, an unknown building or figure.

Backstamp: None

No.	Description	Size	U.S. $	Can. $	U.K. £
1	Yellow roof; blue door, windows; green/white base; circular mottled olive green resin base	45 x 40 (plinth - 55 x 50)	50.00	65.00	32.00

Shamrock Cottage on Simulated Marble Plinth

This *Shamrock Cottage* is glued onto a simulated resin Connemara marble base. Also attached to the base is a miniature tankard with a Guinness label on the front. The miniature tankard is not believed to have been produced by Wade.

Backstamp: None

No.	Description	Size	U.S. $	Can. $	U.K. £
1	Yellow roof; blue door, windows; green/white base; honey tankard; black bands	45 x 40	50.00	65.00	32.00

THIRD VERSION: LIGHT BROWN PEAT, WHITE BASE

1977-Early 1980s

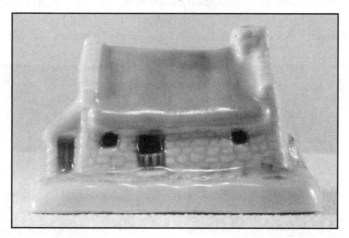

Backstamp: Impressed "Shamrock Pottery Made in Ireland"

No.	Description	Size	U.S. $	Can. $	U.K. £
1.	Yellow roof; blue doors, window; light brown peat; white base1	45 x 40	50.00	65.00	32.00

Shamrock Cottage Third Version Derivatives

Cottage and Tailor on a Map of Ireland

Mid 1950s and 1970s

This model has recently been found with a Shamrock Pottery backstamp, and a brown-faced Leprechaun which would suggest that it was originally produced in the mid 1950s and was reissued in the 1970s, with a later backstamp. The reissued "Tailor" and the reissued *Shamrock Cottage* (1974-1985) were combined by Wade Ireland and placed on a porcelain outline of the map of Ireland to form this unusual and sought-after souvenir model. It was discontinued in 1979.

Backstamp: A. Embossed "Shamrock Pottery Made in Ireland by Wade of Armagh"
          B. Embossed "Made in Ireland"

No.	Name	Description	Size	U.S. $	Can. $	U.K. £
1a	Tailor	Blue hat; grey trousers, shoes; grey-green base	65 x 140	120.00	160.00	90.00
1b	Tailor	Yellow hat; grey trousers, shoes; grey-green base	65 x 140	120.00	160.00	90.00
1c	Tailor	Blue hat, trousers; grey shoes; grey-green base	65 x 140	120.00	160.00	90.00

Shamrock Cottage Third Version Derivatives (cont.)

Shamrock Cottage on Simulated Marble Plinth with Lucky Leprechaun
1970s

In the late 1970s the "Cobbler," "Crock O'Gold" and "Tailor" *Leprechauns* and the reissued *Shamrock Cottage* (1974-1985) were combined and mounted on a rectangular marble base.

Backstamp: None

No.	Name	Description	Size	U.S. $	Can. $	U.K. £
1	Cobbler and Cottage	Beige stool; white shoes; yellow roof; blue windows; dark brown peat	48 x 80	50.00	65.00	32.00
2	Crock O'Gold and Cottage	Yellow hat; blue jacket; yellow roof; blue windows; dark brown peat	44 x 80	50.00	65.00	32.00
3a	Tailor and Cottage	Yellow hat; grey trousers; yellow roof; blue windows; dark brown peat	49 x 80	50.00	65.00	32.00
3b	Tailor and Cottage	Blue hat, trousers; yellow roof; blue windows; dark brown peat	49 x 95	50.00	65.00	32.00

Shamrock Cottage and Pin Tray on Simulated Marble Plinth
1970s

Backstamp: None

No.	Name	Description	Size	U.S. $	Can. $	U.K. £
1	Cottage and pintray	Yellow roof; blue windows; dark brown peat; white/green base; blue-grey pin tray	48 x 80	50.00	65.00	32.00

NOVELTY ANIMALS AND BIRDS

NOVELTY ANIMALS AND BIRDS

Circa 1935-Circa 1949

BABY BIRD

Circa 1935

Backstamp: **A.** Black ink stamp "Flaxman Ware Hand Made Pottery By Wadeheath England" (1)
B. Black ink stamp "Wadeheath Ware England" (2)

No.	Name	Description	Size	U.S. $	Can. $	U.K. £
1a	Baby Bird, large	Mottled green	200 x 165	160.00	200.00	100.00
1b	Baby Bird, large	Pale orange	200 x 165	160.00	200.00	100.00
1c	Baby Bird, large	Yellow	200 x 165	160.00	200.00	100.00
2a	Baby Bird, small	Green	90 x 65	65.00	80.00	40.00
2b	Baby Bird, small	Orange	90 x 65	65.00	80.00	40.00
2c	Baby Bird, small	Yellow	90 x 65	65.00	80.00	40.00

CHEEKY DUCKLING

Backstamp: Black ink stamp "Flaxman Ware Hand Made Pottery by Wadeheath England"

No.	Name	Description	Size	U.S. $	Can. $	U.K. £
1	Cheeky Duckling, large	Blue	180 x 115	250.00	310.00	155.00
2a	Cheeky Duckling, small	Blue	150 x 85	200.00	250.00	125.00
2b	Cheeky Duckling, small	Orange	150 x 85	200.00	250.00	125.00

DUCKLING, HEAD BACK, BEAK CLOSED

Circa 1937-1939

Backstamp: None

No.	Name	Description	Size	U.S. $	Can. $	U.K. £
1a	Duckling, head back, beak closed	Green	95	150.00	160.00	75.00
1b	Duckling, head back, beak closed	Pale green	100	150.00	185.00	95.00

DUCKLING, HEAD FORWARD, BEAK OPEN

Circa 1937-1939

Backstamp: A. Ink stamp "Flaxman Wade Heath England" (1937-1939) (1a)
B. None (1b)

No.	Name	Description	Size	U.S. $	Can. $	U.K. £
1a	Duckling, head forward, beak open	Beige brown	95	150.00	185.00	95.00
1b	Duckling, head forward, beak open	Green	95	150.00	185.00	95.00
1c	Duckling, head forward, beak open	Green	Miniature/60	125.00	150.00	75.00

LAUGHING RABBIT

1937-1939

The shape number for the Laughing Rabbit is 335. This model was scaled-down and issued as Rabbit (Little Laughing Bunny), see page 11.

Backstamp: Black ink stamp "Flaxman Wade Heath England"

No.	Name	Description	Size	U.S. $	Can. $	U.K. £
1a	Laughing Rabbit, large	Bright green	175 x 75	150.00	185.00	95.00
1b	Laughing Rabbit, large	Orange	175 x 75	150.00	185.00	95.00
2a	Laughing Rabbit, medium	Blue	160 x 70	130.00	160.00	80.00
2b	Laughing Rabbit, medium	Brown	160 x 70	130.00	160.00	80.00
2c	Laughing Rabbit, medium	Green	160 x 70	130.00	160.00	80.00
3a	Laughing Rabbit, small	Beige	140 x 65	120.00	150.00	75.00
3b	Laughing Rabbit, small	Blue	140 x 65	120.00	150.00	75.00
3c	Laughing Rabbit, small	Green	140 x 65	120.00	150.00	75.00
4	Old Buck Rabbit	Brown	165 x 128	190.00	275.00	125.00

LAUGHING SQUIRREL

c.1940

This miniature comical squirrel model is very similar in face decoration to one of the Little Laughing Bunny models. As this is the only example of this model seen to date, it may be a prototype that was not put into production.

Backstamp: Ink stamp "Wade England"

No.	Name	Description	Size	U.S. $	Can. $	U.K. £
1	Laughing Squirrel	Fawn; brown mouth, toes	45		Rare	

Note: As this is a unique or one-of-a-kind piece the price must be decided between the buyer and seller.

PONGO

1935-Circa 1949

Pongo was in production from 1935 to 1939 and was reissued for a short time in the late 1940s.

Backstamp: **A.** Black ink stamp "Flaxman Ware Hand Made Pottery By Wadeheath England"
B. Black ink stamp "Wadeheath Ware England"
C. Black ink stamp "Wade Heath England," 1938-1940s

No.	Name	Description	Size	U.S. $	Can. $	U.K. £
1a	Pongo, large	Blue; mauve nose	140 x 128	135.00	165.00	85.00
1b	Pongo, large	Green	145 x 150	135.00	165.00	85.00
1c	Pongo, large	Lilac; mauve nose	140 x 128	135.00	165.00	85.00
1d	Pongo, large	Mottled blue/orange	140 x 128	135.00	165.00	85.00
1e	Pongo, large	Orange	145 x 150	135.00	165.00	85.00
1f	Pongo, large	Orange; mauve nose	140 x 128	135.00	165.00	85.00
2a	Pongo, medium	Blue; mauve nose	128 x 115	135.00	165.00	85.00
2b	Pongo, medium	Lilac; mauve nose	128 x 115	135.00	165.00	85.00
2c	Pongo, medium	Mottled blue/orange	128 x 115	135.00	165.00	85.00
2d	Pongo, medium	Orange; mauve nose	128 x 115	135.00	165.00	85.00
2e	Pongo, medium	Turquoise; black eyes, nose	128 x 115	135.00	165.00	85.00
3	Pongo, miniature	Blue	105 x 95	115.00	145.00	70.00
4a	Pongo, small	Blue; mauve nose	115 x 100	90.00	110.00	55.00
4b	Pongo, small	Green; blue eyes, nose	120 x 110	90.00	110.00	55.00
4c	Pongo, small	Lilac; mauve nose	115 x 100	90.00	110.00	55.00
4d	Pongo, small	Mauve	120 x 110	90.00	110.00	55.00
4e	Pongo, small	Orange; mauve nose	115 x 100	90.00	110.00	55.00
4f	Pongo, small	Pink; black nose	115 x 100	90.00	110.00	55.00

Advertisement for Lucky Fairyfolk

Advertisement for Lucky Leprechauns

STORYBOOK FIGURES

STORYBOOK FIGURES

At the end of World War II the giftware restrictions on potteries were lifted. Although there was plenty of work available to replace war-damaged industrial wares, a few novelty figurines were produced by the Wade Heath Royal Victoria Pottery and by the George Wade Pottery.

Before 1953 these models were produced in the Royal Victoria Pottery and were marked with a green ink stamp. Models produced in 1953 and after, in either the Royal Victoria Pottery or in the George Wade Pottery, were marked with black transfers.

The first nursery rhyme and fairy tale models produced by Wade were coloured in delicate shades of pastel blues, whites and greys. Because they were produced in both potteries, and dies were replaced when worn, there are slight variations in size and in hair colour on the earlier models. Models are listed in alphabetical order for ease of reference.

Alice and the Dodo was produced with a 1930s experimental cellulose glaze, which cracked and flaked when exposed to heat, damp and sunlight. It is rare to find cellulose models in mint condition. Sylvac produced models in a cellulose glaze, these also suffered the same fate as the Wade models.

Some models are marked with a 1935-1937 mark ("Flaxman Ware Hand Made Pottery by Wadeheath England") or any of the 1937-1939 marks ("Flaxman Wade Heath England or Wadeheath Ware England"). Most have an all-over, one-colour matt glaze. All the following storybook models are slip cast, and therefore hollow.

ALICE AND THE DODO

Circa 1935-1938

Alice and the Dodo was produced in the cellulose glaze described above. It is rare to find these models in perfect condition.

Backstamp: **A.** Black hand-painted "Wade Alice 2" with black ink stamp "Made in England" (1)
B. Black hand-painted "Wade Alice" with red ink stamp of leaping deer (2a, 2b, 2c)

No.	Description	Size	U.S. $	Can. $	U.K. £
1	Orange-yellow dress; black band; light brown bird; black beret	130 x 80	450.00	550.00	275.00
2a	Green dress; red band; dark brown bird; blue beret	130 x 80	450.00	550.00	275.00
2b	Pink dress; red band; dark brown bird; blue beret	130 x 80	450.00	550.00	275.00
2c	Blue dress; red band; dark brown bird; blue beret	130 x 80	450.00	550.00	275.00

ANDY CAPP FORTIETH ANNIVERSARY

1997

To celebrate the 40th anniversary of the *Daily Mirror* cartoon series *Andy Capp*, Wade Ceramics produced an *Andy Capp and Flo* cruet, teapot and toast rack. The complete set could be purchased for £35.00 ($58.00 U.S.).

Backstamp: **A.** Printed "Andy Capp Andy © 1997 Mirror Group Newspapers Ltd, Wade" (1)
B. Printed "Andy Capp Flo © 1997 Mirror Group Newspapers Ltd, Wade" (2)
C. Printed "Andy Capp © 1997 Mirror Group Newspapers Ltd, Wade" (3, 4)

No.	Name	Description	Size	U.S. $	Can. $	U.K. £
1	Andy Capp Salt	Light green cap, scarf; black suit; white base	93	20.00	25.00	12.00
2	Flo Pepper	Yellow hair; light green hairband, blouse; black skirt, shoes; white base	103	20.00	25.00	12.00
3	Andy Capp Teapot	Green cap; flesh coloured face; black pot	132	30.00	40.00	20.00
4	Toast Rack	Black; gold line; multicoloured print	70	20.00	25.00	12.00

ANDY CAPP MONEY BOX

1998

Reg Smythe, the creator of *Andy Capp*, died of cancer in 1998, as a mark of respect Wade Ceramics donated £1.00 from the sale of the Andy Capp money box model to cancer research. Original cost direct from the Wade Club was £22.00.

Backstamp: Printed "Andy Capp © 1998 Mirror Group Newspapers LTD Andy Capp Wade England"

No.	Name	Description	Size	U.S. $	Can. $	U.K. £
1	Andy Capp Money Box	Green cap, scarf; black suit, shoes; brown suitcase; grey stool; white base	181	50.00	60.00	30.00

BENGO AND HIS PUPPY FRIENDS, TV PETS

1959-1965

TV Pets was based on a popular British television cartoon series called "Bengo and his Puppy Friends." The cartoon series was created by Austrian cartoonist William Timym, a British resident, who signed his cartoons "Tim." William Timym designed the TV Pets and also the *British Character* models for Wade.

The issue date for "Bengo," "Simon," "Pepi" and "Fifi" was May 1959; "Mitzi" and "Chee-Chee" came into production in September 1959; and "Bruno" and "Droopy" were issued in February 1961. At the beginning of 1965, the last two puppies "Percy" and "Whisky" joined the series, the same year the series came to an end, making a total of ten models in the set. The last two models are difficult to find, as they were only in production for a few months at most. The original price was 3/11d each.

Backstamp: **A.** Black and gold label "Genuine Wade Porcelain Made in England" (1-10)
B. Unmarked (1-10)

No.	Name	Description	Size	U.S. $	Can. $	U.K. £
1	Bengo (Boxer)	Light brown/white; grey muzzle	55 x 50	85.00	125.00	50.00
2	Bruno Junior (Saint Bernard)	Brown rump, head, ears; red tongue	55 x 35	105.00	150.00	70.00
3	Chee-Chee (Pekinese)	Beige; white face, chest, paws	60 x 35	70.00	100.00	45.00
4	Droopy Junior (Basset Hound)	Light brown; white chest; grey ear tips	55 x 40	150.00	150.00	70.00
5	Fifi (Poodle)	Grey-blue head, ears, legs; red bow	55 x 35	50.00	75.00	35.00
6	Mitzi (kitten)	Blue-grey/white; pink mouth	50 x 50	85.00	125.00	50.00
7	Pepi (Chihuahua)	Tan patches; large black eyes; red mouth	55 x 35	105.00	150.00	70.00
8	Percy (Afghan)	Beige; orange patches; grey face	65 x 30	150.00	175.00	90.00
9	Simon (Dalmatian)	White; black spots	60 x 40	85.00	125.00	50.00
10	Whisky (Corgi)	Beige; white face, chest, paws; red tongue	55 x 65	185.00	275.00	125.00

BENGO MONEY BOX

1965

Only one character from the *TV Pets* series was modeled as a money box. Because the original model is standing and had no bulk in which to hold coins, it was unsuitable. A new model of a sitting Bengo was created with a round body to contain the money. The coins slot into the dog's back.

Backstamp: Unmarked

No.	Description	Size	U.S. $	Can. $	U.K. £
1	Beige; white on face, feet; yellow basket	150 x 140	450.00	560.00	280.00

THE BUTCHER, THE BAKER AND THE CANDLESTICK MAKER

1953-Circa 1958

The Butcher, the Baker and the Candlestick Maker is a set of three characters, from a 1940s children's rhyme. It was modelled by Nancy Great-Rex.

Backstamp: **A.** Black transfer "Wade England [name of model]" (1, 2a, 2b, 3)
B. Blue transfer "Wade England [name of model]" (2a, 2b)

No.	Name	Description	Size	U.S. $	Can. $	U.K. £
1	The Butcher	Blue/white apron; grey trousers	95 x 40	295.00	365.00	180.00
2a	The Baker	Blue/white shirt; blue trousers	95 x 30	320.00	395.00	200.00
2b	The Baker	White shirt; blue trousers	95 x 30	320.00	395.00	200.00
3a	The Candlestick Maker	Black coat; grey trousers; yellow candlestick	110 x 25	390.00	480.00	240.00
3b	The Candlestick Maker	Black coat; grey trousers; beige candlestick	110 x 25	390.00	480.00	240.00
3c	The Candlestick Maker	Green coat; grey trousers; beige candlestick	110 x 25	390.00	480.00	240.00
3d	The Candlestick maker	White coat; grey trousers; brown candlestick	110 x 25	390.00	480.00	240.00

DISMAL DESMOND

Circa 1935

This model of "Dismal Desmond," a weeping Dalmatian, is based on a British children's comic character who featured in *Deans Rag Books* during the mid 1930s.

The all-over colourways of "Dismal Desmond" are in Flaxman glazes. The shape number 525 is impressed into the base of the green model.

Dismal Desmond: White with black markings

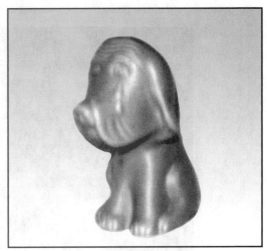

Dismal Desmond: All-over green

Backstamp: Ink stamp "Wadeheath England" with lion (1934-1935)

No.	Description	Size	U.S. $	Can. $	U.K. £
1a	Green	165	370.00	450.00	225.00
1b	Pale blue	165	370.00	450.00	225.00
1c	White; black markings; brownish-red tears, collar	165	450.00	600.00	300.00

GOLDILOCKS AND THE THREE BEARS

STYLE ONE

1953-Circa 1958

Goldilocks and the Three Bears is a set of four models based on the children's fairy tale. It is believed that these models were intended for export only, because they are named "Poppa Bear" and "Mama Bear," which are North American expressions, instead of "Father Bear" and "Mother Bear," as they would be called in Britain.

For *Goldilocks and the Three Bears,* Style Two, see Membership Exclusives, page 232.

Backstamp: Black transfer "Wade England [name of model]"

No.	Name	Description	Size	U.S. $	Can. $	U.K. £
1	Goldilocks	Blonde; blue/white skirt; pink petticoat, bonnet	100 x 60	350.00	435.00	215.00
2	Poppa Bear	Light brown; blue jacket; grey waistcoat	95 x 30	350.00	435.00	215.00
3	Mama Bear	Light brown; blue-grey dress	100 x 65	350.00	435.00	215.00
4	Baby Bear	Brown; blue dungarees	50 x 30	350.00	435.00	215.00

JUMBO JIM

Circa 1930s-1940s

The shape number for *Jumbo Jim* is 331. *Jumbo Jim* is believed to have appeared in a 1930s/40s children's book

Backstamp: **A.** Black ink stamp "Flaxman Wade Heath England" (1a)
B. Ink stamp "Flaxman Wade Heath England" with impressed No 331 (1b)

No.	Name	Description	Size	U.S. $	Can. $	U.K. £
1a	Jumbo Jim	Light brown	180 x 105	380.00	470.00	235.00
1b	Jumbo Jim	Turquoise blue	180 x 105	380.00	470.00	235.00

THE NODDY SET

STYLE ONE

1958-1961

The *Noddy* set consists of four characters created by the English children's writer Enid Blyton. Only four models were issued, with an original price of 3/11d each. Production was discontinued in autumn 1961. The models were not marked but originally had black and gold paper labels.

For *Noddy*, Style Two, see page 398.

Backstamp: Unmarked

No.	Name	Description	Size	U.S. $	Can. $	U.K. £
1	Noddy	Red shirt, shoes; blue hat, trousers, bows	70 x 35	350.00	430.00	215.00
2	Big Ears	Blue jacket; yellow trousers; red hat	70 x 35	285.00	350.00	175.00
3	Mr. Plod	Blue uniform, helmet; yellow buttons	60 x 35	200.00	250.00	125.00
4	Miss Fluffy Cat	Brown coat, collar; yellow hat; red bag	60 x 35	100.00	125.00	65.00

Noddy Style One Derivatives

Toadstool Cottage Money Boxes
Circa 1961

Following Wade's policy of using up unsold stock by converting it into better-selling lines (as with *First Whimsies* on candle holders and *Whimtrays*), "Big Ears" and "Noddy" from the *Noddy* set were placed on toadstool cottage money boxes, with a coin slot in the back rim of the roof. This series had a very limited production run and is extremely rare. The issue date is unknown, but it was probably soon after the *Noddy* set was finished in 1961. These models originally had black and gold foil labels.

Backstamp: **A.** Black and gold foil label "Genuine Wade Porcelain made in England"
B. Unmarked

No.	Name	Description	Size	U.S. $	Can. $	U.K. £
1a	Big Ears	Brown roof with white spots; yellow chimney, flowers; blue windows, door; green grass	110 x 120	390.00	480.00	240.00
1b	Big Ears	Brown roof with white spots; yellow chimney, flowers; blue windows; brown door; green grass	110 x 120	390.00	480.00	240.00
2	Noddy	Brown roof with white spots; yellow chimney, flowers; blue windows, door; green grass	110 x 120	390.00	480.00	240.00

NURSERY FAVOURITES

1972-1981

Nursery Favourites is a series of 20 large nursery rhyme and storybook characters. It was issued in four sets of five models, and each set was sold in a different coloured box. The original selling price for each figure was 7/6d. In 1990 and 1991, five *Nursery Favourites* were commissioned and reissued for Gold Star Gifthouse, see page 307.

SET ONE: DARK GREEN BOXES

1972

Backstamp: Embossed "Wade England"

No.	Name	Description	Size	U.S. $	Can. $	U.K. £
1	Jack	Brown hair, waistcoat; green trousers	75 x 30	45.00	55.00	28.00
2	Jill	Green bonnet, dress	75 x 40	45.00	55.00	28.00
3	Little Miss Muffett	Yellow hair; grey-green dress	60 x 50	45.00	55.00	28.00
4	Little Jack Horner	Green jacket; yellow trousers; brown hair	70 x 40	45.00	55.00	28.00
5	Humpty Dumpty	Honey brown; green suit; red tie	65 x 43	45.00	55.00	28.00

SET TWO: BLUE BOXES

1973

Backstamp: Embossed "Wade England"

No.	Name	Description	Size	U.S. $	Can. $	U.K. £
6	Wee Willie Winkie	Yellow hair; grey nightshirt	75 x 35	30.00	40.00	20.00
7	Mary Had a Little Lamb	Blue bonnet, skirt; grey-blue jacket	75 x 40	45.00	55.00	28.00
8	Polly Put the Kettle On	Brown; pink cap, kettle	75 x 35	45.00	55.00	28.00
9	Old King Cole	Yellow/grey hat; blue-grey cloak	65 x 50	45.00	55.00	28.00
10	Tom Tom the Piper's Son	Grey hat, kilt; brown jacket	65 x 55	45.00	55.00	28.00

SET THREE: YELLOW BOXES

1974

Backstamp: Embossed "Wade England"

No.	Name	Description	Size	U.S. $	Can. $	U.K. £
11	Little Boy Blue	Blue cap, jacket, trousers	75 x 30	60.00	75.00	37.00
12	Mary Mary	Yellow hair; blue dress; pink shoes	75 x 45	60.00	75.00	37.00
13	The Cat and the Fiddle	Brown/grey cat; yellow fiddle	70 x 50	60.00	75.00	37.00
14	The Queen of Hearts	Pink crown, hearts; beige dress	75 x 48	60.00	75.00	37.00
15	Little Tommy Tucker	Yellow hair; blue pantaloons	75 x 30	60.00	75.00	37.00

SET FOUR: PURPLE BOXES

1976

Backstamp: Embossed "Wade England"

No.	Name	Description	Size	U.S. $	Can. $	U.K. £
16	The Three Bears	Grey; green base	70 x 60	70.00	85.00	45.00
17	Little Bo-Peep	Beige bonnet, dress; pink ribbon	70 x 40	110.00	225.00	50.00
18	Goosey Goosey Gander	Beige; pink beak; blue-brown steps	66 x 55	110.00	225.00	50.00
19	Old Woman in a Shoe	Blue bonnet, dress; brown roof, door	60 x 55	110.00	225.00	50.00
20	Puss in Boots	Beige; blue boots	70 x 30	70.00	85.00	45.00

NURSERIES MINIATURES

Circa 1979-1980

The *Nurseries* is a boxed set of five models from the Canadian Red Rose Tea *Miniature Nurseries*. For some reason these figures did not sell well to British collectors, so Wade discontinued the intended series with only five models issued. When these figures are out of their boxes, they are hard to distinguish from the Red Rose Tea models. As the *Nurseries* were advertised after the Corgies and Yorkshire terriers from the *Whimsies Dogs and Puppies* series (issued in 1979), the issue date for this series is set during late 1979.

The value given is for a complete boxed set.

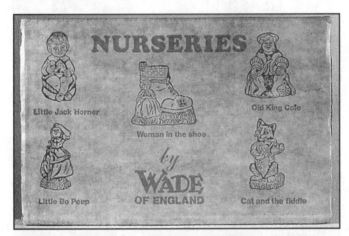

Backstamp: Embossed "Wade England"

No.	Name	Description	Size	U.S. $	Can. $	U.K. £
1	Little Jack Horner	Beige; blue plum; pink cushion	37 x 21			
2a	Old King Cole with Blue Hem	Beige; blue hat; pink sleeves; blue hem	37 x 32			
2b	Old King Cole without Blue Hem	Beige; blue hat; pink sleeves	37 x 32			
3	Old Woman in a Shoe	Honey; red-brown roof	35 x 40			
4	Little Bo-Peep	Light brown; blue apron; green base	44 x 24			
5	The Cat and the Fiddle	Beige; yellow fiddle	47 x 33			
—	5 pce set	Boxed	—	75.00	90.00	45.00

NURSERY RHYMES

1953 - Circa 1958

Although Wade may have intended to add to this series each year, only two *Nursery Rhymes* characters were produced.

Backstamp: Black transfer "Wade [name of model] England"

No.	Name	Description	Size	U.S. $	Can. $	U.K. £
1a	Little Jack Horner	Blue trousers; dark blue braces	70 x 42	475.00	585.00	295.00
1b	Little Jack Horner	Grey trousers, braces	70 x 42	475.00	585.00	295.00
1c	Little Jack Horner	White shirt, trousers	70 x 42	475.00	585.00	295.00
2	Little Miss Muffett	Blonde hair; blue dress; pink petticoat	72 x 66	475.00	585.00	295.00

POGO

1959

"Pogo" is based on a 1940s possum character featured in American children's books, newspapers and comics. The model was produced by Wade (Ulster) Ltd. and modelled by William Harper, who worked for the George Wade Pottery during the 1950s.

Backstamp: Black ink stamp "Pogo Copyright, Walt Kelly, Made in Ireland 1959"

No.	Description	Size	U.S. $	Can. $	U.K. £
1	Grey; blue jacket; blue/pink bird	85 x 30	600.00	740.00	370.00

SAM AND SARAH
(MABEL LUCIE ATTWELL FIGURES)
1959-1961

Manufactured under license to designs by Mabel Lucie Attwell, these two figures of "Sam" and "Sarah," with their pet dogs, were produced to test the public's reaction to a change of style. Apparently, they were not very popular at the time, perhaps due to the high retail price of 6/11d. Subsequently these models, which are sought after by Wade and by Mabel Lucie Attwell collectors, are in high demand.

The issue date for "Sam" and "Sarah" was October 1959, and they were discontinued in summer 1961. Their original price was 6/11d each.

Backstamp: Embossed Raised "Wade Porcelain-Mabel Lucie Attwell © Made in England"

No.	Name	Description	Size	U.S. $	Can. $	U.K. £
1	Sam	Ginger hair; yellow shirt; grey dog	78 x 85	260.00	320.00	160.00
2a	Sarah	Blue shoes; blue/white dress; white/black dog	75 x 100	260.00	320.00	160.00
2b	Sarah	Green shoes; blue/white dress; white/black dog	75 x 100	260.00	320.00	160.00
2c	Sarah	Red shoes; blue/white dress; white/black dog	75 x 100	260.00	320.00	160.00

THOMAS THE TANK ENGINE

STYLE ONE

1986

Thomas the Tank Engine, based on the storybooks by Reverend Wilbert Awdry and on the British television cartoon, was a very short-lived series due to complicated copyright laws. Only two models were produced, "Thomas" and "Percy." They came in two forms, a money box train and a miniature train. A prototype of "The Fat Controller" has been seen, but the model was not put into production. These four models are very rare.

For *Thomas The Tank Engine,* Style Two, see page 273.

Backstamp: **A.** Black transfer "Wade Made in England" (1-4)
  B. Unmarked (1, 3)

No.	Name	Description	Size	U.S. $	Can. $	U.K. £
1	Thomas the Tank Engine, money box	Blue; red markings	110 x 165	325.00	400.00	200.00
2	Thomas the Tank Engine, miniature	Blue; red markings	28 x 40	150.00	180.00	95.00
3	Percy the Small Engine, money box	Green; red markings	110 x 173	325.00	400.00	200.00
4	Percy the Small Engine, miniature	Green; red markings	28 x 38	150.00	180.00	95.00

TINKER, TAILOR, SOLDIER, SAILOR

1953-Circa 1958

Tinker, Tailor, Soldier, Sailor is a series of eight little boys dressed in adult clothes, depicting the characters from a 1940s children's rhyme.

Backstamp: Black transfer "Wade [name of model] England"

No.	Name	Description	Size	U.S. $	Can. $	U.K. £
1a	Tinker	Blue suit; white/grey cap; grey base	55 x 45	250.00	310.00	155.00
1b	Tinker	Pale blue suit; grey checkered cap; grey base	55 x 45	250.00	310.00	155.00
2	Tailor	Blue suit; grey trousers, base	55 x 45	250.00	310.00	155.00
3	Soldier	Blue suit, base; white/grey hat	80 x 45	250.00	310.00	155.00
4a	Sailor	Blue suit, base; white/grey hat	90 x 45	250.00	310.00	155.00
4b	Sailor	Pale blue suit; white/grey hat	90 x 45	250.00	310.00	155.00
5	Rich Man	Blue coat; grey hat, trousers; blue-green base	90 x 45	250.00	310.00	155.00
6a	Poor Man	Blue suit, base; grey hat	75 x 45	250.00	310.00	155.00
6b	Poor Man	Pale blue suit; grey hat	75 x 45	250.00	310.00	155.00
7	Beggar Man	Blue suit; white/blue scarf; blue-green base	65 x 45	250.00	310.00	155.00
8a	Thief	Blue suit; grey mask; blue-green base	80 x 45	250.00	310.00	155.00
8b	Thief	Pale blue suit; grey mask; blue-green base	80 x 45	250.00	310.00	155.00

Comic Animals and Birds

Cheerful Charlie - "Montreal" Pink
1948-1952 (P. 2)

Cheerful Charlie
Colourway Coffee or Grey
1948-1952 (P. 2)

Doleful Dan Posy Bowl
1948 (P. 3)

Mr. and Mrs. Duck with Dilly the Girl and Dack the Boy
1950's (P. 4)

Mr. Penguin
1948-1955 (P. 6)

Mr. Penguin Pepper Pot,
Mrs. Penguin Salt Pot
1948-1955 (P. 7)

Mr. and Mrs. Rabbit with Puff the Boy and Fluff the Girl
1948-1955 (P. 9)

Little Laughing Bunny in Brown, Pink and Grey
1948-1952 (P. 11)

Mouse Family
First issue with yellow tails
1962-1965 (P. 17)

Mouse Family
Second issue with pink tails
1978-1987 (P. 17)

Hippo Family
1978-1987 (P. 16)

Mother Hippo
Dark Blue, first issue, 1961-1965
Light Blue, second issue, 1978-1987 (P. 16)

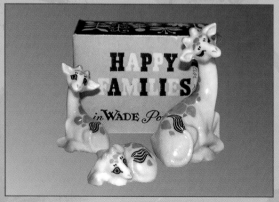

Giraffe Family
Boxed Set, 1961-1965 (P. 16)

Rabbit Family
1963-1965 (P. 19)

Leprechauns and Pixies

Baby Pixie Derivatives

Blue-grey Dish, 1978-1980's (P. 22)

Brown Dish, 1978-1980's (P. 22)

Baby Pixie
1978-1980s (P. 22)

**Leprechaun on Toadstool
with Crock O'Gold**
1975 (P. 26)

**Lucky Leprechaun Derivative with
Crock O'Gold on Marble Plynth**
1975-1985 (P. 36)

Large Leprechaun on Toadstool Money Box
1987 (P. 24)

Larry and Lester Derivative Bookends
1974-1985 (P. 25)

Lucky Fairy Folk

These nicely modelled figures are called **Lucky Fairy Folk**. They are **Leprechaun on Pig, Pixie on Rabbit** and **Pixie on Acorn**.
1956-1986 (P. 27)

Lucky Leprechauns

Lucky Leprechauns can be found with a variety of hat colours. The brown-faced models are the first version and were issued with foil paper labels on the bases. The flesh-coloured face models are the second and third versions. These were unmarked.
1956-1976 (P. 30 and 34)

A classic souvenir model, this **Irish Cottage and Pixie Tailor** sits on a porcelain base outlining the map of Ireland.
1950s-1970s (P. 43)

This brown-faced **Lucky Leprechaun with his Crock O'Gold** is sitting on an Oak Leaf dish.
1957-1959 (P. 31)

Novelty Animals and Birds

Baby Bird
Issued in two sizes and colourways
c.1935 (P. 46)

Cheeky Duckling
Produced in two sizes and two colourways
1935-1939 (P. 46)

Laughing Rabbit
Produced in four sizes and a variety of
colourways,1937-1939 (P. 48)

Duckling, head forward, beak open
1937-1939 (P. 47)

Duckling, head back, beak closed
1937-1939 (P. 47)

Pongo
Issued in three sizes and a variety of colourways
c.1949 (P. 49)

Storybook Figures

Alice and the Dodo
Produced with a new experimental cellulose glaze
1935-1938 (P. 52)

The Andy Capp Salt and **Flo Pepper** pots celebrate the 40th
anniversary of the *Daily Mirror* cartoon series *Andy Capp*
1997 (P. 53)

Bengo and his Puppy Friends: Pepi, Fifi, Simon, and Chee Chee
1959-1965 (P. 54)

Mitzi the Kitten, Bruno Junior, Droopy Junior, Percy and Whiskey. The last two models, **Percy the Afghan** and **Whisky the Corgi**,
were only in production for a few months when the series came to an end.
1959-1965 (P. 54)

Storybook Figures

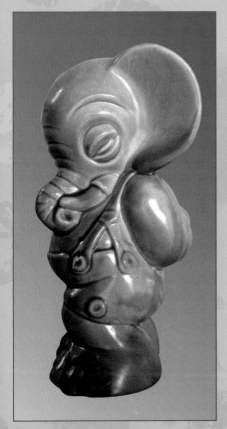

Jumbo Jim
One of Wade's larger Storybook figures
1939-1940 (P. 59)

Goldilocks and the Three Bears
Style One
1953-1958 (P. 58)

The Noddy Set
Noddy, Miss Fluffy Cat, Big Ears and **Mr. Plod the Policeman** are from the Enid
Blyton children's book *Noddy and His Adventures in Toytown*. 1958-1961 (P. 60)

Noddy Style One Derivative
Big Ears on a Toadstool Money Box
1961 (P. 61)

The Butcher, The Baker and The Candlestick Maker
Modelled by Nancy Great-Rex
1953-1958 (P. 56)

Storybook Figures

Little Miss Muffett and Little Jack Horner
1953-1958 (P. 66)

Yogi Bear and friends
Three Hanna-Barbera cartoon characters
1962-1963 (P. 74)

Wynken, Blynken, Nod and I've a Bear Behind
Two versions are shown. The first two with a flower base and the second two with a plain base.
1948-1958 (P. 72)

Sam and Sarah
Mabel Lucie Attwell designs were produced for a short period of time
1959-1961 (P. 68)

TOM AND JERRY

STYLE ONE

1973-1979

Only two models were issued in the *Tom and Jerry* series, courtesy of Metro-Goldwyn-Mayer. The original price for the set of two cartoon character models was 95p.

For *Tom and Jerry,* Style Two, see page 400.

Backstamp: Embossed "Wade England © M.G.M."

No.	Name	Description	Size	U.S. $	Can. $	U.K. £
1	Tom	Blue; yellow/black eyes; pink ears	90 x 55	80.00	100.00	50.00
2	Jerry	Beige; pink ears; green base	50 x 30	80.00	100.00	50.00
—	Set (2)		—	160.00	200.00	100.00

WYNKEN, BLYNKEN, NOD AND I'VE A BEAR BEHIND
Circa 1948-1958

This set of four nursery rhyme characters was based on the poem "Wynken, Blynken and Nod," by American writer Eugene Field: "Wynken, Blynken and Nod one night; sailed off in a wooden shoe; Sailed on a river of crystal light into a sea of dew."

The poem does not include the character "I've a Bear Behind"; this was purely a whim of the Wade modeler. Green moss covers the feet of some models, so their slippers cannot be seen.

The "Wynken, Blynken and Nod" figures were first advertised in a 1948 *Pottery and Glass Trades Review* magazine as a set of three models. "I've a Bear Behind" added later, was based on a scene in the 1938 Walt Disney *Silly Symphony Wynken, Blynken and Nod*, in which when leaning over the side of the "Wooden Shoe" fishing for stars, the buttons popped off the characters pyjama bottoms exposing their bare behinds.

There are two versions of this set to be found: Version One has applied flowers around a green base, and Version Two has a plain green base. Many of these models, along with other Wade Heath and George Wade popular 'Novelties' were exported to Australia, Canada, New Zealand and South Africa during the late 1940s-late 1950s. The "Wynken, Blynken and Nod" models were advertised at $2.50 per set in a Canadian magazine.

There are many examples of Japanese copies of this set to be found. They were made as a genuine 'copy' to boost Japanese pottery sales, and were not made to deliberately deceive people. All were originally backstamped or labelled 'Made in Japan', unfortunately over time the ink stamp wears away and the labels are lost or disintegrate.

A number of English and foreign potteries when they saw that a particular product was getting 'rave' advertising reviews and collectors attention would copy the product idea. Hence you will see Wade and Sylvac models which are almost identical except for a small change in shape, colour and backstamp, or if it is still present the paper label.

It is almost impossible to differentiate the Japanese copies from the Wade models just by look or feel. The best way to be sure is to look through the hole in the base of the model; if you can see light shining through the head or body then it is Japanese egg shell or soft past porcelain (also known as bone china). Wade produced hard paste porcelain, which is much stronger and thicker, and light cannot shine through.

FIRST VERSION: FLOWER BASE

Backstamp: **A.** Green ink stamp "[Name of model] Wade England" (1a, 1b, 2, 3, 4)
B. Black transfer print "Wade England" and green ink stamp "Wade England [model name]" (4)

No.	Name	Description	Size	U.S. $	Can. $	U.K. £
1a	Wynken	Blond hair; blue suit	71 x 38	200.00	260.00	130.00
1b	Wynken	Brown hair; blue suit	75 x 40	200.00	260.00	130.00
2a	Blynken	Blond hair; blue suit	58 x 40	200.00	260.00	130.00
2b	Blynken	Brown hair; blue suit	58 x 40	200.00	260.00	130.00
3	Nod	Blond hair; blue suit	70 x 40	200.00	260.00	130.00
4	I've a Bear Behind	Blond hair; blue suit	70 x 40	200.00	260.00	130.00

SECOND VERSION: GREEN BASE

Backstamp: Black transfer "Wade England [name of model]" 8

No.	Name	Description	Size	U.S. $	Can. $	U.K. £
1	Wynken	Blond hair; blue suit	75 x 40	200.00	250.00	125.00
2a	Blynken	Blond hair; blue suit	58 x 40	200.00	250.00	125.00
2b	Blynken	Light brown hair; blue suit	58 x 40	200.00	250.00	125.00
3	Nod	Light brown hair; blue suit	70 x 40	200.00	250.00	125.00
4	I've a Bear Behind	Light brown hair; blue suit	70 x 40	200.00	250.00	125.00

YOGI BEAR AND FRIENDS

1962-1963

Yogi Bear and Friends is a set of three Hanna-Barbera cartoon characters that were popular on television in the late 1950s/early 1960s. Their original price was 3/6d each.

Backstamp: Unmarked

No.	Name	Description	Size	U.S. $	Can. $	U.K. £
1	Yogi Bear	Beige; yellow/black hat; red tie	62 x 30	140.00	175.00	87.00
2a	Mr. Jinks	Pink; white/yellow/black face; blue bow tie	63 x 30	140.00	175.00	87.00
2b	Mr. Jinks	Yellow; white/yellow/black face; blue tie	63 x 30	140.00	175.00	87.00
3	Huckleberry Hound	Blue; white face; yellow bow tie	60 x 28	140.00	175.00	87.00

WALT DISNEY FIGURES

WALT DISNEY FIGURES

1937 -1984

A small number of Walt Disney character models were produced by Wade Heath Ltd. for approximately three years before giftware production ceased at the onset of World War II. In the early 1960s, Wade again produced Disney figures under license to Walt Disney.

BULLDOGS

Circa 1968

Two model bulldogs have been found, possibly representing Pluto's arch enemy "Butch" and his nephew "Bull." The models are slip cast (hollow). Both bulldogs are sitting and smiling; "Butch" scratches his ribs with his hind leg.

Backstamp: Black printed "Wade Porcelain Copyright Walt Disney Productions Made in England"

No.	Name	Description	Size	U.S. $	Can. $	U.K. £
1	Bull	Cream; grey muzzle, nose	85 x 100	290.00	360.00	180.00
2	Butch	Beige; grey muzzle, nose	90 x 110	290.00	360.00	180.00

DISNEY BLOW UPS

1961-1965

Disney Blow Ups is a set of ten characters from the Disney films *Lady and the Tramp* and *Bambi*. They are referred to as blow-ups because they are larger slip cast versions of the miniature *Hat Box Series* that preceded them. "Tramp," "Jock," "Thumper" and "Dachie" are the hardest of these models to find.

Name	Issue Price	Issue Date
Tramp	17/6d	January 1961
Lady	15/-	January 1961
Bambi	13/6d	January 1961
Scamp	12/6d	January 1961
Si	15/-	Autumn 1961
Am	15/-	Autumn 1961
Thumper	12/6d	Autumn 1961
Trusty	17/6d	Autumn 1961
Jock	13/6d	Autumn 1962
Dachie	15/-	Autumn 1962

Backstamp: A. Black transfer "Wade Porcelain—Copyright Walt Disney Productions—Made in England" (1-10)
B. Black transfer "Wade Porcelain—Copyright Walt Disney Productions—Made in Ireland" (7)

No.	Name	Description	Size	U.S. $	Can. $	U.K. £
1	Tramp	Grey; white face, neck, chest; red tongue	160 x 105	415.00	575.00	275.00
2	Lady	Beige; honey ears; blue collar	110 x 140	250.00	320.00	155.00
3	Bambi	Beige; white spots; pink ears; red tongue	110 x 120	170.00	240.00	115.00
4	Scamp	Grey; pink ears; white/maroon paws	110 x 115	215.00	280.00	120.00
5	Si	Brown; black/lilac ears; blue eyes; red mouth	140 x 110	225.00	300.00	135.00
6	Am	Brown; black/lilac ears; black nose, tail, legs	147 x 85	225.00	300.00	135.00
7	Thumper	Blue; white/yellow, white/red flowers	130 x 80	450.00	600.00	275.00
8	Trusty	Beige; red-brown ears; gold medallion	135 x 80	275.00	350.00	150.00
9	Jock	Grey; pink/mauve ears; gold medallion	100 x 115	950.00	1,300.00	650.00
10	Dachie	Beige; brown ears, eyes; red tongue	125 x 105	950.00	1,300.00	650.00

DONALD DUCK

1937

Backstamp: Black ink stamp "Wade Heath England with lion" (1934-1937)

No.	Description	Size	U.S. $	Can. $	U.K. £
1	White body; yellow beak, legs; blue hat, coat; red bow tie	127	1,300.00	1,600.00	800.00

DOPEY

1939

    This cellulose model of Dopey is a different model than the one used for the 1938 *Snow White* set. He was the only model produced in an intended *Snow White* set for FW Woolworth, England during Christmas 1939, but with the onset of World War II, the order for the rest of the models was cancelled.

Backstamp: None

No.	Description	Size	U.S. $	Can. $	U.K. £
1	Mauve hat; yellow coat; brown shoes	110 x 53	400.00	500.00	250.00

HAPPY CLOCK

CIRCA 1938

A rare find is a *Happy Clock* in the cellulose glaze used by the Wade Heath pottery during the mid-late 1930s. The eyes move from side to side as the clock ticks. Although not marked "Wade," this unusual piece has the same cellulose colours used on the 1930s *Snow White Dwarfs*. More interesting is that the paper label has a BCM/OWL mark which is a known backstamp used on a number of the early Wade Lady Figures.

Happy Clock, Front

Happy Clock, Back

Happy Clock, Bottom

Backstamp: Impressed "Made in England" on back of hat, Paper Label on base with black printed "By permission Walt Disney Mickey Mouse Ltd., Made in England" BCM/OWL Foreign Movement is ink stamped on the wood back plate.

No.	Name	Description	Size	U.S. $	Can. $	U.K. £
1	Happy Clock	Yellow hat and jacket; orange trousers; green shoes	210		Extremely rare	

THE HAT BOX SERIES

These charming Walt Disney cartoon characters were sold in round, striped cardboard boxes which resemble hat boxes, from which this series takes its name. The boxes each had a colour print of the enclosed model on the lid. There are 26 models in this long-running series. The last ten models had only a short production run and are considered scarce. The hardest of all to find are the models from *The Sword in the Stone*, especially the Merlin models.

Three variations of "Jock" can be found. When first produced in 1956, he was not wearing a coat. After Wade was advised that he wore one in the film, he was produced with a blue tartan coat in early 1957. Later that year the coat was changed to green tartan.

The original price for all the models was 2/11d, except for the figures from *The Sword in the Stone*, which sold for 3/6d. The films from which the models were taken are as follows:

Film	Model	Date of Issue
Lady and the Tramp	Lady	January 1956
	Jock, No Coat	January 1956
	Jock, Blue Coat	Early 1957
	Jock, Green Coat	Late 1957
	Tramp	January 1956
	Trusty	January 1956
	Peg	February 1957
	Scamp	February 1957
	Dachie	January 1958
	Si	August 1958
	Am	August 1958
	Boris	February 1960
	Toughy	February 1960
Bambi	Bambi	December 1957
	Flower	December 1957
	Thumper	December 1957
Dumbo	Dumbo	December 1957
Fantasia	Baby Pegasus	January 1958
101 Dalmatians	The Colonel	September 1961
	Lucky	September 1961
	Rolly	September 1961
	Sergeant Tibbs	September 1961
The Sword in the Stone	Archimedes	Autumn 1962
	Madam Mim	Autumn 1962
	Merlin as a Caterpillar	Autumn 1962
	Merlin as a Hare	Autumn 1962
	Merlin as a Turtle	Autumn 1962
	The Girl Squirrel	Autumn 1962

FIRST ISSUE: SET ONE

1956-1965

Backstamp: **A.** Black and gold "Wade England" label (1-6)
B. Blue transfer "Wade England" (1, 3, 6)
C. Unmarked (1-6)

No.	Name	Description	Size	U.S. $	Can. $	U.K. £
1	Lady	Beige; light brown ears; blue collar	40 x 35	40.00	55.00	25.00
2a	Jock, no coat	Blue-grey; purple mouth	40 x 25	65.00	80.00	40.00
2b	Jock, blue tartan coat	Blue coat; purple mouth	40 x 25	60.00	75.00	37.00
2c	Jock, green tartan coat	Green coat; purple mouth	40 x 25	55.00	70.00	35.00
3	Tramp, standing	Grey/white; red tongue	50 x 50	90.00	110.00	55.00
4a	Trusty	Brown; brown nose	55 x 35	55.00	70.00	35.00
4b	Trusty	Brown; black nose	55 x 35	55.00	70.00	35.00
5	Peg	Yellow fringe; red nose, mouth	40 x 35	50.00	65.00	30.00
6	Scamp	Grey; mauve ears, mouth; brown toes	40 x 35	45.00	55.00	28.00

FIRST ISSUE: SET TWO

1956-1965

Backstamp: A. Black and gold "Wade England" label (7-16)
   B. Unmarked (7-16)

No.	Name	Description	Size	U.S. $	Can. $	U.K. £
7	Bambi	Beige; tan/white patches; dark brown eyes	40 x 35	45.00	55.00	28.00
8	Flower	Black/white; blue eyes; red tongue	40 x 25	60.00	75.00	37.00
9a	Thumper	Blue-grey; pink cheeks; red mouth	60 x 35	55.00	70.00	35.00
9b	Thumper	Blue-grey; white cheeks; red mouth	60 x 35	55.00	70.00	35.00
10	Dumbo	Grey/white; pink ears	40 x 38	95.00	120.00	60.00
11	Baby Pegasus	Blue-grey; blue eyes; pink nose, mouth	40 x 30	105.00	130.00	65.00
12	Dachie	Brown; dark brown ears; red mouth	60 x 30	45.00	55.00	28.00
13	Si	Beige; black tail, legs, ears; blue eyes	60 x 30	65.00	80.00	40.00
14	Am	Beige; black tail, legs, ears; eyes closed	60 x 25	55.00	70.00	35.00
15	Boris	Grey; white chest, tail tip; pink in ears	60 x 28	60.00	75.00	37.00
16	Toughy	Brown; white chest, face; red tongue	55 x 30	90.00	110.00	55.00

FIRST ISSUE: SET THREE
1956-1965

Backstamp: A. Black and gold "Wade England" label (17-26)
B. Unmarked (17-26)

No.	Name	Description	Size	U.S. $	Can. $	U.K. £
17	The Colonel	Beige/white; black streak across eye	50 x 34	100.00	125.00	65.00
18	Sergeant Tibbs	Beige; white chest, nose, paws; blue in ears	55 x 30	100.00	125.00	65.00
19	Rolly	White; black spots; red collar; sitting	40 x 30	100.00	125.00	65.00
20	Lucky	White; black spots, ears; red collar; standing	30 x 35	120.00	150.00	75.00
21	Madam Mim	Honey/brown; black neck, wing tips	30 x 28	250.00	310.00	155.00
22	Merlin as a Turtle	Brown-grey; black/white eyes	30 x 45	300.00	375.00	185.00
23	Archimedes	Brown head, back, wings, log	50 x 35	150.00	185.00	95.00
24	Merlin as a Hare	Blue; white tail, chest	55 x 35	200.00	250.00	125.00
25	The Girl Squirrel	Beige; honey brown tail	50 x 30	150.00	185.00	95.00
26	Merlin as a Caterpillar	White/pink/mauve; black/yellow eyes	20 x 45	250.00	310.00	155.00

Note: A counterfeit Disney Hatbox model "Madam Mim" exists. The counterfeit version is much smaller, has a bright blue neck, and very little detailing in the feathers.

First Issue Derivatives

Butter Dish
Circa 1960

From 1955 to 1956, the George Wade Pottery produced a butter dish, to which "Jock" was later added on the back rim.

Jock Butter Dish

Backstamp: Embossed "Wade England"

No.	Name	Description	Size	U.S. $	Can. $	U.K. £
1a	Jock	No coat; blue dish	65 x 80	55.00	70.00	35.00
1b	Jock	No coat; grey dish	65 x 80	55.00	70.00	35.00
1c	Jock	No coat; white dish	65 x 80	55.00	70.00	35.00
1d	Jock	Blue coat, dish	65 x 80	55.00	70.00	35.00
1e	Jock	Green coat; blue dish	65 x 80	55.00	70.00	35.00

First Issue Derivatives (cont.)
Disney Lights (Candle Holders)
Circa 1960

This set is similar in appearance to the 1959-1960 *Zoo Lights*, but the triangular base is much larger, thicker and heavier, and it has an original issue *Hat Box* model sitting on the front edge of the candle holder. The holders are all black and were made for cake-size candles, which stand in a hole on the back edge. These models are rarely found. Examples other than those listed below are believed to exist.

| Flower Candle Holder (3) | Lady Candle Holder (6) | Scamp Candle Holder (8) |

Backstamp: Embossed "Wade"

No.	Name	Description	Size	U.S. $	Can. $	U.K. £
1	Bambi	Beige; black holder	60 x 50	110.00	135.00	70.00
2	Dumbo	White/pink; black holder	60 x 50	110.00	135.00	70.00
3	Flower	Black/white; black holder	60 x 50	110.00	135.00	70.00
4	Jock	Blue-grey/white; green coat; black holder	60 x 50	110.00	135.00	70.00
5	Lady	Beige/white; black holder	60 x 50	110.00	135.00	70.00
6	Lucky	White; black spots, holder	50 x 50	110.00	135.00	70.00
7	Rolly	White; black spots, holder	60 x 50	110.00	135.00	70.00
8	Scamp	Grey; mauve ears, mouth; brown toes; black holder	60 x 50	110.00	135.00	70.00
9	Thumper	Blue-grey/white; black holder	80 x 50	110.00	135.00	70.00

First Issue Derivatives (cont.)

Card Trumps

Circa 1960

These unusual pieces are of "Merlin as a Hare." One is glued onto a Bakelite stand which has plastic playing card trumps hanging from the frame, and the other is fixed to a Bouldray tray which has a brass card trump frame on it.

Merlin as Hare Card Trump

Backstamp: Raised "Bouldray Wade Porcelain 2 Made in England"

No.	Name	Description	Size	U.S. $	Can. $	U.K. £
1	Merlin as a Hare	Bakelite brown stand, frame; blue/grey Merlin; white plastic cards	90 x 75	160.00	225.00	110.00
2	Merlin as a Hare	Brass frame; blue tray; blue/grey Merlin; white plastic cards	90 x 75	160.00	225.00	110.00

First Issue Derivatives (cont.)

Kennel Money Boxes

1962

This series comprises a set of five money boxes in the shape of a dog kennel, with an original issue *Hat Box* figure standing in front of the entrance. The coin slot is in the kennel roof. The issue date for these money boxes was spring 1962, and they originally sold for 9/11d. Over time, the glue holding the model to the base breaks down, thus the money boxes can be found minus the dog model.

| Lady | Lucky | Rolly |

Backstamp: Unmarked

No.	Name	Description	Size	U.S. $	Can. $	U.K. £
1	Lady	Beige; blue kennel	95 x 105	200.00	250.00	125.00
2	Lucky	White; blue kennel	95 x 105	200.00	250.00	125.00
3a	Jock, green coat	Blue-grey; blue kennel	95 x 105	200.00	250.00	125.00
3b	Jock, no coat	Blue-grey; blue kennel	95 x 105	200.00	250.00	125.00
4	Rolly	White; blue kennel	95 x 105	200.00	250.00	125.00
5	Scamp	Grey; blue kennel	95 x 105	200.00	250.00	125.00

SECOND ISSUE: DISNEY'S

1981-1985

In spring 1981 George Wade and Son renewed its license with Walt Disney Productions Ltd. and reissued six models from the *Hat Box* series, using the original moulds. The new series was named "Disney's."

At first glance the reissues are hard to distinguish from the earlier figures, as the original moulds were used, some of which were worn, the model features are flat compared to the originals which is most noticeable on the "Scamp" model. There is only a slight variation in colour on the re-issued models. The name of "Dachie" was changed to "Dachsie."

Four new models from the Disney film, *The Fox and the Hound,* "Tod," "Copper," "Chief" and "Big Mama" were added in February 1982. In 1985 the last two models in the set, a new shape "Tramp" and a reissued "Peg" were issued.

When first issued the models were sold in round, numbered plastic hat box-shaped containers, later the plastic boxes were discontinued and the Disney's were then sold in oblong numbered cardboard boxes, which had two types of labels: type one — a long label that sealed the box flap, type two — a short 'name' label. "Tramp" and "Peg," were only issued in cardboard boxes.

Models are listed in chronological order.

Backstamp: Black and gold label "Walt Disney Productions Wade England"

No.	Name	Description	Size	U.S. $	Can. $	U.K. £
1	Lady	Dark brown ears; light blue collar	40 x 35	40.00	60.00	30.00
2	Scamp	Pink mouth, ears; facial markings flat	40 x 35	40.00	60.00	30.00
3	Jock, green tartan coat	Green coat; pink mouth; orange collar	40 x 25	40.00	60.00	30.00
4	Dachsie	Light brown ears; pink mouth	60 x 30	40.00	60.00	30.00
5	Bambi	Light brown eyes	40 x 35	40.00	60.00	30.00
6	Thumper	Light grey; pink mouth, cheeks; pale orange flower	60 x 35	40.00	60.00	30.00
7	Copper	Beige; brown patch, ears; white chest, paws	45 x 50	60.00	75.00	38.00
8	Tod	Red-brown; dark brown paws	45 x 50	60.00	75.00	38.00
9	Big Mama	Beige head, back, wings; orange beak	45 x 45	75.00	90.00	45.00
10	Chief	Grey; white chest; black eyes; red tongue	50 x 20	60.00	75.00	38.00
11	Tramp, seated	Grey; red tongue	47 x 30	60.00	75.00	38.00
12	Peg	Beige fringe; brown nose; pink mouth	40 x 35	40.00	60.00	30.00

Note: Prices listed are for pieces only or pieces in cardboard boxes. Models that are found in their original round plastic boxes will command a premium of 10-20% above list price.

LITTLE HIAWATHA AND HIS FOREST FRIENDS

1937

These models are from Walt Disney's cartoon *Little Hiawatha*. The models shown can be seen in a Wade Heath advertisement dated August 2nd, 1937. Along side Hiawatha are a deer, a bear cub and another character which has not been identified, but is thought to be an opossum or possum. In the cartoon Little Hiawatha goes on a hunting trip in the forest and meets many small animals he cannot bear to shoot with his bow and arrow. In a conversation with Tony Wade, he referred to the four models in the advertisement as "Hiawatha and his Forest Friends." "Hiawatha" was produced with a cellulose glaze, so it is difficult to find in mint condition.

Little Hiawatha

Little Hiawatha's friend Opossum

Advertisement from the August 1937 issue of "Pottery and Glass Trade Review"
Little Hiawatha, Deer, Bear Cub, Opossum (Possum) and Pluto

Backstamp: A. Black hand-painted "'Hiawatha' Wade England"
B. Unmarked (4)

No.	Name	Description	Size	U.S. $	Can. $	U.K. £
1	Bear Cub	Unknown	Unknown		Rare	
2	Deer	Unknown	Unknown		Rare	
3a	Little Hiawatha	Yellow feather; red trousers	100 x 50	450.00	550.00	275.00
3b	Little Hiawatha	Red feather; blue trousers	100 x 50	450.00	550.00	275.00
4	Possum / Opossum	Beige; black eyebrows, eyes, nose	90	410.00	500.00	250.00

MICKEY MOUSE

1935

A rare model of *Mickey Mouse* was produced by the Wadeheath Pottery at the same time as a children's toy Mickey Mouse tea set. This model was first advertised along with the toy tea set in March 1935.

Backstamp: Black ink stamp "Wadeheath Ware by Permission Walt Disney Mickey Mouse Ltd Made in England" (1935)

No.	Description	Size	U.S. $	Can. $	U.K. £
1a	Black and white body; yellow gloves; blue shorts; orange shoes; brown suitcase	90	2,250.00	2,500.00	1,250.00
1b	Black and white body; yellow gloves; green shorts; orange shoes; brown suitcase	90	2,250.00	2,500.00	1,250.00
1c	Black and white body; yellow gloves; orange shorts and shoes; brown suitcase	95	2,250.00	2,500.00	1,250.00
1d	Black and white body; yellow gloves and shoes; blue shorts; brown suitcase	90	2,250.00	2,500.00	1,250.00

PLUTO

1937-1938

Some *Pluto* models may have the impressed shape number 205.

Backstamp: Black ink stamp "Wadeheath by permission of Walt Disney, England"

No.	Description	Size	U.S. $	Can. $	U.K. £
1a	Grey; black ears, nose, eyes	100 x 162	450.00	550.00	280.00
1b	Orange-brown; black ears, nose, eyes	100 x 162	450.00	550.00	280.00
1c	White; black ears, nose and eyes	100 x 162	450.00	550.00	280.00

PLUTO'S PUPS

1937

Pluto's quintuplet puppies, the "Quinpuplets," were from the Walt Disney cartoon film of the same name. In the film they were not given names, but one pup reappeared in a 1942 Disney cartoon as "Pluto Junior."

Pup sitting, front paws up and Puppy, lying on back

Pup, sitting

Pup, sniffing ground

Pup, looking back

Backstamp: **A.** Black ink stamp "Flaxman Wadeheath England"(3a)
B. Black ink stamp "Wadeheath by permission of Walt Disney, England" (1a, 1b, 1c, 2a, 2b, 3b, 3c, 3d, 3e, 3f, 4a, 4b, 5)

No.	Name	Description	Size	U.S. $	Can. $	U.K. £
1a	Pup, lying on back	Beige	62 x 112	450.00	560.00	280.00
1b	Pup, lying on back	Green	62 x 112	450.00	560.00	280.00
1c	Pup, lying on back	Orange	62 x 112	450.00	560.00	280.00
2a	Pup, sitting	Grey; blue ears, eyes, nose	100 x 62	450.00	560.00	280.00
2b	Pup, sitting	Orange	100 x 62	450.00	560.00	280.00
3a	Pup, sitting, front paws up	Beige	95 x 85	450.00	560.00	280.00
3b	Pup, sitting, front paws up	Grey; blue ears, eyes, nose	95 x 85	450.00	560.00	280.00
3c	Pup, sitting, front paws up	Light blue; dark blue ears, eyes	95 x 85	450.00	560.00	280.00
3d	Pup, sitting, front paws up	Light grey; dark blue ears, eyes	95 x 85	450.00	560.00	280.00
3e	Pup, sitting, front paws up	Orange	95 x 85	450.00	560.00	280.00
3f	Pup, sitting, front paws up	Orange; blue ears, eyes, nose	95 x 85	450.00	560.00	280.00
4a	Pup, sniffing ground	Beige	62 x 112	450.00	560.00	280.00
4b	Pup, sniffing ground	Orange	62 x 112	450.00	560.00	280.00
5a	Pup, looking back	Grey; blue ears, eyes, nose	100 x 62	450.00	560.00	280.00
5b	Pup, looking back	Orange	100 x 62	450.00	560.00	280.00

SAMMY SEAL

1937 / 1948

Sammy Seal is believed to have appeared in a Disney Short in which *Mickey Mouse* carries him home unknowingly in his picnic basket after a visit to the zoo. A miniature model of *Sammy* has been found which is approximately the same height size as the *Arundel Chick*. The miniature version has no backstamp.

Backstamp: Black ink stamp "Wadeheath England by permission Walt Disney"

No.	Description	Size	U.S. $	Can. $	U.K. £
1a	Beige	150 x 150	450.00	560.00	280.00
1b	Grey; black eyes, nose	150 x 150	450.00	560.00	280.00
1c	Off white; brown eyes	150 x 150	450.00	560.00	280.00
1d	Orange	150 x 150	450.00	560.00	280.00
1e	Orange, black eyes, nose	150 x 150	450.00	560.00	280.00
1f	Pink; black eyes, nose	150 x 150	450.00	560.00	280.00
1g	White; black eyes, nose	150 x 150	450.00	560.00	280.00
2	Orange, black eyes, nose	110 x 110	450.00	560.00	280.00
3a	Beige; black eyes, nose	85 x 70	400.00	500.00	250.00
3b	Orange; black eyes, nose	85 x 70	400.00	500.00	250.00

SNOW WHITE AND THE SEVEN DWARFS

STYLE ONE

1938

The George Wade Pottery held a Walt Disney license to produce Disney models, and the Wade Heath Royal Victoria Pottery issued this first *Snow White* set to coincide with the release of the Walt Disney film, *Snow White and the Seven Dwarfs*. These models were produced with a cellulose glaze.

Backstamp: **A.** Black hand-painted "Wade [name of model]," plus red ink stamp with a leaping deer and "Made in England" (1)
B. Black hand-painted "Wade [name of model]," plus red ink stamp "Made in England" (2, 3, 4, 6, 7, 8, 9)
C. Unmarked (5)

No.	Name	Description	Size	U.S. $	Can. $	U.K. £
1	Snow White	Yellow dress; red bodice	180 x 65	450.00	600.00	300.00
2	Bashful	Orange coat; blue trousers	100 x 45	275.00	340.00	170.00
3	Doc	Orange jacket; maroon trousers	110 x 55	275.00	340.00	170.00
4	Dopey	Red coat; green trousers	110 x 45	275.00	340.00	170.00
5	Grumpy	Maroon jacket; green trousers	100 x 60	275.00	340.00	170.00
6	Happy	Orange jacket; red trousers	125 x 55	275.00	340.00	170.00
7	Sleepy	Orange-brown jacket; blue trousers	100 x 35	275.00	340.00	170.00
8	Sneezy	Blue jacket; red trousers	100 x 35	275.00	340.00	170.00
—	8 pce set	Boxed	—	3,500.00	4,000.00	2,000.00

SNOW WHITE AND THE SEVEN DWARFS
STYLE TWO
1981-1984

This issue of *Snow White and the Seven Dwarfs*, modelled by Alan Maslankowski, was first offered through mail order by Harper's Direct Mail Marketing just before Christmas 1981, then distributed in stores during the next spring.

Snow White, First Version

Snow White, Second Version

Backstamp: A. Black and gold label "© Walt Disney Productions Wade England" (1a, 8)
B. Black transfer "© Walt Disney Productions Wade England" (1b, 2-8)
C. Black transfer "Wade Made in England" (1a, 2, 4, 6)

No.	Name	Description	Size	U.S. $	Can. $	U.K. £
1a	Snow White, First Version	Head straight; smiling; pink spots on sleeves; light blue bodice; pale yellow skirt	95 x 100	210.00	320.00	145.00
1b	Snow White, Second Version	Head back; pink stripes on sleeves; light blue bodice with pink heart; pale yellow skirt	95 x 100	210.00	320.00	145.00
2	Bashful	Orange coat; grey hat; beige shoes	80 x 45	210.00	320.00	145.00
3	Doc	Blue coat; grey trousers; beige hat, shoes	80 x 50	210.00	320.00	145.00
4	Dopey	Beige coat; red hat; pale blue shoes	80 x 50	210.00	320.00	145.00
5	Grumpy	Red coat; beige hat; brown shoes	75 x 45	210.00	320.00	145.00
6	Happy	Brown vest; beige hat; blue trousers	85 x 50	210.00	320.00	145.00
7	Sleepy	Pale green coat, shoes; orange hat	80 x 50	210.00	320.00	145.00
8	Sneezy	Navy coat; blue trousers; brown hat, shoes	80 x 45	210.00	320.00	145.00
—	8 pce set	Boxed	—	1,750.00	2,250.00	1,200.00

SNOW WHITE AND THE SEVEN DWARFS BROOCHES

Circa 1938

Miniature lapel brooches were produced in the cellulose glaze used by the Wadeheath pottery during the mid-late 1930s, one of Snow White's face and full figure brooches of the dwarfs. The brooches have only been found in Canada and the USA. They were probably produced for Walt Disney staff during the North American promotion of the film *Snow White and the Seven Dwarfs*. They have an unusual "Wade Burslem England" backstamp, which adds to the belief that they were a special promotion.

Backstamp: Embossed "[name of character] Made in England Wade Burslem England"

No.	Name	Description	Size	U.S. $	Can. $	U.K. £
1	Snow White	Black hair and eyes; red bow and mouth	40		Very Rare	
2	Bashful	Green hat; orange coat; blue trousers; brown shoes	35		Very Rare	
3	Doc	Green hat; orange coat; maroon trousers; yellow belt buckle; blue shoes	35		Very Rare	
4	Dopey	Unknown	35		Very Rare	
5	Grumpy	Orange hat; orange-brown coat; blue trousers; orange brown shoes	37		Very Rare	
6	Happy	Light blue hat; brown coat; green trousers; red-brown shoes	35		Very Rare	
7	Sleepy	Green hat; brown coat; purple trousers; red shoes	35		Very Rare	
8	Sneezy	Green hat; blue coat; orange-red trousers; orange shoes	35		Very Rare	

**WHIMSIES
1954-1993**

BALLY-WHIM IRISH VILLAGE

1984-1987

Due to the success of the *English Whimsey-on-Why* models, Wade Ireland introduced a set of eight Irish village houses. Because the Wade Ireland pottery ceased production of giftware in August 1987, only one *Bally-Whim Irish Village* set was made. Each model is marked in a hollow under the base. The model number is on the side.

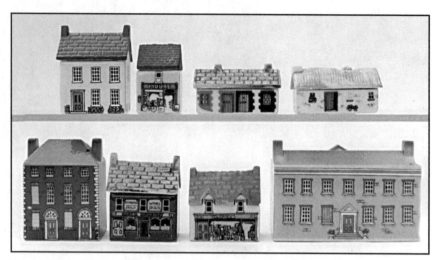

Backstamp: Embossed "Wade Ireland"

No.	Name	Description	Size	U.S. $	Can. $	U.K. £
1	Undertaker's House	Beige; brown roof, door	50 x 38	32.00	40.00	20.00
2	Moore's Post Office	Cream; brown roof	38 x 25	32.00	40.00	20.00
3	Barney Flynn's Cottage	Grey roof; red windows, door	28 x 45	32.00	40.00	20.00
4	Kate's Cottage	Yellow-brown roof	23 x 45	32.00	40.00	20.00
5	The Dentist's House	Dark brown; grey roof; red door	50 x 45	32.00	40.00	20.00
6	Mick Murphy's Bar	Green/grey	35 x 38	32.00	40.00	20.00
7	W. Ryan's Hardware Store	Yellow/brown roof	35 x 38	32.00	40.00	20.00
8	Bally-Whim House	Grey; blue roof; honey door	40 x 82	32.00	40.00	20.00

DOGS AND PUPPIES

1969-1982

This *Dogs and Puppies* series was advertised and labeled on the boxes as *Whimsies*. The models are of a mother dog and her two puppies, which were produced intermittently between 1969 and 1982. The mother dog was sold in one box and her two puppies in another. The boxes resemble books, and the inside of the lid has a description of the dog's breed printed on it. The first three sets were packaged in blue boxes, the last two sets in red. The original price was 7/6d per box.

SET ONE: ALSATIAN

1969-1982

Backstamp: Black and gold label "Genuine Wade Porcelain Made in England"

No.	Name	Description	Size	U.S. $	Can. $	U.K. £
1	Mother	Brown/honey brown	60 x 75	35.00	45.00	20.00
2	Puppy, seated	Brown/honey brown	40 x 45	16.00	20.00	10.00
3	Puppy, lying	Brown/honey brown	35 x 45	16.00	20.00	10.00

SET TWO: CAIRN

1969-1982

Backstamp: Black and gold label "Genuine Wade Porcelain Made in England"

No.	Name	Description	Size	U.S. $	Can. $	U.K. £
1	Mother	Honey brown; brown ears, nose	65 x 70	35.00	45.00	20.00
2	Puppy, standing	Honey brown; brown ears, nose	40 x 50	16.00	20.00	10.00
3	Puppy, lying	Honey brown; brown ears, nose	35 x 50	16.00	20.00	10.00

SET THREE: RED SETTER

1973-1982

Backstamp: Black and gold label "Genuine Wade Porcelain Made in England"

No.	Name	Description	Size	U.S. $	Can. $	U.K. £
1	Mother	Red-brown	60 x 75	35.00	45.00	20.00
2	Puppy, lying, facing left	Red-brown	40 x 45	16.00	20.00	10.00
3	Puppy, lying, facing right	Red-brown	40 x 45	16.00	20.00	10.00

SET FOUR: CORGI

1979-1982

Backstamp: Black and gold label "Genuine Wade Porcelain Made in England"

No.	Name	Description	Size	U.S. $	Can. $	U.K. £
1	Mother	Honey brown; brown ears, nose; green base	60 x 60	45.00	55.00	28.00
2	Puppy, lying	Honey brown; brown ears, nose; green base	30 x 45	25.00	32.00	16.00
3	Puppy, seated	Honey brown; brown ears, nose; green base	45 x 40	25.00	32.00	16.00

SET FIVE: YORKSHIRE TERRIER

1979-1982

Backstamp: Black and gold label "Genuine Wade Porcelain Made in England"

No.	Name	Description	Size	U.S. $	Can. $	U.K. £
1	Mother	Black/brown; honey brown face, chest	55 x 70	65.00	80.00	40.00
2	Puppy, seated	Black/brown; honey brown face, chest	40 x 40	50.00	60.00	30.00
3	Puppy, walking	Black/brown; honey brown face, chest	35 x 45	50.00	60.00	30.00

Dogs And Puppies Derivatives

Dog Pipe Stands

1973-1981

The *Dog Pipe Stands* have a mother dog from the 1969-1982 *Dogs and Puppies* series on the back rim of a stand. The original price was 72p each. A colour variation of the Alsatian, in an all-over honey glaze, has been found in the U.S.A.

Backstamp: Embossed "Wade England"

No.	Name	Description	Size	U.S. $	Can. $	U.K. £
1a	Alsatian	Brown/honey brown; green stand	60 x 115	35.00	45.00	20.00
1b	Alsatian	Honey; green stand	60 x 115	40.00	50.00	25.00
2	Cairn	Honey brown; green stand	60 x 115	35.00	45.00	20.00
3	Corgi	Honey brown; green stand	60 x 115	45.00	55.00	28.00
4	Red Setter	Red-brown; green stand	60 x 115	35.00	45.00	20.00
5	Yorkshire Terrier	Black/brown; green stand	60 x 115	65.00	80.00	40.00

Cat And Puppy Dishes

1974-1981

The *Cat and Puppy Dishes* is a series of 11 basket dishes with the puppies from the 1969-1982 *Dogs and Puppies* series sitting in them. The only change is the addition of a new model and the first in the series, the "Tabby Cat." With the exception of style 1b, the baskets are coloured in mottled greys and browns. The puppy dishes were packaged in pastel boxes marked "Pup-in-a-Basket" in North America.

Backstamp: Embossed "Wade England"

No.	Name	Description	Size	U.S. $	Can. $	U.K. £
1a	Tabby Cat	Brown stripes	50 x 75	35.00	48.00	24.00
1b	Tabby Cat	Brown stripes; dark brown basket	50 x 75	35.00	48.00	24.00
2	Alsatian puppy, seated	Brown/honey-brown	40 x 75	28.00	40.00	20.00
3	Alsatian puppy, lying	Brown/honey brown	35 x 75	28.00	40.00	20.00
4	Cairn puppy, standing	Honey brown	40 x 75	28.00	40.00	20.00
5	Cairn puppy, lying	Honey brown	35 x 75	28.00	40.00	20.00
6	Red Setter puppy, lying, facing left	Red-brown	40 x 75	28.00	40.00	20.00
7	Red Setter puppy, lying, facing right	Brown	40 x 75	28.00	40.00	20.00
8	Corgi puppy, seated	Honey brown	45 x 75	30.00	48.00	24.00
9	Corgi puppy, lying	Honey brown	30 x 75	30.00	48.00	24.00
10	Yorkie puppy, sitting	Grey/brown	30 x 75	42.00	55.00	28.00
11	Yorkie puppy, standing	Grey/brown	35 x 75	42.00	55.00	28.00

ENGLISH WHIMSIES

1971-1984

In 1971, 25 of the original Red Rose Tea Canada models were individually boxed and sold by Wade as a retail line. Unlike their famous forerunners, *First Whimsies*, this series has five models per set, with each figure sold in its own numbered box. The boxes in each set were the same colour (for example, set one was dark blue, set two was red, etc.). An updated list of models was added to the back of the boxes each year.

A new set was usually issued annually, although on some occasions when demand was strong, two sets were issued per year. A further 35 new models were added to the 25 original Canadian models, making an English series of 60 models.

Note that the "Trout" when it was first issued was unmarked, and the back of the base differed slightly from the second issue, which is marked "Wade England" on the back rim. The "Hedgehog" has two pads on the base. The "Hippo," "Bison" and "Pig" come in more than one size, due to the replacement of broken dies. In fact, there can be slight size variations in all the models listed below.

The black "Zebra" was glazed dark grey with black stripes, but after the first production run through the kiln, it emerged looking black all over, with very few markings to show it was a zebra. The Wade management then decided to change the colour to beige. The black "Zebra" is rare. The "Bullfrog" is the same model as the Red Rose Tea "Frog," but has been changed from green-yellow to brown. The "Kitten" can be found with or without a backstamp.

English Whimsies was offered as a pocket-money line to children for a price of 2/2d each.

SET ONE: DARK BLUE BOX

1971

Without backstamp (left), with backstamp (right)

Backstamp: Embossed "Wade England"

No.	Name	Description	Size	U.S. $	Can. $	U.K. £
1	Fawn	Brown; blue ears	30 x 30	5.00	6.00	3.00
2	Rabbit	Beige; ears open	30 x 30	5.00	6.00	3.00
3	Mongrel	Dark brown back; light brown front	35 x 35	5.00	6.00	3.00
4	Kitten	Dark/light brown; pink wool	30 x 30	5.00	6.00	3.00
5	Spaniel	Honey; green base	35 x 35	5.00	6.00	3.00

SET TWO: RED BOX
1972

Backstamp: Embossed "Wade England"

No.	Name	Description	Size	U.S. $	Can. $	U.K. £
6	Duck	Blue/brown, yellow beak	30 x 40	7.00	10.00	5.00
7	Corgi	Honey brown	30 x 35	7.00	10.00	5.00
8	Beaver	Grey-brown; honey-brown face	35 x 45	3.00	4.00	2.00
9	Bushbaby, Type 1	Brown; blue ears; black nose	30 x 30	3.00	4.00	2.00
10	Fox	Dark brown body, tail; fawn brown face, chest	30 x 30	6.00	10.00	4.00

SET THREE: DARK GREEN BOX
1972

Backstamp: A. Embossed "Wade" between front feet and "England" on back of model (11)
B. Embossed "Wade England" (12-15)
C. Unmarked (15)

No.	Name	Description	Size	U.S. $	Can. $	U.K. £
11	Bear Cub	Grey; beige face	30 x 40	5.00	6.00	3.00
12	Otter	Beige; blue base	30 x 35	5.00	6.00	3.00
13	Setter	Brown; grey-green base	35 x 50	5.00	6.00	3.00
14	Owl	Dark brown; light brown chest, face	35 x 20	5.00	6.00	3.00
15	Trout	Brown; black patch; red tail; grey-green base	30 x 30	5.00	6.00	3.00

SET FOUR: YELLOW BOX

1973

Large Hippo (left), Small Hippo (right)

Backstamp: Embossed "Wade England"

No.	Name	Description	Size	U.S. $	Can. $	U.K. £
16	Lion	Light brown; dark brown head, mane	35 x 45	7.00	8.00	4.00
17	Elephant	Grey; some may have black eyes	35 x 28	12.00	15.00	7.00
18	Giraffe	Beige	35 x 35	5.00	6.00	3.00
19	Chimpanzee	Dark brown; light brown face, patches	35 x 35	5.00	6.00	3.00
20a	Hippo	Large; honey brown	25 x 45	16.00	20.00	10.00
20b	Hippo	Small; honey brown	20 x 40	5.00	6.00	3.00

SET FIVE: DARK RED BOX

1974

Backstamp: A. Embossed "Wade England" (21, 23, 25)
B. Embossed in recessed base "Wade England" (22)

No.	Name	Description	Size	U.S. $	Can. $	U.K. £
21	Squirrel	Grey; beige head, legs; yellow acorn	35 x 30	5.00	6.00	3.00
22	Hedgehog, Type 2	Dark brown; light brown face; black nose	23 x 40	5.00	6.00	3.00
23	Pine Marten	Honey	30 x 30	5.00	6.00	3.00
24	Fieldmouse	Honey; yellow corn; green on base	35 x 25	9.00	12.00	6.00
25	Alsatian	Grey; tan face	30 x 40	5.00	6.00	3.00

SET SIX: LIGHT BLUE BOX

1975

A colour variation of the "Horse" has been found. The original horse was issued in a dark grey colourway, however, the origin of the beige model is unknown. Due to the mould being renewed there are three sizes of the Pig. This model was used in the *English Whimsies* series, and both the Red Rose Tea (Canada) Ltd. and Red Rose Tea (U.S.A) Ltd. promotions.

Pigs in three sizes

Backstamp: Embossed "Wade England"

No.	Name	Description	Size	U.S. $	Can. $	U.K. £
26	Collie	Golden brown; green base	35 x 35	10.00	12.00	6.00
27	Cow	Honey brown	35 x 35	10.00	12.00	6.00
28a	Pig	Large; beige; green base	27 x 44	25.00	32.00	16.00
28b	Pig	Medium; beige; green base	25 x 40	20.00	25.00	12.00
28c	Pig	Small; beige; green base	25 x 35	20.00	25.00	12.00
29a	Horse	Beige; dark brown/green base	38 x 30	20.00	25.00	12.00
29b	Horse	Dark grey; green base	38 x 30	20.00	25.00	12.00
30	Lamb	Fawn brown; green base	35 x 28	10.00	12.00	6.00

SET SEVEN: ORANGE BOX

1976

Black Zebra, faint stripes (left); Zebra, beige (right)

Backstamp: Embossed "Wade England"

No.	Name	Description	Size	U.S. $	Can. $	U.K. £
31	Rhino	Grey; green base	25 x 35	5.00	7.00	4.00
32	Leopard	Yellow/brown; green base	17 x 45	8.00	12.00	6.00
33	Gorilla, standing	Grey; grey-green base	35 x 25	6.00	9.00	4.00
34	Camel	Light grey; green base	35 x 35	9.00	12.00	6.00
35a	Zebra	Black; faint stripes	40 x 35	60.00	90.00	45.00
35b	Zebra	Beige; green base	40 x 35	12.00	12.00	6.00

SET EIGHT: MAGENTA BOX

1977

Backstamp: Embossed "Wade England"

No.	Name	Description	Size	U.S. $	Can. $	U.K. £
36	Donkey	Light brown; green base	30 x 30	14.00	20.00	10.00
37	Barn Owl	Light brown; dark brown head, back; blue base	35 x 20	20.00	28.00	14.00
38	Cat	Light brown/ginger; grey-green base	40 x 17	20.00	28.00	14.00
39	Mouse, seated	Beige; grey-blue base	40 x 25	15.00	22.00	11.00
40	Ram	White; grey face; green base	30 x 30	15.00	22.00	11.00

SET NINE: MID BLUE BOX

1978

Backstamp: A. Embossed "Wade England" (41, 42, 43, 45)
B. Embossed "Wade England" in recessed base (44)

No.	Name	Description	Size	U.S. $	Can. $	U.K. £
41	Dolphin	Grey-brown; blue base	30 x 40	35.00	50.00	20.00
42	Pelican	Honey; brown back; yellow beak; green base	45 x 40	20.00	30.00	15.00
43	Angel Fish	Dark grey; blue base	35 x 30	10.00	15.00	7.00
44	Turtle	Greenish-grey	15 x 50	10.00	15.00	7.00
45	Seahorse	Honey yellow; grey-blue base	50 x 17	20.00	30.00	15.00

SET TEN: LIGHT GREEN BOX

1979

Backstamp: Embossed "Wade England"

No.	Name	Description	Size	U.S. $	Can. $	U.K. £
46	Kangaroo	Dark brown; light brown base	45 x 25	12.00	18.00	9.00
47	Orang-outan	Ginger	30 x 30	5.00	8.00	4.00
48	Tiger	Honey; green base	35 x 25	15.00	20.00	10.00
49	Koala	Yellow-brown; black nose; green base	35 x 25	20.00	30.00	14.00
50	Langur, Type 1	Light brown; dark brown stump; green leaves	35 x 30	5.00	8.00	4.00

SET ELEVEN: DARK BROWN BOX

1979

Large Bison (left), Small Bison (right)

Backstamp: A. Embossed "Wade England" (51a, 51b, 54, 55)
B. Embossed in recessed base "Wade England" (52, 53)

No.	Name	Description	Size	U.S. $	Can. $	U.K. £
51a	Bison	Large; honey brown; dark brown head, mane	32 x 45	12.00	18.00	9.00
51b	Bison	Small; honey brown; dark brown head, mane	28 x 40	5.00	6.00	3.00
52	Bluebird	Beige body, tail; blue wings, head	15 x 35	10.00	12.00	6.00
53	Bullfrog	Brown	15 x 30	18.00	26.00	13.00
54	Wild Boar	Light brown; green base	30 x 40	9.00	10.00	5.00
55	Raccoon	Brown; grey-green base	25 x 35	15.00	18.00	9.00

SET TWELVE: DEEP BLUE BOX
1980

Backstamp: Embossed "Wade England"

No.	Name	Description	Size	U.S. $	Can. $	U.K. £
56	Penguin	Grey; white face, chest; yellow beak, feet	38 x 19	20.00	30.00	15.00
57	Seal Pup	Beige; blue base	25 x 37	20.00	30.00	15.00
58	Husky	Grey; grey/green base	35 x 30	20.00	30.00	15.00
59	Walrus	Light brown; grey base	30 x 30	10.00	12.00	6.00
60	Polar Bear, head forward	White; black nose; blue base	30 x 30	22.00	26.00	13.00

English Whimsies Derivatives

English Whimtrays
1971-1984

These *Whimtrays* were made with models from the *English Whimsies* series.

Photograph not available
at press time

Backstamp: Embossed "Whimtrays Wade Porcelain Made in England"

No.	Name	Description	Size	U.S. $	Can. $	U.K. £
1	Duck	Blue/brown; yellow beak; black tray	50 x 75	18.00	24.00	12.00
2	Fawn	Brown; blue ears; black tray	50 x 75	18.00	24.00	12.00
3	Trout	Brown; black patch; red tail; black tray	50 x 75	18.00	24.00	12.00

WHOPPAS

1976-1981

Whoppas are the big brothers of *Whimsies* and were in production from 1976 to 1981. They were issued in three sets of five models. The original price was 65p each.

SET ONE: RED BOX

1976-1981

Backstamp: Embossed "Wade England"

No.	Name	Description	Size	U.S. $	Can. $	U.K. £
1a	Polar Bear, head forward	Beige brown; blue base	35 x 55	28.00	35.00	18.00
1b	Polar Bear, head forward	White; grey-blue base	35 x 55	28.00	35.00	18.00
2	Hippo	Grey; green base	35 x 50	28.00	35.00	18.00
3	Brown Bear	Red-brown; brown base	35 x 45	28.00	35.00	18.00
4	Tiger	Honey; green base	30 x 60	28.00	35.00	18.00
5	Elephant	Grey; green base	55 x 50	28.00	35.00	18.00

SET TWO: GREEN BOX
1977-1981

Backstamp: Embossed "Wade England"

No.	Name	Description	Size	U.S. $	Can. $	U.K. £
6	Bison	Brown; green base	40 x 50	30.00	38.00	19.00
7	Wolf	Grey; green base	60 x 45	30.00	38.00	19.00
8	Bobcat	Light brown; dark brown spots; green base	55 x 50	30.00	38.00	19.00
9	Chipmunk	Brown; brown base	55 x 40	35.00	42.00	21.00
10	Racoon	Brown; black stripes; eye patches; green base	40 x 50	35.00	42.00	21.00

SET THREE: BROWN BOX
1978-1981

Backstamp: Embossed "Wade England"

No.	Name	Description	Size	U.S. $	Can. $	U.K. £
11	Fox	Red-brown; green base	30 x 60	35.00	42.00	21.00
12	Badger	Brown; cream stripe; green base	35 x 45	35.00	42.00	21.00
13	Otter	Brown; blue base	30 x 55	35.00	42.00	21.00
14	Stoat	Brown; green base	35 x 55	35.00	42.00	21.00
15	Hedgehog	Brown; green base	30 x 50	35.00	42.00	21.00

FIRST WHIMSIES

1954-1958

Following the end of World War II, the massive program to replace war-damaged houses and factories created a heavy demand for industrial ceramics. By the early 1950s, this demand had slackened, and new products had to be produced in order to avoid worker layoffs in the George Wade Potteries. With many years of experience making small pressed articles for industrial use, coupled with a unique ability in specialist tool-making, it was decided to manufacture a range of miniature animals.

The first set of five models was produced in 1954 and was designed for children to spend their pocket money on. When Mr. Wade's secretary referred to the models as whimsical, the series was named *Whimsies* (and later referred to as the *First Whimsies*).

The original models were packaged and sold in sets of five pieces for 5/9d. Only those models on bases wide enough for a Wade stamp were marked; free-standing models with open-cast legs generally had no room for marks. All boxes were marked "Wade Whimsies," but once the unmarked figures were removed from their boxes, there was no way to tell that they were Wade.

Whimsies models had their first showing at the British Industries Fair in 1954. At first, the reaction of dealers and wholesalers to the five tiny models was discouraging. But the following day, when the public was allowed into the show, they quickly changed their attitude when they saw the growing numbers of children and parents queuing to buy *Whimsies*.

For the next six years, Wade produced and sold nine sets of five and one set of four miniature animal models. Today these *First Whimsies* are highly sought after by collectors all over the world.

The "Spaniel with Ball" in the beige rump colourway is so rarely seen it is now believed to have been a prototype and not put into full production.

SET ONE: ENGLISH ANIMALS

1954-1958

Backstamp: A. Embossed "Wade" (1, 2)
B. Unmarked (3, 4, 5)

No.	Name	Description	Size	U.S. $	Can. $	U.K. £
1	Leaping Fawn	White; green base	40 x 40	48.00	60.00	25.00
2	Horse	Light brown; green/brown base	35 x 50	48.00	60.00	25.00
3	Spaniel with ball	White; beige rump, tail	25 x 40	30.00	40.00	20.00
4	Poodle	Light brown; white markings	35 x 35	40.00	58.00	25.00
5	Squirrel	Light grey	25 x 50	25.00	37.00	18.00

Note: Whimsies animals are arranged in issue order.

SET TWO: ENGLISH ANIMALS

1954-1958

Backstamp: A. Black and gold label "Genuine Wade Porcelain Made in England" (1, 3)
B. Unmarked (1, 2, 3, 4, 5)

No.	Name	Description	Size	U.S. $	Can. $	U.K. £
1	Bull	Brown legs; green base	45 x 55	85.00	120.00	60.00
2	Lamb	Brown muzzle, front legs; green base	45 x 25	60.00	80.00	35.00
3	Kitten	White; grey face, paws, tail; blue bow	15 x 40	85.00	120.00	60.00
4	Hare	Light grey/white, white base	30 x 45	45.00	65.00	32.00
5	Dachshund	Beige	35 x 45	85.00	120.00	60.00

SET THREE: ENGLISH COUNTRY ANIMALS

1955-1958

Backstamp: A. Unmarked (1, 2, and 3)
B. Embossed "Wade" (4, 5)

No.	Name	Description	Size	U.S. $	Can. $	U.K. £
1	Badger	Grey; black/white face	30 x 40	35.00	50.00	25.00
2	Fox Cub	Light brown	35 x 35	75.00	110.00	55.00
3	Stoat	Grey tail; red eyes	20 x 35	55.00	80.00	40.00
4	Shetland Pony	Grey mane; green base	35 x 40	40.00	60.00	30.00
5	Retriever	Brown; white legs; green/white base	30 x 40	35.00	50.00	25.00

SET FOUR: AFRICAN JUNGLE ANIMALS

1955-1958

Backstamp: A. Unmarked (1, 5)
B. Black ink stamp "Wade Made in England" (2, 3, 4)

No.	Name	Description	Size	U.S. $	Can. $	U.K. £
1	Lion	Light brown	30 x 35	55.00	80.00	40.00
2	Crocodile	Green-brown	15 x 40	75.00	110.00	55.00
3	Monkey and Baby	Brown; green stump	45 x 25	40.00	60.00	30.00
4	Rhinoceros	Grey; green base	45 x 45	40.00	60.00	30.00
5	Baby Elephant	Grey	40 x 40	55.00	80.00	40.00

SET FIVE: HORSES

1956-1959

This is the only *First Whimsies* set of four figures and, despite its title, it includes a Beagle dog.

Backstamp: A. Embossed "Wade"
B. Unmarked (4)

No.	Name	Description	Size	U.S. $	Can. $	U.K. £
1a	Mare	Light brown; brown tail, mane; green base	45 x 40	45.00	65.00	32.00
1b	Mare	White; brown mane, tail, hooves; green base	45 x 40	45.00	65.00	32.00
2a	Foal	Light brown; brown mane, tail; green base	40 x 40	45.00	65.00	32.00
2b	Foal	Dark brown; green base	40 x 40	45.00	65.00	32.00
2c	Foal	White; brown mane, tail, hooves; green base	45 x 40	45.00	65.00	32.00
3a	Colt	Light brown; brown mane, tail; green base	40 x 40	45.00	65.00	32.00
3b	Colt	White; brown mane, tail, hooves; green base	40 X 40	45.00	65.00	32.00
4	Beagle	Brown patches; green base	20 x 20	85.00	125.00	50.00

SET SIX: POLAR ANIMALS

1956-1959

The original price was 6/6d for the set.

Backstamp: Unmarked

No.	Name	Description	Size	U.S. $	Can. $	U.K. £
1	King Penguin	Black back, head, flippers; yellow beak, feet	35 x 20	50.00	65.00	32.00
2	Husky	Fawn/white; grey ears, muzzle	30 x 25	50.00	65.00	32.00
3	Polar Bear	Grey muzzle; blue base	45 x 45	50.00	65.00	32.00
4	Baby Seal	Light grey; white base	25 x 25	30.00	45.00	22.00
5a	Polar Bear Cub	White; brown eyes, nose, claws	20 x 30	40.00	60.00	30.00
5b	Polar Bear Cub	Pink; brown eyes, nose, claws	20 x 30	40.00	60.00	30.00

SET SEVEN: PEDIGREE DOGS

1957-1961

The original price for Set Seven was 6/6d for a box of five models.

A variation in the St. Bernard dog has been found, in Type 1 the barrel has two vertical ridges, in Type 2, the barrel has one horizontal ridge. There are also slight variations in the brown glazes.

St. Bernard, Type 2 (left), Type 1 (right)

Backstamp: Unmarked

No.	Name	Description	Size	U.S. $	Can. $	U.K. £
1	Alsatian	Grey/brown, green-brown base	35 x 40	30.00	45.00	22.00
2	West Highland Terrier	White	25 x 30	50.00	65.00	32.00
3	Corgi	Beige/white	25 x 30	50.00	65.00	32.00
4	Boxer	Brown; grey face; brown-green base	35 x 40	50.00	65.00	32.00
5a	Saint Bernard, Type 1	Brown/white; beige barrel	40 x 45	65.00	80.00	40.00
5b	Saint Bernard, Type 2	Dark brown/white; beige barrel	40 x 45	65.00	80.00	40.00

SET EIGHT: ZOO ANIMALS

1957-1961

Two "Panda" figures were issued by Wade, one larger than the other. The smaller one, with a black band across its chest, is the right model for this set; the larger, 35 by 25 millimetre figure is out of proportion to the other models in the set. The larger model may have been produced first, then found to be too large and was set aside for possible use in special offers or premiums. Whether or not it was actually used in a premium set or simply sold off is not known. The original price per box was 5/9d.

Backstamp: Unmarked

No.	Name	Description	Size	U.S. $	Can. $	U.K. £
1	Bactrian Camel	Light brown; dark brown humps; green base	40 x 40	50.00	65.00	32.00
2	Cockatoo	Yellow crest; grey base	30 x 30	55.00	80.00	40.00
3a	Giant Panda, large	Black/white	35 x 25	35.00	50.00	25.00
3b	Giant Panda, small	Black/white; black band on chest	30 x 18	40.00	60.00	30.00
4	Lion Cub	Brown; white chest	25 x 25	35.00	50.00	25.00
5	Llama	Grey face; brown-green base	45 x 30	45.00	60.00	30.00

SET NINE: NORTH AMERICAN ANIMALS

1958-1961

The "Grizzly Cub" (model 4a), is the figure issued as part of this set. Models 4b and 4c were issued at a later time. The original issue price was 6/6d per set.

Backstamp: A. Unmarked (1, 2, 4a, 4b, 4c, 5)
B. Embossed "Wade" (3)
C. Embossed "Wade England" (3)

No.	Name	Description	Size	U.S. $	Can. $	U.K. £
1	Snowy Owl	Brown eyes, claws	28 x 30	50.00	65.00	32.00
2	Raccoon	Grey/black, white base	30 x 30	45.00	60.00	30.00
3	Grizzly Bear	Brown/white; green base	50 x 25	70.00	95.00	45.00
4a	Grizzly Cub	Light brown, green base	25 x 25	40.00	60.00	30.00
4b	Grizzly Cub	Brown; pink ears	25 x 30	40.00	60.00	30.00
4c	Grizzly Cub	White; pink ears	25 x 25	45.00	65.00	32.00
5	Cougar	Brown; white face, feet	20 x 45	70.00	95.00	45.00

SET TEN: FARM ANIMALS

1959-1961

These are the hardest of all *First Whimsies* models to find. This was the last set made and was only in production for a short time.

The "Shire Horse" and "Swan" in this set have been unlawfully reproduced and sold as authentic *First Whimsies*. The "Shire Horse" fake is slightly larger, it leans backwards in an ungainly way (most will not stand) and its nose is longer. It does not have the appearance of a real horse, but looks more like a caricature. The counterfeit "Swan" has a thicker neck and shorter beak, and the detailing of the feathers is not as fine as on the original.

The original price was 5/9d per boxed set.

Backstamp: Unmarked

No.	Name	Description	Size	U.S. $	Can. $	U.K. £
1	Pig	Pink; green base	20 x 35	75.00	110.00	55.00
2	Italian Goat	Grey; white face, chest; green base	30 x 30	75.00	110.00	55.00
3a	Foxhound	Beige patches; green base	25 x 45	75.00	110.00	55.00
3b	Foxhound	Light brown patches; green/white base	25 x 45	75.00	110.00	55.00
4a	Shire Horse	Creamy beige; brown mane and tail	50 x 50	235.00	290.00	145.00
4b	Shire Horse	White; grey mane; brown hooves	50 x 40	235.00	290.00	145.00
4c	Shire Horse	Red brown; cream mane; cream/black hooves	50 x 50	300.00	370.00	185.00
5	Swan	Yellow beak; black tip	25 x 35	170.00	250.00	125.00

First Whimsies Derivatives Disney Lights, Candleholder

Circa 1960

A "Panda" model has been found on a Disney Light candle holder base, which is much thicker and heavier than the Zoo light candle holder base.

Photograph not available
at press time

No.	Name	Description	Size	U.S. $	Can. $	U.K. £
1	Panda, large	Black/white; black base	55 x 50	40.00	50.00	25.00

English Whimsies and First Whimsies Derivatives Irish Whimtrays
Circa 1985

In the mid-1980s, Wade Ireland reissued *Whimtrays*, but as the original mould for the tray was worn, a new one was designed. The plinth on which the figure sits is not gently rounded, as was that on the original George Wade model. Instead, it bends much farther out into the dish, making it easy to distinguish the two styles of trays. A few surplus *First Whimsies* were sent to Ireland to be used up on the Irish Whimtrays. The following have been found attached to the Irish tray: Cockatoo, Husky, Polar Bear Cub, and the King Penguin which is in a new colourway.

Duck (2b)

Husky (4a)

Trout (7c)

Backstamp: Embossed "Made in Ireland, Irish Porcelain, Wade 'Eire tir a dheanta'" in a circle around a crown and shamrock

No.	Name	Description	Size	U.S. $	Can. $	U.K. £
1	Cockatoo (FW)	Yellow crest; black tray	50 x 77	38.00	46.00	23.00
2a	Duck (EW)	Blue/brown; blue tray	50 x 77	24.00	30.00	15.00
2b	Duck (EW)	Blue/brown; green tray	50 x 77	24.00	30.00	15.00
3a	Fawn (EW)	Brown; black tray	50 x 77	24.00	30.00	15.00
3b	Fawn (EW)	Brown; green tray	50 x 77	24.00	30.00	15.00
4a	Husky (FW)	Fawn/white; blue tray	50 x 77	38.00	46.00	23.00
4b	Husky (FW)	Fawn/white; green tray	50 x 77	38.00	46.00	23.00
5a	King Penguin (FW)	Black/white; black tray	50 x 77	38.00	46.00	23.00
5b	King Penguin (FW)	Black/white; green tray	45 x 77	38.00	46.00	23.00
6a	Polar Bear Cub (FW)	White; black tray	40 x 77	38.00	46.00	23.00
6b	Polar Bear Cub (FW)	White; green tray	40 x 77	38.00	46.00	23.00
7a	Trout (EW)	Brown; black tray	50 x 77	24.00	30.00	15.00
7b	Trout (EW)	Brown; blue tray	50 x 77	24.00	30.00	15.00
7c	Trout (EW)	Brown; green tray	50 x 77	24.00	30.00	15.00

Note: The following initials indicate the origin of the models:
EW: *English Whimsies*
FW: *First Whimsies*

First Whimsies Derivatives Mare And Foal Dish

1963

The *Mare and Foal Dish* has two models from the *First Whimsies Horses,* set 5, on the rim of a figure-eight shaped dish. The original price was 6/6d. This dish is rare.

Backstamp: Embossed "Wade Porcelain Made in England"

No.	Name	Description	Size	U.S. $	Can. $	U.K. £
1	Mare and foal dish	Light brown horses; black dish	110 x 20	75.00	110.00	55.00

First Whimsies Derivatives Snack Tray

Mid 1960s

This snack tray is possibly part of a set of four or five sections that would make up a circular table centre decoration. Only one example, which has a First Whimsies Racoon on the back edge of the tray, has been found to date

Backstamp: Unknown

No.	Name	Description	Size	U.S. $	Can. $	U.K. £
1	Snack tray	Grey, white, black raccoon; yellow tray	115		Rare	

First Whimsies Derivative Whimtrays
1958-1965

Whimtrays are small round dishes with a *First Whimsies* animal on the back edge of the tray. The issue date was January 1958 (except for the Bactrian Camel, Cockatoo, Giant Panda, Llama and Lion Cub *Whimtrays*, which were issued in August 1958), and they originally sold for 2/6d each. The trays come in black, blue, yellow and pink.

The following *Whimtrays* are listed in alphabetical order.

Bactrian Camel (2)

Racoon (2)

Backstamp: Embossed "Whimtrays Wade Porcelain Made in England"

No.	Name	Description		Size	U.S. $	Can. $	U.K. £
1a	Alsatian	Grey/brown;	black tray	55 x 75	35.00	50.00	25.00
1b	Alsatian		blue tray	55 x 75	35.00	50.00	25.00
1c	Alsatian		pink tray	55 x 75	35.00	50.00	25.00
1d	Alsatian		yellow tray	55 x 75	35.00	50.00	25.00
2a	Bactrian Camel	Light brown;	black tray	60 x 75	35.00	50.00	25.00
2b	Bactrian Camel		blue tray	60 x 75	35.00	50.00	25.00
2c	Bactrian Camel		pink tray	60 x 75	35.00	50.00	25.00
2d	Bactrian Camel		yellow tray	60 x 75	35.00	50.00	25.00
3a	Baby Seal	Grey;	black tray	40 x 75	35.00	50.00	25.00
3b	Baby Seal		blue tray	40 x 75	35.00	50.00	25.00
3c	Baby Seal		pink tray	40 x 75	35.00	50.00	25.00
3d	Baby Seal		yellow tray	40 x 75	35.00	50.00	25.00
4a	Boxer	Brown;	black tray	45 x 75	35.00	50.00	25.00
4b	Boxer		blue tray	45 x 75	35.00	50.00	25.00
4c	Boxer		pink tray	45 x 75	35.00	50.00	25.00
4d	Boxer		yellow tray	45 x 75	35.00	50.00	25.00
5a	Cockatoo	Yellow crest;	black tray	50 x 75	35.00	50.00	25.00
5b	Cockatoo		blue tray	50 x 75	35.00	50.00	25.00
5c	Cockatoo		pink tray	50 x 75	35.00	50.00	25.00
5d	Cockatoo		yellow tray	50 x 75	35.00	50.00	25.00
6a	Corgi	Beige/white;	black tray	45 x 75	35.00	50.00	25.00
6b	Corgi		blue tray	45 x 75	35.00	50.00	25.00
6c	Corgi		pink tray	45 x 75	35.00	50.00	25.00
6d	Corgi		yellow tray	45 x 75	35.00	50.00	25.00
7a	Giant Panda	Black/white;	black tray	50 x 75	35.00	50.00	25.00
7b	Giant Panda		blue tray	50 x 75	35.00	50.00	25.00
7c	Giant Panda		pink tray	50 x 75	35.00	50.00	25.00
7d	Giant Panda		yellow tray	50 x 75	35.00	50.00	25.00
8a	Giant Panda, small	Black/white;	black tray	45 x 75	35.00	50.00	25.00
8b	Giant Panda, small		blue tray	45 x 75	35.00	50.00	25.00
8c	Giant Panda, small		pink tray	45 x 75	35.00	50.00	25.00
8d	Giant Panda, small		yellow tray	45 x 75	35.00	50.00	25.00

First Whimsies Derivatives Whimtrays (cont.)
1958-1965

No.	Name	Description		Size	U.S. $	Can. $	U.K. £
9a	Grizzly Bear	Brown/white;	black tray	65 x 75	35.00	50.00	25.00
9b	Grizzly Bear		blue tray	65 x 75	35.00	50.00	25.00
9c	Grizzly Bear		pink tray	65 x 75	35.00	50.00	25.00
9d	Grizzly Bear		yellow tray	65 x 75	35.00	50.00	25.00
10a	Grizzly Cub	Brown;	black tray	45 x 75	35.00	50.00	25.00
10b	Grizzly Cub		blue tray	45 x 75	35.00	50.00	25.00
10c	Grizzly Cub		pink tray	45 x 75	35.00	50.00	25.00
10d	Grizzly Cub		yellow tray	45 x 75	35.00	50.00	25.00
11a	Hare	Light grey/white;	black tray	50 x 75	35.00	50.00	25.00
11b	Hare		blue tray	50 x 75	35.00	50.00	25.00
11c	Hare		pink tray	50 x 75	35.00	50.00	25.00
11d	Hare		yellow tray	50 x 75	35.00	50.00	25.00
12a	Husky	Fawn/white;	black tray	50 x 75	35.00	50.00	25.00
12b	Husky		blue tray	50 x 75	35.00	50.00	25.00
12c	Husky		pink tray	50 x 75	35.00	50.00	25.00
12d	Husky		yellow tray	50 x 75	35.00	50.00	25.00
13a	King Penguin	Black/white;	black tray	50 x 75	35.00	50.00	25.00
13b	King Penguin		blue tray	50 x 75	35.00	50.00	25.00
13c	King Penguin		pink tray	50 x 75	35.00	50.00	25.00
13d	King Penguin		yellow tray	50 x 75	35.00	50.00	25.00
14a	Lion Cub	Brown;	black tray	45 x 75	35.00	50.00	25.00
14b	Lion Cub		blue tray	45 x 75	35.00	50.00	25.00
14c	Lion Cub		pink tray	45 x 75	35.00	50.00	25.00
14d	Lion Cub		yellow tray	45 x 75	35.00	50.00	25.00
15a	Llama	Grey face;	black tray	65 x 75	35.00	50.00	25.00
15b	Llama		blue tray	65 x 75	35.00	50.00	25.00
15c	Llama		pink tray	65 x 75	35.00	50.00	25.00
15d	Llama		yellow tray	65 x 75	35.00	50.00	25.00
16a	Mare	Light brown;	black tray	55 x 75	35.00	50.00	25.00
16b	Mare		blue tray	55 x 75	35.00	50.00	25.00
16c	Mare		pink tray	55 x 75	35.00	50.00	25.00
16d	Mare		yellow tray	55 x 75	35.00	50.00	25.00
17a	Monkey and Baby	Brown;	black tray	65 x 75	35.00	50.00	25.00
17b	Monkey and Baby		blue tray	65 x 75	35.00	50.00	25.00
17c	Monkey and Baby		pink tray	65 x 75	35.00	50.00	25.00
17d	Monkey and Baby		yellow tray	65 x 75	35.00	50.00	25.00
18	Piglet	Pink/green;	black tray	35 x 75	75.00	110.00	55.00
19a	Polar Bear	White;	black tray	65 x 75	35.00	50.00	25.00
19b	Polar Bear		blue tray	65 x 75	35.00	50.00	25.00
19c	Polar Bear		pink tray	65 x 75	35.00	50.00	25.00
19d	Polar Bear		yellow tray	65 x 75	35.00	50.00	25.00
20a	Polar Bear Cub	White;	black tray	40 x 75	35.00	50.00	25.00
20b	Polar Bear Cub		blue tray	40 x 75	35.00	50.00	25.00
20c	Polar Bear Cub		pink tray	40 x 75	35.00	50.00	25.00
20d	Polar Bear Cub		yellow tray	40 x 75	35.00	50.00	25.00
21a	Raccoon	Grey/black;	black tray	50 x 75	35.00	50.00	25.00
21b	Raccoon		blue tray	50 x 75	35.00	50.00	25.00
21c	Raccoon		pink tray	50 x 75	35.00	50.00	25.00
21d	Raccoon		yellow tray	50 x 75	35.00	50.00	25.00
22a	Snowy Owl	White;	black tray	44 x 75	35.00	50.00	25.00
22b	Snowy Owl		blue tray	44 x 75	35.00	50.00	25.00
22c	Snowy Owl		pink tray	44 x 75	35.00	50.00	25.00
22d	Snowy Owl		yellow tray	44 x 75	35.00	50.00	25.00
23a	Spaniel	White;	black tray	45 x 75	35.00	50.00	25.00
23b	Spaniel		blue tray	45 x 75	35.00	50.00	25.00
23c	Spaniel		pink tray	45 x 75	35.00	50.00	25.00
23d	Spaniel		yellow tray	45 x 75	35.00	50.00	25.00

First Whimsies Derivatives Whimtrays (cont.)
1958-1965

No.	Name	Description		Size	U.S. $	Can. $	U.K. £
24a	Squirrel	Light grey;	black tray	45 x 75	35.00	50.00	25.00
24b	Squirrel		blue tray	45 x 75	35.00	50.00	25.00
24c	Squirrel		pink tray	45 x 75	35.00	50.00	25.00
24d	Squirrel		yellow tray	45 x 75	35.00	50.00	25.00
25a	Swan	White;	black tray	40 x 75	100.00	150.00	75.00
25b	Swan		blue tray	40 x 75	100.00	150.00	75.00
25c	Swan		pink tray	40 x 75	100.00	150.00	75.00
25d	Swan		yellow tray	40 x 75	100.00	150.00	75.00
26a	West Highland Terrier	White;	black tray	40 x 75	35.00	50.00	25.00
26b	West Highland Terrier		blue tray	40 x 75	35.00	50.00	25.00
26c	West Highland Terrier		pink tray	40 x 75	35.00	50.00	25.00
26d	West Highland Terrier		yellow tray	40 x 75	35.00	50.00	25.00

First Whimsies Derivatives Zoo Lights, Candle Holders
1957-1960

George Wade's policy of using unsold models by adding them to new items produced many different "Stick-em-on-Somethings," such as *Zoo Lights*, *Whimtrays* and *Disney Lights*. Luckily for collectors, single models of *First Whimsies* animals, which were eluding capture in their original form, were attached to an oval base with a candle holder on the back to become *Zoo Lights*. Almost all the *First Whimsies* animals are on *Zoo Lights*. The candle holders come in black, yellow, blue and pink, and all the animals are in their original colour glazes.

The *Zoo Lights* were first issued prior to Christmas 1957 as *Animal Candlesticks* (with the exception of the Camel, Llama and Panda, which were issued in August 1958), and were discontinued in January 1960. They are listed in alphabetical order.

Backstamp: Embossed "Wade Porcelain Made in England"

No.	Name	Description		Size	U.S. $	Can. $	U.K. £
1a	Alsatian	Grey/brown;	black holder	47 x 48	40.00	60.00	30.00
1b	Alsatian		blue holder	47 x 48	40.00	60.00	30.00
1c	Alsatian		pink holder	47 x 48	40.00	60.00	30.00
1d	Alsatian		yellow holder	47 x 48	40.00	60.00	30.00
2a	Baby Seal	Light grey;	black holder	35 x 48	40.00	60.00	30.00
2b	Baby Seal		blue holder	35 x 48	40.00	60.00	30.00
2c	Baby Seal		pink holder	35 x 48	40.00	60.00	30.00
2d	Baby Seal		yellow holder	35 x 48	40.00	60.00	30.00

First Whimsies Derivatives Zoo Lights Candle holders (cont.)
1957-1960

No.	Name	Description		Size	U.S. $	Can. $	U.K. £
3a	Bactrian Camel	Light brown;	black holder	52 x 48	40.00	60.00	30.00
3b	Bactrian Camel		blue holder	52 x 48	40.00	60.00	30.00
3c	Bactrian Camel		pink holder	52 x 48	40.00	60.00	30.00
3d	Bactrian Camel		yellow holder	52 x 48	40.00	60.00	30.00
4a	Badger	Grey/black/white; black holder		40 x 48	40.00	60.00	30.00
4b	Badger		blue holder	40 x 48	40.00	60.00	30.00
4c	Badger		pink holder	40 x 48	40.00	60.00	30.00
4d	Badger		yellow holder	40 x 48	40.00	60.00	30.00
5a	Boxer	Brown;	black holder	45 x 48	40.00	60.00	30.00
5b	Boxer		blue holder	45 x 48	40.00	60.00	30.00
5c	Boxer		pink holder	45 x 48	40.00	60.00	30.00
5d	Boxer		yellow holder	45 x 48	40.00	60.00	30.00
6a	Cockatoo	Yellow crest;	black holder	44 x 48	40.00	60.00	30.00
6b	Cockatoo		blue holder	44 x 48	40.00	60.00	30.00
6c	Cockatoo		pink holder	44 x 48	40.00	60.00	30.00
6d	Cockatoo		yellow holder	44 x 48	40.00	60.00	30.00
7a	Corgi	Beige/white;	black holder	37 x 48	40.00	60.00	30.00
7b	Corgi		blue holder	37 x 48	40.00	60.00	30.00
7c	Corgi		pink holder	37 x 48	40.00	60.00	30.00
7d	Corgi		yellow holder	37 x 48	40.00	60.00	30.00
8a	Giant Panda, small	Black/white;	black holder	40 x 48	40.00	60.00	30.00
8b	Giant Panda, small		blue holder	40 x 48	40.00	60.00	30.00
8c	Giant Panda, small		pink holder	40 x 48	40.00	60.00	30.00
8d	Giant Panda, small		yellow holder	40 x 48	40.00	60.00	30.00
9a	Grizzly Bear	Brown/white;	black holder	60 x 48	40.00	60.00	30.00
9b	Grizzly Bear		blue holder	60 x 48	40.00	60.00	30.00
9c	Grizzly Bear		pink holder	60 x 48	40.00	60.00	30.00
9d	Grizzly Bear		yellow holder	60 x 48	40.00	60.00	30.00
10a	Hare	Light grey/white; black holder		40 x 48	40.00	60.00	30.00
10b	Hare		blue holder	40 x 48	40.00	60.00	30.00
10c	Hare		pink holder	40 x 48	40.00	60.00	30.00
10d	Hare		yellow holder	40 x 48	40.00	60.00	30.00
11a	Husky	Fawn/white;	black holder	44 x 48	40.00	60.00	30.00
11b	Husky		blue holder	44 x 48	40.00	60.00	30.00
11c	Husky		pink holder	44 x 48	40.00	60.00	30.00
11d	Husky		yellow holder	44 x 48	40.00	60.00	30.00
12a	King Penguin	Black/white;	black holder	44 x 48	40.00	60.00	30.00
12b	King Penguin		blue holder	44 x 48	40.00	60.00	30.00
12c	King Penguin		pink holder	44 x 48	40.00	60.00	30.00
12d	King Penguin		yellow holder	44 x 48	40.00	50.00	30.00
13a	Lion Cub	Brown;	black holder	37 x 48	40.00	60.00	30.00
13b	Lion Cub		blue holder	37 x 48	40.00	60.00	30.00
13c	Lion Cub		pink holder	37 x 48	40.00	60.00	30.00
13d	Lion Cub		yellow holder	37 x 48	40.00	60.00	30.00
14a	Llama	Grey face;	black holder	55 x 48	40.00	60.00	30.00
14b	Llama		blue holder	55 x 48	40.00	60.00	30.00
14c	Llama		pink holder	55 x 48	40.00	60.00	30.00
14d	Llama		yellow holder	55 x 48	40.00	60.00	30.00
15a	Mare	Light brown;	black holder	55 x 48	40.00	60.00	30.00
15b	Mare		blue holder	55 x 48	40.00	60.00	30.00
15c	Mare		pink holder	55 x 48	40.00	60.00	30.00
15d	Mare		yellow holder	55 x 48	40.00	60.00	30.00
15e	Mare	White;	royal blue holder	55 x 48	40.00	60.00	30.00
16a	Polar Bear Cub	White;	black holder	35 x 48	40.00	60.00	30.00
16b	Polar Bear Cub		blue holder	35 x 48	40.00	60.00	30.00
16c	Polar Bear Cub		pink holder	35 x 48	40.00	60.00	30.00
16d	Polar Bear Cub		yellow holder	35 x 48	40.00	60.00	30.00

First Whimsies Derivatives Zoo Lights Candle holders (cont.)
1957-1962

No.	Name	Description		Size	U.S. $	Can. $	U.K. £
17a	Poodle	Light brown;	black holder	44 x 48	40.00	50.00	30.00
17b	Poodle		blue holder	44 x 48	40.00	50.00	30.00
17c	Poodle		pink holder	44 x 48	40.00	50.00	30.00
17d	Poodle		yellow holder	44 x 48	40.00	50.00	30.00
18a	Retriever	Brown/white;	black holder	40 x 48	40.00	50.00	30.00
18b	Retriever		blue holder	40 x 48	40.00	50.00	30.00
18c	Retriever		pink holder	40 x 48	40.00	50.00	30.00
18d	Retriever		yellow holder	40 x 48	40.00	50.00	30.00
19a	Spaniel	White;	black holder	35 x 48	40.00	50.00	30.00
19b	Spaniel		blue holder	35 x 48	40.00	50.00	30.00
19c	Spaniel		pink holder	35 x 48	40.00	50.00	30.00
19d	Spaniel		yellow holder	35 x 48	40.00	50.00	30.00
20a	Squirrel	Light grey;	black holder	35 x 48	40.00	50.00	30.00
20b	Squirrel		blue holder	35 x 48	40.00	50.00	30.00
20c	Squirrel		pink holder	35 x 48	40.00	50.00	30.00
20d	Squirrel		yellow holder	35 x 48	40.00	50.00	30.00
21a	West Highland Terrier	White;	black holder	35 x 48	40.00	50.00	30.00
21b	West Highland Terrier		blue holder	35 x 48	40.00	50.00	30.00
21c	West Highland Terrier		pink holder	35 x 48	40.00	50.00	30.00
21d	West Highland Terrier		yellow holder	35 x 48	40.00	50.00	30.00

FIRST WHIMSIE BLOW UP SPANIEL

50th ANNIVERSARY 2004

To celebrate fifty years of Whimsies, Wade produced a blow-up model of the first Whimsie "Spaniel with Ball" from Set One of the *First Whimsies*. Although the backstamp dates are 1953-2003, an *Evening Sentinel* newspaper article reveals that the models were actually exhibited for the first time at a Trade Fair in May 1954. William Harper was the modeller of the *First Whimsies*. Included with the blow up model was a reissue (using the original mould) of the miniature First Whimsie "Spaniel," but this time he holds a gold ball in his mouth. The edition size of the models is limited to orders received before March 31st, 2004. The issue price of the two models is £39.95, and the club members price was £35.00.

Spaniel with Ball (left); Blow Up Spaniel with Ball (right)

Backstamp: A. Blow Up: Printed "Celebrating 50 Years of the Whimsie 1953-2003 Made in England" with red "Wade" logo
B. Whimsie: Embossed "Wade"

No.	Name	Description	Size	U.S. $	Can. $	U.K. £
1.	Blow Up Spaniel with Ball	White; grey ears, markings; bright blue ball	70 x 135		Priced per pair	
2.	Spaniel with Ball	White; grey ears, markings; gold ball	25 x 40	65.00	80.00	40.00

NEW COLOURWAY WHIMSIES

SET ONE: ANIMALS

1998 and 2000

Wade reissued six *Whimsies* models in new colourways. Four models, the "Gorilla," "Hippo," "Leopard" and "Racoon" are from the Red Rose Tea Canada and *English Whimsies* series; and two, the "Mole" and the "Safari Park Lion," are Tom Smith models. The "Safari Park Lion" is identical in colour to the original model, except the base is a brighter green.

In 2000, Wade Ceramics sold these models in two ways; singly or in boxed sets. Set one was reissued in a limited edition of 3,000 boxed sets of six models for £15.95. A label on the back of the box reads, "Introduced 2000 Limited Edition of 3000 No. ..." It goes on to list the models in the box, two of which are incorrectly named. The Seal is actually the *Tom Smith* 'Mole' and the Wolf is actually the *English Whimsies / Red Rose Tea* "Racoon." The *English Whimsies* 'Gorilla' model has been renamed Ape. Models are listed in correct name order.

The New Colourway Whimsies were available on-line and from the Wade Factory Shop in September 2003 at the U.K. prices listed below.

Backstamp: Embossed "Wade England" on rim

No.	Name	Description	Size	U.S. $	Can. $	U.K. £
1	Gorilla, standing / Ape (RRC & EW)	Beige; grey-blue base	25 x 35	7.00	8.00	4.00
2	Hippo (RRC & EW)	Light grey; blue base	23 x 35	7.00	8.00	4.00
3	Leopard (RRC & EW)	Pale honey; bright green base	17 x 45	7.00	8.00	4.00
4	Mole / Seal (TS)	Light grey; pale green base	25 x 40	7.00	8.00	4.00
5	Racoon / Wolf (EW)	Light grey; black nose, striped tail	25 x 35	7.00	8.00	4.00
6	Safari Park Lion (TS)	Honey; bright green base	30 x 45	7.00	8.00	4.00
—	6 pce set	Boxed	—	35.00	50.00	20.00

Note: The following initials indicate the origin of the models.
     EW: *English Whimsies*
     TS: Tom Smith
     RRC: Red Rose Tea

NEW COLOURWAY WHIMSIES (cont.)

SET TWO: ANIMALS
2000-2001

During 2000-2001 Wade reissued more *Whimsie* models in new colourways. Five models, the "Beaver," "Elephant," "Kitten," "Polar Bear," and "Zebra" are from the *Red Rose Tea Canada* and *English Whimsies* series. The "Polar Bear" is in the same colourway as the original *English Whimsie* model except for a black nose. The "Puppy" was originally the "Spaniel Puppy" from the *Tom Smith Family Pets Set*. The models could be purchased in two ways direct from Wade Ceramics: as a boxed set of six models for £15.99, or individually boxed for £2.99 each. The second set was not issued in a limited edition.

Backstamp: Embossed "Wade England" on rim

No.	Name	Description	Size	U.S. $	Can. $	U.K. £
1	Beaver (RRC & EW)	Light grey, dark brown stump	35 x 45	7.00	8.00	4.00
2	Elephant (RRC & EW)	Honey; bright green base	35 x 28	7.00	8.00	4.00
3	Kitten, seated (RRC & EW)	Apricot; dark brown wool	30 x 30	7.00	8.00	4.00
4	Polar Bear, head forward (EW)	White; blue base	30 x 30	7.00	8.00	4.00
5	Spaniel Puppy (TS)	Honey; dark brown ears	25 x 30	7.00	8.00	4.00
6	Zebra (EW)	White; black stripes	40 x 35	7.00	8.00	4.00
—	6 pce set	Boxed	—	35.00	50.00	20.00

Note: The following initials indicate the origin of the models.

EW: *English Whimsies*
TS: Tom Smith
RRC: Red Rose Tea

NEW COLOURWAY WHIMSIES (cont.)
SET THREE and FOUR: MINIATURE NURSERIES
2000-2001

Wade reissued ten of the original *Red Rose Tea Canada Miniature Nurseries* and two of the *Tom Smith Miniature Nursery* models and reglazed them in new colourways. Each series was issued as a boxed set of six models for £15.95.

Set Three

Set Four

Backstamp: Embossed "Wade England" on rim

SET THREE

No.	Name	Description	Size	U.S. $	Can. $	U.K. £
1	Hickory Dickory Dock (RRC)	Apricot; dark brown mouse	44 x 20	7.00	8.00	4.00
2	Humpty Dumpty (RRC)	Pale honey; black bow tie, shoes; grey wall	36 x 25	7.00	8.00	4.00
3	Old Woman Who Lived in a Shoe (RRC)	Apricot; dark brown door; green base	35 x 40	7.00	8.00	4.00
4	Puss in Boots (RRC)	Blue; black eyes, nose, boots	43 x 20	7.00	8.00	4.00
5	Queen of Hearts (RRC)	Pale honey; dark red hearts	42 x 25	7.00	8.00	4.00
6	Red Riding Hood (RRC)	Grey; yellow basket; black shoes	44 x 24	7.00	8.00	4.00
—	6 pce set	Boxed		35.00	50.00	20.00

SET FOUR

No.	Name	Description	Size	U.S. $	Can. $	U.K. £
1	Little Bo-Peep (RRC)	Blue; dark brown crook; pink bow	44 x 24	7.00	8.00	4.00
2	Little Boy Blue (RRC)	Blue; green hat; dark brown shoes; yellow horn	41 x 25	7.00	8.00	4.00
3	Cat and the Fiddle (RRC)	Apricot; dark brown fiddle; tan bow	47 x 33	7.00	8.00	4.00
4	Gingerbread Man (RRC)	Honey; yellow hair; green base	43 x 30	7.00	8.00	4.00
5	Ride-a-Cock Horse (RRC)	Apricot; orange hair; black shoes	45 x 55	7.00	8.00	4.00
6	Tom, Tom the Piper's Son (RRC)	Honey; grey tam, kilt, socks; black shoes	39 x 33	7.00	8.00	4.00
—	6 pce set	Boxed	—	35.00	50.00	20.00

Note: The following initials indicate the origin of the models.
TS: Tom Smith
RRC: Red Rose Tea

NEW COLOURWAY WHIMSIES (cont.)
SET FIVE: FARMYARD
2003

In this set five models are from the original *Whimsieland*, Set Three, issued in 1985, and the sixth is the Pony from Set One: Pets. Although the same models, five of them are easily distinguished from the originals by the new colourways. The pig is in the original colours and therefore harder to distinguish, however the base is a brighter green than the model previously issued. The models could be purchased as a boxed set of six or as individual models. The issue price for the boxed set was £17.50, and the individual models were priced at £3.50.

Set Five: Farmyard Animals

No.	Name	Description	Size	U.S. $	Can. $	U.K. £
1	Cockerel	White; red comb; blue wings, tail; grey base	50 x 35	5.00	7.00	3.50
2	Cow	White; tan patches; green base	30 x 45	5.00	7.00	3.50
3	Duck	White; yellow beak; blue wings; green base	45 x 35	5.00	7.00	3.50
4	Goat	White; brown patch; green base	35 x 35	5.00	7.00	3.50
5	Pig	Pink; bright green base	30 x 35	5.00	7.00	3.50
6	Pony	White; brown patches; green base	37 x 47	5.00	7.00	3.50
—	6 pce set	Boxed	—	32.00	35.00	17.50

POLAR BLOW UPS

1962-1963

The *Polar Blow Ups* set is a series of slightly modified blow ups of three of the *First Whimsies Polar Animals*, set six. They are slip cast, hollow models, which because of high production costs, were never put into full production. Only a few hundred of these models are believed to exist. A blow up of the Polar set "Husky" has been seen and a description of colour and size has been reported; there are also unconfirmed reports of a "Dolphin," "Mermaid," and a "Penguin," but no written or visual evidence has been found.

For the previously listed *Walrus* see *The Charlton Standard Catalogue of Wade, Volume One, General Issues, Wade Ireland Animals.*

Backstamp: A. Black and gold label "Genuine Wade Porcelain Made in England" (1-7)
B. Unmarked (1-7)

No.	Name	Description	Size	U.S. $	Can. $	U.K. £
1	Polar Bear Mother	White/beige; pink tongue; blue/beige/white fish	150 x 120	350.00	475.00	235.00
2	Polar Bear Cub	White/beige; pink mouth	100 x 100	350.00	475.00	235.00
3	Seal	Greenish black; pink tongue	120 x 105	350.00	475.00	235.00
4	Husky	Beige/white	150 x 100		Rare	

WHIMSIE-LAND

1984-1988

Although the *English Whimsies* series was discontinued in 1984, George Wade and Son Ltd. continued to produce a range of inexpensive miniature animals, called the *Whimsie-land* series. Five sets of this series were issued between 1984 and 1988. There are five models per set, making a total of 25 figures.

All *Whimsie-land* models were issued in pastel coloured boxes with a complete numbered list of all the models in the series printed on the bottom. All these figures are marked on the back of the base. The original price was 49p each. A model of the *Whimsie-Land* 'Pony' has been found fixed on a small display card, this example was probably used for display purposes .

When the packaging department at the pottery ran out of a specific animal box in this series, a small paper label would be glued over the original printed name on surplus boxes: for example, the Whimsie-land Fox box can be found with an 'Owl' label.

Note: The Elephant in this series is sometimes confused with the *English Whimsies* Elephant, as the pose is similar. However, the *Whimsie-land* Elephant has open-cast legs.

SET ONE: PETS

1984

Backstamp: Embossed "Wade England"

No.	Name	Description	Size	U.S. $	Can. $	U.K. £
1	Retriever	Beige; white face, underparts; green base	32 x 60	25.00	30.00	15.00
2	Puppy	Beige; white face, chest; pink tongue	35 x 36	25.00	30.00	15.00
3	Rabbit	Dark brown ears; honey; red-brown	50 x 25	25.00	30.00	15.00
4a	Kitten, lying, facing left	Grey; white face; blue wool	20 x 42	25.00	30.00	15.00
4b	Kitten, lying, facing left	Grey; white face; pink wool	20 x 42	25.00	30.00	15.00
5	Pony	White; grey mane, tail; green base	37 x 47	25.00	30.00	15.00

SET TWO: WILDLIFE
1984

Backstamp: Embossed "Wade England"

No.	Name	Description	Size	U.S. $	Can. $	U.K. £
6	Lion	Honey; brown mane; tail tip	30 x 50	15.00	22.00	10.00
7	Tiger	Brown; dark stripes, base	22 x 50	15.00	22.00	10.00
8	Elephant	Grey; grey-green base	35 x 40	25.00	36.00	18.00
9	Panda	White; grey markings; green base	37 x 20	25.00	36.00	18.00
10	Giraffe	Beige; black hooves; green base	50 x 35	30.00	45.00	22.00

SET THREE: FARMYARD
1985

Backstamp: Embossed "Wade England"

No.	Name	Description	Size	U.S. $	Can. $	U.K. £
11	Cockerel	White; grey markings; pink tail, comb; grey/green base	50 x 35	32.00	40.00	20.00
12	Duck	White; grey back, tail; yellow beak; green base	45 x 35	32.00	40.00	20.00
13	Cow	White; black patches; green base	30 x 45	32.00	40.00	20.00
14	Pig	Pink; green base	30 x 35	32.00	40.00	20.00
15	Goat	White; grey patch; green base	35 x 35	32.00	40.00	20.00

SET FOUR: HEDGEROW

1986

Backstamp: Embossed "Wade England"

No.	Name	Description	Size	U.S. $	Can. $	U.K. £
16	Fox	Red-brown; honey face, chest, feet	35 x 35	25.00	35.00	18.00
17	Owl	White; yellow/black eyes	35 x 25	15.00	22.00	10.00
18	Hedgehog	Grey-brown; beige	25 x 35	15.00	22.00	10.00
19	Badger	Grey; white face; black markings	25 x 35	15.00	22.00	10.00
20	Squirrel	White; grey	35 x 25	15.00	22.00	10.00

SET FIVE: BRITISH WILDLIFE

1987

Backstamp: Embossed "Wade England"

No.	Name	Description	Size	U.S. $	Can. $	U.K. £
21	Pheasant	Honey; grey-blue head; red-brown tail	35 x 50	35.00	50.00	25.00
22	Field Mouse	Brown; beige berry; green base	35 x 30	35.00	50.00	25.00
23	Golden Eagle	Brown; dark brown base	35 x 40	35.00	50.00	25.00
24	Otter	Brown; blue-grey base	40 x 40	35.00	50.00	25.00
25	Partridge	White; black beak; green base	35 x 35	35.00	50.00	25.00

Whimsie-land Derivatives

Money Box
1987

In 1987 Wade issued three money boxes based on the earlier "Fawn," "Disney Kennel" and "Noddy Toadstool Cottage" money boxes. Because the original moulds were worn, Wade made new moulds, which produced larger, heavier and less delicate-looking models than the originals. New colours were also used. The *Whimsie-land* Puppy was used on a newly modelled Disney Kennel money box. The money boxes were sold in plain, unmarked boxes. For other money boxes see pages 24, 69 and 158.

Kennel and Puppy

Backstamp: Unmarked

No.	Name	Description	Size	U.S. $	Can. $	U.K. £
1	Kennel and Puppy	Brown roof; honey walls	95 x 125	45.00	60.00	28.00

Whimsie-Land Derivatives Whimtrays
1987

During the summer of 1987, Wade produced a set of kidney-shaped trays it called *New Whimtrays*. Because the new *Whimsie-land* animals were used on them, they are often referred to as *Whimsie-land trays*.

Backstamp: Embossed "Wade England"

No.	Name	Description	Size	U.S. $	Can. $	U.K. £
1a	Duck	Black tray	90 x 110	25.00	38.00	20.00
1b	Duck	Blue tray	90 x 110	25.00	38.00	20.00
1c	Duck	Green tray	90 x 110	25.00	38.00	20.00
2a	Owl	Black tray	90 x 110	25.00	38.00	20.00
2b	Owl	Blue tray	90 x 110	25.00	38.00	20.00
2c	Owl	Green tray	90 x 110	25.00	38.00	20.00
3a	Pony	Black tray	90 x 110	25.00	38.00	20.00
3b	Pony	Blue tray	90 x 110	25.00	38.00	20.00
3c	Pony	Green tray	90 x 110	25.00	38.00	20.00
4a	Puppy	Black tray	90 x 110	25.00	38.00	20.00
4b	Puppy	Blue tray	90 x 110	25.00	38.00	20.00
4c	Puppy	Green tray	90 x 110	25.00	38.00	20.00
5a	Squirrel	Black tray	90 x 110	25.00	38.00	20.00
5b	Squirrel	Blue tray	90 x 110	25.00	38.00	20.00
5c	Squirrel	Green tray	90 x 110	25.00	38.00	20.00

Whimsie-land Derivatives Key Rings
1988

After the Whimsie-land series and the New Whimtrays were discontinued, surplus models were converted into key rings by adding a small chain and a ring. The Whimsie-land "Panda" was reglazed in black and white for this series.

Photograph not available
at press time

Backstamp: Embossed "Wade England"

No.	Name	Description	Size	U.S. $	Can. $	U.K. £
1	Badger	Grey; black markings	25 x 35	20.00	30.00	15.00
2	Duck	White/grey; yellow beak	45 x 35	20.00	30.00	15.00
3	Kitten, lying, facing left	Grey/white; pink wool	20 x 42	20.00	30.00	15.00
4	Panda	Black/white	37 x 20	20.00	30.00	15.00
5	Puppy	Beige/white	35 x 36	20.00	30.00	15.00

WHIMSEY-IN-THE-VALE

1993

In 1993 two sets of houses were produced and named *Whimsey-in-the-Vale*. Each set consists of five models, and unlike the *Whimsey-on-Why models* were boxed individually and unnumbered.

The moulds from the 1980-1988 *Whimsey-on-Why* houses were used to make the following models in the *Whimsey-in-the-Vale* series:

Whimsey-on-Why Models became Whimsey-in-the-Vale Models

Why Knott Inn	Antique Shop
Whimsey Service Station	Florist Shop
Briar Row	Jubilee Terrace
The Fire Station	St. John's School
St. Sebastians Church	St. Lawrence Church
The Barley Mow	Boars Head Pub
The Antique Shop	Post Office
The Post Office	Rose Cottage
The Market Hall	Town Garage
The Stag Hotel	Vale Farm

SET ONE

Backstamp: Embossed "Wade England"

No.	Name	Description	Size	U.S. $	Can. $	U.K. £
1	Antique Shop	White; beige roof; green/yellow trim	33 x 39	15.00	22.00	10.00
2	Florist Shop	White; light brown roof; green/yellow trim	40 x 38	15.00	22.00	10.00
3	Jubilee Terrace	White; beige roof; yellow stonework	33 x 78	22.00	30.00	15.00
4	St. John's School	White; dark brown roof; green windows, doors	33 x 30	15.00	22.00	10.00
5	St. Lawrence Church	Grey; green doors	55 x 77	15.00	22.00	10.00

SET TWO

Backstamp: A. Embossed "Wade England" (6, 7, 8, 10)
B. Unmarked (9)

No.	Name	Description	Size	U.S. $	Can. $	U.K. £
6	Boar's Head Pub	White; brown roof, windows; yellow doors	35 x 77	15.00	22.00	10.00
7	Post Office	White; dark brown roof; blue doors	35 x 37	15.00	22.00	10.00
8	Rose Cottage	White; beige roof; yellow windows, doors	40 x 38	15.00	22.00	10.00
9	Town Garage	White; beige roof; blue doors, windows	35 x 50	16.00	24.00	12.00
10	Vale Farm	Light brown; grey roof; dark brown beams	42 x 66	16.00	24.00	12.00

WHIMSEY-ON-WHY

1980-1987

Whimsey-on-Why is a series of miniature porcelain houses based upon a mythical English village called Whimsey-on-Why. The highly accurate detail was achieved by the use of fired-on enamel transfers, which included the number of the model in an unobtrusive place. The original price for a set of eight models was £10, or the houses could be bought individually at prices ranging from 79p for a small model to £2.15 for a larger size.

SET ONE

1980-1981

Set One was issued in spring 1980. The original price for "Pump Cottage" was 79p. "Morgan's the Chemist," "Dr Healer's House" and the "Tobacconist's Shop" sold for 99p. "The Why Knott Inn" was 89p, "Bloodshott Hall" and "The Barley Mow" were £1.85 and "St. Sebastian's Church" was £2.15. All models are numbered.

Backstamp: Embossed "Wade England"

No.	Name	Description	Size	U.S. $	Can. $	U.K. £
1	Pump Cottage	Brown thatch, beams	28 x 39	15.00	22.00	10.00
2	Morgan's the Chemist	Grey roof; yellow windows	40 x 39	22.00	30.00	15.00
3	Dr. Healer's House	Brown roof, door	40 x 39	25.00	37.00	18.00
4	Tobacconist's Shop	Brown roof; red doors	33 x 39	15.00	22.00	10.00
5	Why Knott Inn	Beige thatch; black beams	33 x 39	20.00	30.00	15.00
6	Bloodshott Hall	Red-brown; grey roof	50 x 80	25.00	37.00	18.00
7	St. Sebastian's Church	Grey; brown door	55 x 77	45.00	60.00	30.00
8	The Barley Mow	Beige roof; black wood	35 x 77	32.00	50.00	25.00

SET TWO

1981-1982

This set was issued in spring 1981. "The Greengrocer's Shop" and "The Antique Shop" originally sold for 99p each. The price for the "Whimsey Service Station" and for "The Post Office" was £1.10. "The Whimsey School" cost £1.50, "The Watermill" and "The Stag Hotel" were £1.85 and "The Windmill" was £2.15.

Backstamp: A. Embossed "Wade England" (9-15)
B. Unmarked (16)

No.	Name	Description	Size	U.S. $	Can. $	U.K. £
9	The Greengrocer's Shop	Grey roof; green windows	35 x 35	15.00	22.00	10.00
10	The Antique Shop	Purple-brown roof	35 x 37	25.00	37.00	18.00
11	Whimsey Service Station	Beige roof; green pumps	40 x 38	25.00	37.00	18.00
12	The Post Office	Beige roof; yellow/blue windows	40 x 38	15.00	22.00	10.00
13	Whimsey School	Brown; grey roof; blue window	38 x 51	50.00	70.00	35.00
14	The Watermill	Red-brown; beige thatch	42 x 66	25.00	37.00	18.00
15	The Stag Hotel	Grey roof; black wood	45 x 66	25.00	37.00	18.00
16	The Windmill	White; copper pin	60 x 30	90.00	135.00	70.00

SET THREE

1982-1983

Set Three was issued in spring 1982. "The Tinker's Nook" originally sold for 89p, the "Whimsey Station" cost 99p, "Merryweather Farm" was £2.15, "The Vicarage" was £1.65, "The Manor" was £1.85, "Briar Row" was £1.95 and "Broomyshaw Cottage" and "The Sweet Shop" were each £1.10. "Tinker's Nook" has been found with a Wade Ireland Backstamp.

Backstamp: A. Embossed "Wade England" (18-24)
B. "Wade Ireland" (17)

No.	Name	Description	Size	U.S. $	Can. $	U.K. £
17	Tinker's Nook	Red-brown roof; yellow/white windows	38 x 22	15.00	22.00	10.00
18	Whimsey Station	Red-brown; brown roof; yellow/blue windows	135 x 39	25.00	35.00	20.00
19	Merryweather Farm	Cream; brown roof; blue/yellow windows	48 x 55	60.00	90.00	45.00
20	The Vicarage	Pink; beige roof; blue/yellow windows	41 x 51	60.00	90.00	45.00
21	Broomyshaw Cottage	Beige; brown roof; blue/yellow windows	40 x 40	15.00	22.00	10.00
22	The Sweet Shop	Grey roof; black wood; blue windows	40 x 40	15.00	22.00	10.00
23	Briar Row	Beige thatch; yellow/blue windows	33 x 78	50.00	70.00	35.00
24	The Manor	Red-brown; brown roof; blue/yellow windows	42 x 66	25.00	37.00	18.00

SET FOUR

1984-1985

Only three new *Whimsey-on-Why* models were released during 1984. "The District Bank," "The Old Smithy" and "The Picture Palace" were issued the same year Wade Ireland introduced its *Bally-Whim Irish Village* (marketed by George Wade & Son Ltd.). The remaining five models of this set were produced in early 1985.

The original price for the "District Bank" was £1.75, "The Old Smithy" was £1.30 and "The Picture Palace" was £2.35. The original prices for the remaining models are not known.

A model of the *Bally-Whim Irish Village* "Undertaker's House" (#1), with a beige glaze, has been found with the transfer print of the *Whimsey-on-Why* "District Bank" (# 25) applied. This model is clearly marked with an embossed "Wade Ireland 1" on the base. The reason for this change of model shape has not been determined.

District Bank (25b)

Fire Station, brown roof (left), honey roof (right)

Backstamp: A. Embossed "Wade England" (25-31)
B. Embossed "Wade Ireland" (26)
C. Unmarked (32)

No.	Name	Description	Size	U.S. $	Can. $	U.K. £
25a	The District Bank	Red-brown; brown roof	43 x 40	15.00	22.00	10.00
25b	The District Bank	Beige walls; dark grey roof	50 x 58	22.00	28.00	14.00
26	The Old Smithy	Yellow thatch; black wood	25 x 45	15.00	22.00	10.00
27	The Picture Palace	Black wood; red lettering	45 x 65	25.00	37.00	18.00
28	The Butcher Shop	Brown roof; green/grey front	33 x 25	25.00	37.00	18.00
29	The Barber Shop	Grey roof; green/yellow front	33 x 25	32.00	48.00	24.00
30	Miss Prune's House	Grey roof; black wood; yellow door	38 x 38	18.00	24.00	12.00
31a	The Fire Station	Brown roof; red fire engine	33 x 30	25.00	37.00	18.00
31b	The Fire Station	Honey roof; red fire engine	33 x 30	22.00	28.00	14.00
32	The Market Hall	Brown roof	35 x 50	25.00	37.00	18.00

SET FIVE

1987-Circa 1988

The last *Whimsey-on-Why* set, issued in 1987, comprises four models. This brought the series to a close with a total of 36 models. The original prices of this set are unknown. For similar models, see the section on *Whimsey-in-the-Vale*.

Backstamp: Embossed "Wade England"

No.	Name	Description	Size	U.S. $	Can. $	U.K. £
33	The School Teacher's House	Grey roof, walls	38 x 38	45.00	65.00	35.00
34	The Fishmonger's Shop	Brown roof	43 x 27	45.00	65.00	35.00
35	The Police Station	Blue; brown roof	43 x 27	45.00	65.00	35.00
36	The Library	Brown; grey roof	50 x 38	45.00	66.00	35.00

MISCELLANEOUS SETS

MISCELLANEOUS SETS

ALPHABET AND LONDON TRAINS

1958-1959

The *Alphabet Train* comprises a miniature engine pulling six carriages and was intended to be educational, as well as fun, for children to play with. The carriages have various numbers on their roofs and letters of the alphabet on both sides. The *London Train* has a single letter on the roof of each carriage (forming the name *London*), with scenes of Tower Bridge, St. Paul's Cathedral, Trafalgar Square, Piccadilly Circus, Big Ben or Westminster Abbey on each side.

The issue date for both sets was August 1958, and they originally sold for 6/11d. They were discontinued in January 1959. The trains are very rare. As they are only seen in complete sets, no individual prices are given below.

Alphabet Set

Backstamp: Unmarked

No.	Name	Description	Size	U.S. $	Can. $	U.K. £
1	Alphabet Set: engine, tender, 6 carriages	Blue engine	27 x 205	900.00	1,200.00	450.00

London Set

No.	Name	Description	Size	U.S. $	Can. $	U.K. £
1	London Set: engine, tender, 6 carriages	Grey engine	27 x 205	1,000.00	1,500.00	600.00

ANGELS

1963

The *Angels* is a small series of models which were only produced for a short time. They were modelled in three different positions standing, sitting and kneeling and coloured in pastel shades of pink, green, yellow and blue. These figures are also found on angel dishes and on angel candle holders. The *Angels* originally sold for 1/11 each.

Angels Kneeling, Sitting and Standing

KNEELING ANGEL

Backstamp: Unmarked

No.	Description	Size	U.S. $	Can. $	U.K. £
1a	Blue dress; brown hair	40 x 25	90.00	110.00	55.00
1b	Blue dress; yellow hair	40 x 25	90.00	110.00	55.00
1c	Green dress; brown hair	40 x 25	90.00	110.00	55.00
1d	Green dress; yellow hair	40 x 25	90.00	110.00	55.00
1e	Pink dress; brown hair	40 x 25	90.00	110.00	55.00
1f	Pink dress; yellow hair	40 x 25	90.00	110.00	55.00
1g	Yellow dress; brown hair	40 x 25	90.00	110.00	55.00
1h	Yellow dress; yellow hair	40 x 25	90.00	110.00	55.00

SITTING ANGEL

Backstamp: Unmarked

No.	Description	Size	U.S. $	Can. $	U.K. £
2a	Blue dress; brown hair	40 x 30	90.00	110.00	55.00
2b	Blue dress; yellow hair	40 x 30	90.00	110.00	55.00
2c	Green dress; brown hair	40 x 30	90.00	110.00	55.00
2d	Green dress; yellow hair	40 x 30	90.00	110.00	55.00
2e	Pink dress; brown hair	40 x 30	90.00	110.00	55.00
2f	Pink dress; yellow hair	40 x 30	90.00	110.00	55.00
2g	Yellow dress; brown hair	40 x 30	90.00	110.00	55.00
2h	Yellow dress; yellow hair	40 x 30	90.00	110.00	55.00

STANDING ANGEL

Backstamp: Unmarked

No.	Description	Size	U.S. $	Can. $	U.K. £
3a	Blue dress; brown hair	40 x 30	90.00	110.00	55.00
3b	Blue dress; yellow hair	40 x 30	90.00	110.00	55.00
3c	Green dress; brown hair	40 x 30	90.00	110.00	55.00
3d	Green dress; yellow hair	40 x 30	90.00	110.00	55.00
3e	Pink dress; brown hair	40 x 30	90.00	110.00	55.00
3f	Pink dress; yellow hair	40 x 30	90.00	110.00	55.00
3g	Yellow dress; brown hair	40 x 30	90.00	110.00	55.00
3h	Yellow dress; yellow hair	40 x 30	90.00	110.00	55.00

Angel Derivatives

Angel Candle Holders

The angel models were mounted on the front of triangular-shaped candle holders (the same candle holders that were used for the 1960 *Disney Lights*). All the candle holders are black, and they were sold with a candy-twist candle for an original price of 2/11d each.

Kneeling Angel Candle Holder

Backstamp: Embossed "Wade"

No.	Description	Size	U.S. $	Can. $	U.K. £
1a	Blue dress; brown hair	58 x 50	100.00	120.00	60.00
1b	Blue dress; yellow hair	58 x 50	100.00	120.00	60.00
1c	Green dress; brown hair	58 x 50	100.00	120.00	60.00
1d	Green dress; yellow hair	58 x 50	100.00	120.00	60.00
1e	Pink dress; brown hair	58 x 50	100.00	120.00	60.00
1f	Pink dress; yellow hair	58 x 50	100.00	120.00	60.00
1g	Yellow dress; brown hair	58 x 50	100.00	120.00	60.00
1h	Yellow dress; yellow hair	58 x 50	100.00	120.00	60.00

Sitting Angel Candle Holder

Backstamp: Embossed "Wade"

No.	Description	Size	U.S. $	Can. $	U.K. £
2a	Blue dress; brown hair	58 x 50	100.00	120.00	60.00
2b	Blue dress; yellow hair	58 x 50	100.00	120.00	60.00
2c	Green dress; brown hair	58 x 50	100.00	120.00	60.00
2d	Green dress; yellow hair	58 x 50	100.00	120.00	60.00
2e	Pink dress; brown hair	58 x 50	100.00	120.00	60.00
2f	Pink dress; yellow hair	58 x 50	100.00	120.00	60.00
2g	Yellow dress; brown hair	58 x 50	100.00	120.00	60.00
2h	Yellow dress; yellow hair	58 x 50	100.00	120.00	60.00

Standing Angel Candle Holder

Backstamp: Embossed "Wade"

No.	Description	Size	U.S. $	Can. $	U.K. £
3a	Blue dress; brown hair	58 x 50	100.00	120.00	60.00
3b	Blue dress; yellow hair	58 x 50	100.00	120.00	60.00
3c	Green dress; brown hair	58 x 50	100.00	120.00	60.00
3d	Green dress; yellow hair	58 x 50	100.00	120.00	60.00
3e	Pink dress; brown hair	58 x 50	100.00	120.00	60.00
3f	Pink dress; yellow hair	58 x 50	100.00	120.00	60.00
3g	Yellow dress; brown hair	58 x 50	100.00	120.00	60.00
3h	Yellow dress; yellow hair	58 x 50	100.00	120.00	60.00

Angel Derivatives Dishes

The dishes, similar to the *Whimtrays*, are black and the angel figure is positioned on the back rim. They originally sold for 2/11d each.

Angel Dishes - Kneeling, Standing and Sitting

Kneeling Angel Dish

Backstamp: Embossed Angel Dish, "Wade Porcelain, Made in England"

No.	Description	Size	U.S. $	Can. $	U.K. £
1a	Blue dress; brown hair	40 x 75	100.00	120.00	60.00
1b	Blue dress; yellow hair	40 x 75	100.00	120.00	60.00
1c	Green dress; brown hair	40 x 75	100.00	120.00	60.00
1d	Green dress; yellow hair	40 x 75	100.00	120.00	60.00
1e	Pink dress; brown hair	40 x 75	100.00	120.00	60.00
1f	Pink dress; yellow hair	40 x 75	100.00	120.00	60.00
1g	Yellow dress; brown hair	40 x 75	100.00	120.00	60.00
1h	Yellow dress; yellow hair	40 x 75	100.00	120.00	60.00

Standing Angel Dish

No.	Description	Size	U.S. $	Can. $	U.K. £
2a	Blue dress; brown hair	40 x 75	100.00	120.00	60.00
2b	Blue dress; yellow hair	40 x 75	100.00	120.00	60.00
2c	Green dress; brown hair	40 x 75	100.00	120.00	60.00
2d	Green dress; yellow hair	40 x 75	100.00	120.00	60.00
2e	Pink dress; brown hair	40 x 75	100.00	120.00	60.00
2f	Pink dress; yellow hair	40 x 75	100.00	120.00	60.00
2g	Yellow dress; brown hair	40 x 75	100.00	120.00	60.00
2h	Yellow dress; yellow hair	40 x 75	100.00	120.00	60.00

Sitting Angel Dish

No.	Description	Size	U.S. $	Can. $	U.K. £
3a	Blue dress; brown hair	40 x 75	100.00	120.00	60.00
3b	Blue dress; yellow hair	40 x 75	100.00	120.00	60.00
3c	Green dress; brown hair	40 x 75	100.00	120.00	60.00
3d	Green dress; yellow hair	40 x 75	100.00	120.00	60.00
3e	Pink dress; brown hair	40 x 75	100.00	120.00	60.00
3f	Pink dress; yellow hair	40 x 75	100.00	120.00	60.00
3g	Yellow dress; brown hair	40 x 75	100.00	120.00	60.00
3h	Yellow dress; yellow hair	40 x 75	100.00	120.00	60.00

Walt Disney Figures

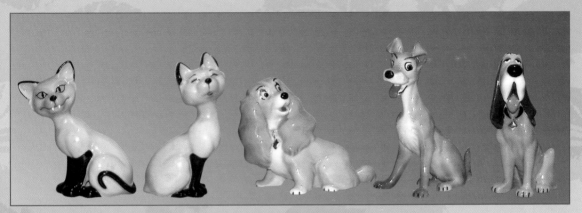

Disney Blow Ups
Si, Am, Lady, Tramp and **Trusty**
1961-1965 (P. 77)

Little Hiawatha
Produced in the "New" cellulose glaze
1937 (P. 89)

Hat Box Series, First Issue, Set Two
Bambi, Flower, Thumper, Dumbo, Baby Pegasus, Dachie, Si, Am, Boris, and **Toughy**
1956-1965 (P. 82)

Hat Box Derivative
Thumper on Disney Light (Candle Holder)
1960 (P. 85)

Hat Box Series First Issue, Part of Set Three
Merlin as a Hare, The Girl Squirrel, and **Merlin as a Caterpillar**
1956-1965 (P. 83)

English Whimsies

Set One: Fawn, Rabbit, Mongrel, Kitten, Spaniel
1971 (P. 104)

Set Eight: Donkey, Barn Owl, Cat, Mouse, Ram
1977 (P. 108)

Set Eleven: Bison, Bluebird, Wild Boar, Bullfrog, Raccoon
1979 (P. 110)

Set Twelve: Penguin, Seal Pup, Husky, Walrus, Polar Bear
1980 (P. 111)

First Whimsies

Set One: English Animals; Leaping Fawn, Horse, Spaniel with Ball, Poodle, and Squirrel
1954-1958 (P. 114)

Set Two: English Animals; Bull, Lamb, Kitten, Hare, and Dachshund
1954-1958 (P. 115)

Set Three: English Country Animals; Badger, Fox Cub, Stoat, Shetland Pony, Retriever
1955-1958 (P. 115)

Set Four: African Jungle Animals; Lion, Crocodile, Monkey and Baby, Rhinoceros, Baby Elephant
1955-1958 (P. 116)

First Whimsies

Set Five: Horses; Light Brown Mare, White Mare, Light Brown Foal, White Foal, Light Brown Colt, White Colt, Beagle
1956-1959 (P. 116)

Set Six: Polar Animals; King Peng uin, Husky, Polar Bear, Baby Seal, Polar Bear Cub
1956-1959 (P. 117)

Set Seven: Pedigree Dogs; Alsatian, West Highland Terrier, Corgi, Boxer, Dark Brown Saint Bernard, Light Brown Saint Bernard
1957-1961 (P. 118)

Set Eight: Zoo Animals; Llama, Lion Cub, Giant Panda, Bactrian Camel, Cockatoo
1957-1961 (P. 119)

First Whimsies

Set Nine: North American Animals; Snowy Owl, Raccoon, Grizzly Bear, Cub in light brown, brown, and white, Cougar
1958-1961 (P. 119)

Set Ten: Farm Animals; Pig, Italian Goat, Beige Shire Horse, White Shire Horse, Foxhound, Swan
1957-1961 (P. 120)

First Whimsies Derivatives Whimtrays

Yellow Tray with Grizzly Bear Cub

Black Tray with Corgi

Black Tray with Bactrian Camel

Yellow Tray with Cockatoo
1958-1965 (P. 123-125)

Yellow Tray with Llama

New Colourway Whimsies

Set One: Animals; Gorilla, Hippo, Leopard, Lion, Mole, Racoon
1998-2000 (P. 128)

Set Two: Animals; Kitten, Elephant, Polar Bear, Spaniel Puppy, Beaver, Zebra
2000-2001 (P. 129)

Set Three: Nurseries; Puss in Boots, Queen of Hearts, Red Riding Hood, Hickory Dickory Dock, Humpty Dumpty, Old Woman Who Lived in a Shoe, 2000-2001 (P. 130)

Set Four: Nurseries; Cat and the Fiddle, Gingerbread Man, Little Bo-Peep, Little Boy Blue, Ride-a-Cock Horse, Tom, Tom the Piper's Son, 2000-2001 (P. 130)

Polar Blow Ups

Polar Bear Mother, Polar Bear Cub, Seal Polar Blow Ups were produced for only one year. The models are based on the First Whimsies Set Six: Polar Animals
1962-1963 (P. 132)

Whimsey-On-Why

Set One: Pump Cottage, Morgan's the Chemist, Dr. Healer's House, Tobacconist's Shop, Why Knott Inn, Bloodshot Hall, St. Sebastian's Church, The Barley Mow, 1980-1981 (P. 140)

Set Two: The Greengrocer's Shop, The Antique Shop, Whimsey Service Station, The Post Office, Whimsey School, The Watermill, The Stag Hotel, The Windmill, 1981-1982 (P. 141)

Set Three: Tinker's Nook, Whimsey Station, Merryweather Farm, The Vicarage, Broomyshaw Cottage, The Sweet Shop, Briar Row, The Manor, 1982-1983 (P. 142)

Set Four: The District Bank, The Old Smithy, The Picture Palace, The Butcher Shop, The Barber Shop, Miss Prune's House, The Fire Station, The Market Hall, 1984-1985 (P. 143)

The British Character Set

The British Characters: Billingsgate Porter, Lawyer, Pearly King and Queen. The hat colours differ in the Pearly Queen. 1959 (P. 152)

Child Studies

Child Studies is a set of four (three shown) children in National Costume. The decorated bases reflect the country: **Daffodil (Wales), Thistle (Scotland), Shamrock (Ireland),** and **Grass (England).** 1962 (P. 153)

Children and Pets

The Children and Pets, was a set of three models produced in a limited edition for Wade Club members. **Welcome Home** was the first model issued. **Fireside Friend** the second and **Togetherness** was the last model. Only 500 sets were made when the series was discontinued. 1993-1994 (P. 154)

Welcome Home

Fireside Friend

Togetherness

BEAR AMBITIONS

1995

The *Bear Ambitions* set of six named Teddy Bears was reissued in 1996 for Tom Smith and Company (the British Christmas Cracker manufacturers) in three different glaze colours for their Christmas Time Crackers series, see page 388. See also Ripley Teddy Bears Picnic for green colourways, page 228.

Backstamp: Embossed "Wade England"

No.	Name	Description	Size	U.S. $	Can. $	U.K. £
1	Admiral Sam	Honey	50	7.00	8.00	4.00
2	Alex the Aviator	Honey	45	7.00	8.00	4.00
3	Artistic Edward	Honey	40	7.00	8.00	4.00
4	Beatrice Ballerina	Honey	50	7.00	8.00	4.00
5	Locomotive Joe	Honey	50	7.00	8.00	4.00
6	Musical Marco	Honey	45	7.00	8.00	4.00

THE BRITISH CHARACTER SET

1959

The *British Character* set, also known to collectors as *London Characters,* includes four models: the "Pearly King," "Pearly Queen," "Lawyer" and the "Billingsgate Porter," who in the famous Billingsgate Fish Market tradition, is carrying a basket of fish on his head. They were produced for only one year and are rarely seen and highly sought after. This set was designed by William Timym, who also designed the series "Bengo and his Puppy Friends, TV Pets" (see page 55).

Backstamp: A. Black and gold label "Genuine Wade Porcelain" (1-4)
B. Unmarked (1-4)

No.	Name	Description	Size	U.S. $	Can. $	U.K. £
1	Pearly King	White pearlised suit, cap: yellow brim	68 x 28	195.00	240.00	120.00
2a	Pearly Queen	White pearlised dress, jacket; yellow ribbon; lower hat brim black	68 x 38	195.00	240.00	120.00
2b	Pearly Queen	Blue/pink pearlised dress; lower hat brim grey	68 x 38	195.00	240.00	120.00
2c	Pearly Queen	Blue/pink pearlised dress; lower hat brim pink	68 x 38	195.00	240.00	120.00
2d	Pearly Queen	Blue/pink pearlised dress; lower hat brim white	68 x 38	195.00	240.00	120.00
3	Lawyer	White wig; black gown, shoes; brown base	68 x 28	195.00	240.00	120.00
4a	Billingsgate Porter	Pearlised fish; black hat, badge and shoes; green tie; blue trousers; and base	75 x 28	195.00	240.00	120.00
4b	Billingsgate Porter	Pearlised fish; black hat, green tie; blue badge, trousers, and base; brown shoes	75 x 28	195.00	240.00	120.00

CHILD STUDIES

1962

Child Studies was a short-lived set of four children in national costumes, representing England, Ireland, Scotland and Wales. Each model stands on a circular base, which has an embossed flower design on it.

Their issue date was spring 1962, and they sold for an original price of 21/- each.

Backstamp: A. Blue transfer "Wade England" (1-4)
B. Unmarked (1-4)

No.	Name	Description	Size	U.S. $	Can. $	U.K. £
1	English Boy	Yellow hair; black hat; red jacket; blue waistcoat; grassy base	120 x 40	600.00	750.00	375.00
2	Irish Girl	Green kilt; shamrock base	115 x 40	850.00	1,050.00	525.00
3	Scots Boy	Blue kilt; black tam, jacket; thistle base	120 x 40	600.00	750.00	375.00
4	Welsh Girl	Striped skirt; checkered shawl; daffodil base	135 x 40	600.00	750.00	375.00

Note: Models have been found without the facial feathers. They may have been rejected during the quality control inspection process.

CHILDREN AND PETS

1993-1994

Children and Pets is a series comprising three figures modelled by Ken Holmes. Each piece was to be issued in a limited edition of 2,500, with the edition number appearing on the base. However, only 500 of the "Togetherness" model was issued before the series was discontinued.

The first model, "Welcome Home," was issued in June 1993, "Fireside Friend" was produced in the latter half of 1993 and "Togetherness" was issued in late autumn 1994. The models have polished wood bases with recessed tops shaped in the same outline as the figure above.

Children and Pets was sold direct from the Wade pottery as a mail order and was limited to two models per customer. The original price was £25.00 each.

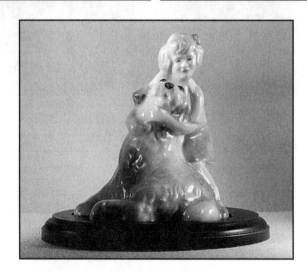

Backstamp: Black transfer "Wade Limited Editions [name of model] Modelled by Ken Holmes"

No.	Name	Description	Size	U.S. $	Can. $	U.K. £
1	Welcome Home	Yellow jacket; brown trousers; white/black dog	100 x 125	55.00	70.00	35.00
2	Fireside Friend	Pink blanket; brown or black ears	90 x 110	55.00	70.00	35.00
3	Togetherness	Green skirt, ribbon; white/grey dog	130 x 95	125.00	150.00	75.00

COLLECTABLE LIMITED EDITION CRACKERS

MINIATURE NURSERY RHYMES

2001

As there were eight models in the set and only six crackers in a box, extra models could be purchased direct from Wade Ceramics at a cost of £2.99 each.

Ten complete sets were produced in an all-over gold glaze. As there were only six crackers to the box, two contained an extra model. A ticket allowing the finder to take four guests on a tour of the Wade Pottery was inserted into one of the boxes of crackers.

The cost direct from Wade was £19.99.

Backstamp: Embossed "Wade England"

No.	Name	Description	Size	U.S. $	Can. $	U.K. £
1a	Dr. Foster	Grey; black umbrella; brown bag	43 x 26	6.00	8.00	4.00
1b	Dr. Foster	Gold	43 x 26			Rare
2a	Goosey Gander	White; yellow beak, feet	33 x 36	6.00	8.00	4.00
2b	Goosey Gander	Gold	33 x 36			Rare
3a	Jack	Beige; brown hair; green base	34 x 33	6.00	8.00	4.00
3b	Jack	Gold	34 x 33			Rare
4a	Jill	Beige; yellow hair; green base	28 x 39	6.00	8.00	4.00
4b	Jill	Gold	28 x 39			Rare
5a	Little Jack Horner	Green; yellow hair; brown shoes	37 x 21	6.00	8.00	4.00
5b	Little Jack Horner	Gold	37 x 21			Rare
6a	Little Miss Muffett	Beige; yellow hair; black spider	39 x 35	6.00	8.00	4.00
6b	Little Miss Muffett	Gold	39 x 35			Rare
7a	Mother Goose	Pale honey; green hat; Goose: yellow beak, feet	41 x 31	6.00	8.00	4.00
7b	Mother Goose	Gold	41 x 31			Rare
8a	Wee Willie Winkie	Blue; dark brown hair	44 x 24	6.00	8.00	4.00
8b	Wee Willie Winkie	Gold	44 x 24			Rare
—	6 pce set	Boxed	—	30.00	45.00	20.00
—	8 pce set	Boxed (gold)	—		Rare	

DINOSAUR COLLECTION

SET ONE and SET TWO

1993 and 2001

The *Dinosaur Collection* was issued in the wake of a series of documentary films about dinosaurs and the popular movie, *Jurassic Park*, released in early 1993. The subject stirred the imagination of the public, and it sparked the revival of dinosaur exhibits and a subsequent flood of dinosaur toys and models.

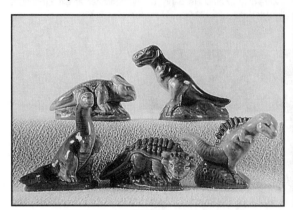

Set One

Set Two

Backstamp: Embossed "Wade England"

SET ONE

No.	Name	Description	Size	U.S. $	Can. $	U.K. £
1	Camarasaurus	Brown/honey; green base	52 x 45	12.00	18.00	9.00
2	Euoplocephalus	Red-brown/honey; green base	26 x 55	12.00	18.00	9.00
3	Spinosaurus	Beige; grey spines; brown base	40 x 60	12.00	18.00	9.00
4	Protoceratops	Brown; green base	25 x 58	12.00	18.00	9.00
5a	Tyrannosaurus Rex	Dark brown/honey; green base	44 x 62	12.00	18.00	9.00
5b	Tyrannosaurus Rex	Grey; greenish-brown base	44 x 62	12.00	18.00	9.00

SET TWO

The Protoceratops model in this second set is a reissued model from the 1993 set, but is much lighter in colour. The second set, which contained six models, was issued in 2001, and the original cost direct from Wade was £18.00 per set.

No.	Name	Description	Size	U.S. $	Can. $	U.K. £
6	Corythosaurus	Apricot; blue-grey base	50 x 65	6.00	8.00	4.00
7	Nodosaurus	Grey; grey-green base	27 x 58	6.00	8.00	4.00
8	Protoceratops	Beige; green base	25 x 58	6.00	8.00	4.00
9	Saurclephus	Green; brown base	45 x 52	6.00	8.00	4.00
10	Scutellosaurus	Honey; brown base	32 x 62	6.00	8.00	4.00
11	Vulcanodon	Blue; mottled brown-green base	50 x 67	6.00	8.00	4.00

DRUM BOX SERIES

1957-1959

In the advertising literature of the time, Wade called this set the *Animal Band*, later changing it to the *Drum Box* series. The set consists of five comical animals, four playing a musical instrument and the fifth, "Dora" the donkey, is the soprano. They were sold in round cardboard drum-design boxes, from which the series got its name. The original price for each model was 3/11d. They were issued in May 1957 and discontinued in spring 1959.

Backstamp: Unmarked

No.	Name	Description	Size	U.S. $	Can. $	U.K. £
1	Jem	Red collar; grey trousers; black tie, eye patch	45 x 25	100.00	120.00	60.00
2	Clara	White dress; yellow stripes; brown cello	50 x 25	100.00	120.00	60.00
3	Harpy	Blue dress; mauve/white harp	45 x 28	100.00	120.00	60.00
4	Trunky	White shirt, trousers; black tie	50 x 35	100.00	120.00	60.00
5	Dora	White dress; red hem; yellow base	55 x 25	160.00	200.00	100.00

FAWN MONEY BOX

FIRST VERSION

Circa 1963

This figure is different from "Bambi," a *Disney Blow Up*, and has a coin slot in the back. It is believed that a few other *Disney Blow Ups* were remodeled as money boxes. There are unconfirmed reports of a "Lady Money Box," "Jock Money Box" and "Thumper Money Box," but no visual or written evidence has been found. Because of high production costs, only a limited number of the "Fawn Money Box" were made.

Fawn Money Box, First Version   Fawn Money Box, Second Version

Backstamp: **A.** Black transfer "Made in England"
              B. Unmarked

No.	Name	Description	Size	U.S. $	Can. $	U.K. £
1	Fawn	Brown; orange-brown patches	120 x 105	100.00	130.00	65.00

SECOND VERSION

1987

In 1987 Wade issued three money boxes based on the earlier "Fawn Disney Kennel" and "Noddy Toadstool Cottage" money boxes. Because the original moulds were worn, Wade made new moulds, which produced larger, heavier and less delicate-looking models than the originals. New colours were also used. These models were sold in plain, unmarked boxes. For other money boxes see pages 24, 69, and 136.

Backstamp: **A.** Black "Wade Made in England"
              B. Black "Wade England" on cap that covers hole in base

No.	Name	Description	Size	U.S. $	Can. $	U.K. £
1	Fawn	Light brown; brown markings	130 x 125	45.00	60.00	30.00

FLYING BIRDS

1956-1961

Wade produced two sets in the *Flying Birds* series, "Swallows" and "Swifts." These models were first produced in England, then their production was moved to Wade (Ulster) Ltd. The *Flying Birds* series was sold in boxed sets of three models of the same colour. The "Swifts" models were the last production run and are harder to find. The original price for a set of three "Swallows" was 5/9d, which was later increased to 5/11d.

FIRST ISSUE: WADE ENGLAND

Set One: Swallows (1956-1960)

Set One: Swifts (1958-1959)

SET ONE: SWALLOWS
1956-1960

Backstamp: Unmarked

No.	Description	Size	U.S. $	Can. $	U.K. £
1a	Beige wings, tail	65 x 68	18.00	26.00	12.00
1b	Blue wings, tail	65 x 68	18.00	26.00	12.00
1c	Green wings, tail	65 x 68	18.00	26.00	12.00
1d	Grey wings, tail	65 x 68	18.00	26.00	12.00
1e	Salmon pink wings, tail	65 x 68	18.00	26.00	12.00
1f	Yellow wings, tail	65 x 68	20.00	30.00	15.00
—	Boxed set (3)	—	55.00	70.00	35.00
—	Boxed set (3—yellow)	—	60.00	90.00	45.00

SET TWO: SWIFTS
1958-1959

The original price for three "Swifts" was 6/11d.

Backstamp: Unmarked

No.	Description	Size	U.S. $	Can. $	U.K. £
1	Blue wings, tail	86 x 76	28.00	42.00	20.00
—	Boxed set (3)	—	85.00	125.00	65.00

SECOND ISSUE: WADE ULSTER

Following the production of the *Flying Birds* series in the George Wade Pottery, the models were made by Wade (Ulster) Ltd. As with the George Wade production, two sets were made. In this case, however, the numbers of the sets were reversed. Set 1 was now the "Swifts;" set 2 was the "Swallows."

SET ONE: SWIFTS
1960-1961

The original price for three "Swifts" was 6/11d.

Backstamp: Unmarked

No.	Description	Size	U.S. $	Can. $	U.K. £
1a	Blue head, wings	86 x 76	28.00	42.00	20.00
1b	Yellow head, wings	86 x 76	28.00	42.00	20.00
—	Boxed set (3)	—	85.00	125.00	65.00

SET TWO: SWALLOWS
1960-1961

On the front of the original box was printed, "Flying Birds Made in Ireland by Wade Co. Armagh, The Mourne Range of Porcelain Miniatures." "The Mourne Range of Wade Porcelain Miniatures" is on the end of the box and inside is "No. 2 The Mourne Range of Porcelain Miniatures, Made in Ireland by Wade Co. Armagh." The original price for a box of three "Swallows" was 5/11d per boxed set.

Backstamp: Unmarked

No.	Description	Size	U.S. $	Can. $	U.K. £
1a	Beige wings, tail	65 x 68	18.00	26.00	12.00
1b	Blue wings, tail	65 x 68	18.00	26.00	12.00
1c	Green wings, tail	65 x 68	18.00	26.00	12.00
1d	Grey wings, tail	65 x 68	18.00	26.00	12.00
1e	Yellow wings, tail	65 x 68	18.00	26.00	12.00
—	Boxed set (3)	—	60.00	90.00	45.00

THE FISH WAITER

June 1998

This model of a fish dressed as a waiter and holding a plate in his left fin was first available from the Wade shop. It was later sold at the Arundel and Buffalo shows.

The Fish Waiter was produced in a limited edition of 1,500, and the original cost direct from Wade was £15.00.

Backstamp: Black Printed "Genuine Wade Porcelain"

No.	Name	Description	Size	U.S. $	Can. $	U.K. £
1	Fish Waiter	Grey fish; green eyes; black coat, bow tie; white vest; brown trousers; tan feet; orange base	140	40.00	50.00	25.00

GOODIE BOXES

1998-2001

A *Goodie Box* of randomly packed previously issued Wade models was offered to members of the O.I.W.C.C. for the first time in October 1998. The cost was £35.00, and the Wade models had a guaranteed value of £60.00. The first 500 members to contact Wade would receive a new model, "Rosie the Kitten," in either a honey or white glaze. Randomly packaged, there were 400 models in a honey glaze and 100 in white.

ROSIE THE KITTEN

October 1998

Backstamp: Embossed "Wade England" in recessed base.

No.	Name	Description	Size	U.S. $	Can. $	U.K. £
1a	Rosie the Kitten	Honey; black eyes	115	55.00	70.00	35.00
1b	Rosie the Kitten	White; black eyes	115	150.00	190.00	95.00

FIZZY THE FAWN

October 1999

In 1999, Wade again offered the *Goodie Box* at a cost of £35. The first 525 (U.K.) customers would receive a new model, "Fizzy the Fawn." Randomly packaged, there were 450 models in a honey colourway and 75 in white.

Backstamp: Embossed "Wade England"

No.	Name	Description	Size	U.S. $	Can. $	U.K. £
1a	Fizzy the Fawn	Honey; black eyes, nose	95	45.00	60.00	30.00
1b	Fizzy the Fawn	White; black eyes, nose	95	135.00	200.00	95.00

CRUNCHIE THE FOAL

October 2000

As in previous years, the *Goodie Box* was offered at £35.00 with a guaranteed value of £60.00. This time the offering was open to U.K. and U.S.A. collectors. The special edition to the first 525 collectors was 'Crunchie the Foal' which was available in a honey (450) or white (75) glaze. The white foals were randomly distributed among the boxes. Cost in the U.K. £35.00 and $68.00 in the U.S.

Backstamp: Embossed "Wade England"

No.	Name	Description	Size	U.S. $	Can. $	U.K. £
1a	Crunchie the Foal	Honey; black eyes, nose	70 x 73	45.00	60.00	35.00
1b	Crunchie the Foal	White; black eyes, nose	70 x 73	100.00	150.00	75.00

STILTON THE MOUSE

October 2001

In 2001, the Wade *Goodie box* again cost £35.00. Guaranteed to contain models to the value of £60.00, the first 500 collectors that ordered the Goodie box would receive a "Stilton the Mouse." Telephone orders only were accepted from October 2nd onwards. There were 425 honey glazed and 75 white mice. The white mice were randomly distributed amongst the boxes.

Backstamp: Embossed "Wade England"

No.	Name	Description	Size	U.S. $	Can. $	U.K. £
1a	Stilton the Mouse	Honey; black eyes, nose	60	45.00	60.00	35.00
1b	Stilton the Mouse	White; black eyes, nose	60	100.00	150.00	75.00

TOOTS THE OWL

October 2002

In 2002 the *Goodie Box* model was "Toots the Owl." The first 500 people to telephone their order received "Toots" in their parcel. There were 425 honey glazed and 75 white owls produced, The white models were randomly distributed among the boxes. The cost of the Goodie Box was £40.00.

Backstamp: Printed "Toots the Owl Goodie Box Special 2002" with "Wade" logo

No.	Name	Description	Size	U.S. $	Can. $	U.K. £
1a	Toots the Owl	Honey; black eyes, beak; yellow feet	68	55.00	70.00	35.00
1b	Toots the Owl	White; black eyes, beak; yellow feet	68	80.00	100.00	80.00

DIGGER THE MOLE

October 2003

In 2003 the *Goodie Box* model was "Digger the Mole." There was a change of colour for the Goodie Box special for this year, instead of white the colourway was changed to black. The first 500 people to telephone their order received "Digger" in their parcel. There were 500 grey glazed and 75 black moles produced, The black models were randomly distributed among the boxes.

The cost of the Goodie Box was £40.00 and was guaranteed to contain a selection of Wade items, including "Digger the Mole" to a value of £70.00.

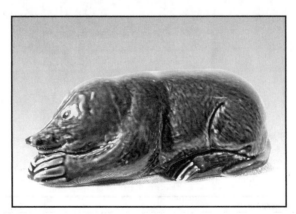

Backstamp: Unknown

No.	Name	Description	Size	U.S. $	Can. $	U.K. £
1a	Digger the Mole	Light grey; black eyes	Unk.	55.00	70.00	35.00
1b	Digger the Mole	Mottled black	Unk.	80.00	100.00	50.00

THE HONEY BUNCH BEARS

1998

A set of three teddy bears named the *Honey Bunch* was introduced at the Trentham Gardens show on March 22nd 1998. The models were later available from the Wade Shop. The original cost was £18.00 for the set. See also *Collect It!* Fairs, page 202.

The *Honey Bunch Bears*, sets one and two, were available on-line and from the Wade Factory Shop in September 2003, at the original issue price listed below.

SET ONE

Backstamp: Embossed "Wade"

No.	Description	Colourways	Size	U.S. $	Can. $	U.K. £
1	Bear, arms raised, bee on chest	Honey; black/white bee	55	10.00	12.00	6.00
2	Bear, seated, bee on face	Honey; black/white bee	57	10.00	12.00	6.00
3	Bear with honey pot, bee on shoulder	Honey; black/white bee	57	10.00	12.00	6.00

SET TWO

A second set of *Honey Bunch Bears* was introduced at the combined Wade and Jim Beam Fair held in Buffalo, July 18-19th, 1998. The cost was £18.00 for the set.

No.	Description	Colourways	Size	U.S. $	Can. $	U.K. £
4	Bear, lying, with sunglasses	Honey; black sunglasses	55	10.00	12.00	6.00
5	Bear, sleeping with bee	Honey; black/white bee	55	10.00	12.00	6.00
6	Bear, seated, waving, bee on hip	Honey; black/white bee	57	10.00	12.00	6.00

HORSE SETS

1974-1981

Two sets of horses were produced intermittently between 1974 and 1981. Each set comprised a "Mare" and her two foals. Although the models were sold with black and gold "Wade England" labels stuck on the bases, most of them either peeled off or wore off. But even without labels, the distinctive Wade glaze and their ribbed bases make these models easily recognizable. A variation in the glaze colour of the "Standing Foal" from Set One has been found, it is in an all-over honey glaze.

SET ONE

1974-1981

Backstamp: A. Black and gold label "Wade England" (1-3)
B. Unmarked (1-3)

No.	Name	Description	Size	U.S. $	Can. $	U.K. £
1	Mare	Dark brown; light brown face	75 x 76	18.00	20.00	10.00
2	Foal, lying	Dark brown; light brown face	32 x 55	18.00	20.00	10.00
3a	Foal, standing	Dark brown; light brown face	48 x 48	18.00	20.00	10.00
3b	Foal, standing	Honey	48 x 48	32.00	40.00	20.00
—	3 pce set	Boxed	—	60.00	90.00	45.00

SET TWO

1978-1981

Backstamp: A. Black and gold label "Wade England" (1-3)
B. Embossed "Wade England" on rim (1-3)
C. Unmarked (1-3)

No.	Name	Description	Size	U.S. $	Can. $	U.K. £
1	Mare	Honey; light brown mane	65 x 70	40.00	60.00	30.00
2	Foal, lying	Honey; light brown mane	30 x 46	40.00	60.00	30.00
3	Foal, sitting	Honey; light brown mane	38 x 38	40.00	60.00	30.00
—	3 pce set	Boxed	—	100.00	150.00	70.00

KISSING BUNNIES

Circa 1948-1950s

Care has to be taken when purchasing unmarked *Kissing Bunnies* models, as they were also produced by Joseph Szeiler and Sylvac as well as being copied by other ceramic manufacturers including those in Japan.

Kissing Bunnies, large eyes   Kissing Bunnies, small eyes

Backstamp: Black transfer print "Wade England"

No.	Description	Size	U.S. $	Can. $	U.K. £
1a	White bunny; beige bunny; large eyes	64 x 80	115.00	170.00	85.00
1b	White bunny; grey bunny; large eyes	64 x 80	115.00	170.00	85.00
1c	White bunny; grey bunny; white tail; large eyes	64 x 80	115.00	170.00	85.00
1d	White bunny; grey ears, tail; brown bunny; white tail; small eyes	64 x 80	115.00	170.00	85.00
1e	White bunny; grey tail; grey bunny; large eyes	64 x 80	115.00	170.00	85.00

Kissing Bunnies Derivatives

Circa 1948

This ashtray is similar in design to a model produced by Sylvac in the late 1940s known as an "Angular ashtray with Kissing Rabbits," and carrying an impressed design No. of 1532.

Ashtray

Backstamp: Ink stamp "Made in England Reg No 824" (the rest of the numbers are missing)

No.	Name	Description	Size	U.S. $	Can. $	U.K. £
1	Kissing Bunnies	White and brown bunnies; light green tray	85	110.00	150.00	75.00

Kissing Bunnies Mustard Pot

Backstamp: Green-brown ink stamp "Wade England"

No.	Name	Description	Size	U.S. $	Can. $	U.K. £
1a	Kissing Bunnies	Blue; bramble-ware mustard pot	70 x 87	100.00	150.00	75.00
1b	Kissing Bunnies	Cream; bramble-ware mustard pot	70 x 87	100.00	150.00	75.00
1c	Kissing Bunnies	Green; bramble-ware mustard pot	70 x 87	100.00	150.00	75.00
1d	Kissing Bunnies	White; multicoloured bramble-ware mustard pot, flower, base	70 x 87	110.00	165.00	85.00

MINIKINS

1955-1958

Minikins were issued in three separate series, with four different-shaped *Minikins* in each. They were sold to the retailer in boxes of 48 models (12 of each shape). *Minikins* were modelled by William Harper

The models are completely covered in white glaze, with decorative motifs on their bodies, different coloured ears and six eye styles. The combinations of eye expression, ear colour and body decoration could produce a total of 48 styles of *Minikins* in each set.

None of the *Minikins* was marked. Advertisements show that series B was offered for sale for Christmas 1956, and the demise of series C is mentioned in Wade's August 1958 "Wholesalers Newsletter." The original price was 1/- each.

MINIKINS SHOP COUNTER PLAQUE

1955-1958

These small half-circular plaques would have been used by the retailer in his shop display for *Minikins,* as they were not made for general sale. The wording on one plaque is "Porcelain Wade Minikins made in England." On the other 1/- (One Shilling) each has been added to the plaque.

No price shown

Price shown

Backstamp: None

No.	Description	Size	U.S. $	Can. $	U.K. £
1a	White; black lettering	28	200.00	300.00	150.00
1b	White; black lettering 1/- each	28	200.00	300.00	150.00

SERIES A: CATS AND RABBITS
1955-1958

Cat Walking (left), Cat Standing (right)

Cat Walking

Backstamp: Unmarked

No.	Description	Size	U.S. $	Can. $	U.K. £
1a	White; blue ears, tail; black/brown eyes	20 x 38	30.00	40.00	18.00
1b	White; blue ears, tail; green/black eyes; red nose	20 x 38	30.00	40.00	18.00
1c	White; yellow ears, tail; black/brown eyes	20 x 38	30.00	40.00	18.00
1d	White; yellow ears, tail; black/green eyes	20 x 38	30.00	40.00	18.00

Cat Standing

Backstamp: Unmarked

No.	Description	Size	U.S. $	Can. $	U.K. £
2a	Brown; black eyes, nose	30 x 17	30.00	40.00	18.00
2b	White; green ears; black eyes, nose; blue patches	30 x 17	30.00	40.00	18.00
2c	White; green ears; black eyes; blue patches	30 x 17	30.00	40.00	18.00
2d	White; green ears; black/green eyes; blue patches	30 x 17	30.00	40.00	18.00
2e	White; yellow ears; black eyes; green starburst	30 x 17	30.00	40.00	18.00
2f	White; yellow ears; black eyes; red starburst	30 x 17	30.00	40.00	18.00
2g	White; yellow ears; black/green eyes; blue starburst	30 x 17	30.00	40.00	18.00
2h	White; yellow ears; black/green eyes; green daisy	30 x 17	30.00	40.00	18.00

Rabbit Sitting (left), Narrow-Eared Rabbit (right)

Rabbit Sitting

Backstamp: Unmarked

No.	Description	Size	U.S. $	Can. $	U.K. £
3a	Brown; turquoise ears; black eyes, nose	30 x 18	30.00	40.00	18.00
3b	White; blue ears, nose; small black eyes	30 x 18	30.00	40.00	18.00
3c	White; green ears; eyes open; red nose; blue patch	30 x 18	30.00	40.00	18.00
3d	White; green ears; winking eyes; red nose; blue patch	30 x 18	30.00	40.00	18.00
3e	White; green/yellow ears; eyes open; red nose	30 x 18	30.00	40.00	18.00
3f	White; green/yellow ears; winking eyes; red nose	30 x 18	30.00	40.00	18.00
3g	White; red ears/nose; winking eyes; blue patch	30 x 18	30.00	40.00	18.00
3h	White; turquoise ears, nose; small black eyes	30 x 18	30.00	40.00	18.00

Narrow-Eared Rabbit

Backstamp: Unmarked

No.	Description	Size	U.S. $	Can. $	U.K. £
4a	White; green ears; large black/brown eyes; black nose; blue patch	30 x 18	30.00	40.00	18.00
4b	White; yellow ears; large black eyes; red nose; blue patch;	30 x 18	30.00	40.00	18.00
4c	White; yellow ears; large black/brown eyes; black nose; blue patch	30 x 18	30.00	40.00	18.00
4d	White; yellow ears; large black eyes; red nose; blue OXO design	30 x 18	30.00	40.00	18.00
4e	White; yellow ears; large black eyes; red nose; green OXO design	30 x 18	30.00	40.00	18.00
4f	White; yellow ears; large black/brown eyes; red nose; green/red OXO design	30 x 18	30.00	40.00	18.00

SERIES B: BULL, COW, MOUSE AND RABBIT
1956-1958

Mouse   Rabbit   Bull   Cow

Bull

Backstamp: Unmarked

No.	Description	Size	U.S. $	Can. $	U.K. £
1a	Brown; small black eyes, nose; black spot (front and back)	20 x 25	30.00	40.00	18.00
1b	Brown; small black eyes, nose; black spot/yellow X (back and front)	20 x 25	30.00	40.00	18.00
1c	White; small black eyes, nose; black spot (front and back)	20 x 25	30.00	40.00	18.00
1d	White; large black/blue eyes; black nose; black spot/yellow X (front and back)	20 x 25	30.00	40.00	18.00
1e	White; green hair; large black eyes, nose; green daisy (front); red/green L-plate (back)	20 x 25	30.00	40.00	18.00
1f	White; green hair; black eyes, nose; green heart/blue arrow (front); orange heart/green arrow (back)	20 x 25	30.00	40.00	18.00
1g	White; green hair; large black eyes, nose; orange daisy (front); black daisy (back)	20 x 25	30.00	40.00	18.00
1h	White; green hair; black eyes, nose; red/blue notes (front); orange heart/ blue arrow (back)	20 x 25	30.00	40.00	18.00
1i	White; green hair; large black eyes, nose; red/blue notes (front); red/green L-plate (back)	20 x 25	30.00	40.00	18.00
1j	White; green hair; large black eyes, nose; red/blue notes (front); red/blue L-plate (back)	20 x 25	30.00	40.00	18.00
1k	White; green hair; large black eyes, nose; red/blue notes (front); red L-plate (back)	20 x 25	30.00	40.00	18.00
1l	White; yellow hair; black eyes, nose; blue/green notes (front); blue heart/ yellow arrow (back)	20 x 25	30.00	40.00	18.00
1m	White; yellow hair; black eyes, nose; blue/green notes (front); red/green L-plate (back)	20 x 25	30.00	40.00	18.00
1n	White; yellow hair; large black eyes; red heart / blue arrow front; red L (back)	20 x 25	30.00	40.00	18.00
1o	White; yellow hair; large brown eyes; blue and yellow flower (front); red musical notes with green lines (back)	20 x 25	30.00	40.00	18.00

Cow

Backstamp: Unmarked

No.	Description	Size	U.S. $	Can. $	U.K. £
2a	White; green ears; black eyes; blue nose; orange daisy (front); blue daisy (back)	22 x 20	30.00	40.00	18.00
2b	White; green ears; black eyes; blue nose; orange/green notes (front) orange heart/blue arrow (back)	22 x 20	30.00	40.00	18.00
2c	White; pink ears; black eyes; red nose; red daisy (front); red heart/ green arrow (back)	22 x 20	30.00	40.00	18.00
2d	White; yellow ears; black eyes; blue nose; orange/blue notes (front); orange heart/green arrow (back)	22 x 20	30.00	40.00	18.00
2e	White; yellow ears; black eyes; blue nose; red heart/arrow (front); yellow daisy (back)	22 x 20	30.00	40.00	18.00
2f	White; yellow ears; black eyes; red nose; blue daisy (front); orange L (back)	22 x 20	30.00	40.00	18.00
2g	White; yellow ears; black eyes; red nose; blue daisy (front); red/ blue notes (back)	22 x 20	30.00	40.00	18.00
2h	White; yellow ears; black eyes; red nose; green daisy (front); red daisy (back)	22 x 20	30.00	40.00	18.00
2i	White; yellow ears; black eyes; red nose; blue heart/green arrow (front); blue daisy (back)	22 x 20	30.00	40.00	18.00
2j	White; yellow ears; black eyes; blue nose; red heart and green arrow (front); red/blue notes (back)	22 x 20	30.00	40.00	18.00

Mouse

Backstamp: Unmarked

No.	Description	Size	U.S. $	Can. $	U.K. £
3a	Brown; small black eyes, nose	25 x 23	30.00	40.00	18.00
3b	Brown; small black eyes, nose; dark blue patch	25 x 23	30.00	40.00	18.00
3c	White all over	25 x 23	25.00	40.00	18.00
3d	White; small black eyes, nose; blue patch	25 x 23	30.00	40.00	18.00
3e	White; green ears, nose; large black eyes; orange daisy (front); green daisy (back)	25 x 23	30.00	40.00	18.00
3f	White; green ears, nose; large black eyes; orange/green notes (front); orange daisy (back)	25 x 23	30.00	40.00	18.00
3g	White; green ears, nose; large black eyes; red/green L-plate (back and front)	25 x 23	30.00	40.00	18.00
3h	White; pink ears; large black eyes; green nose; blue/red notes (front); blue daisy (back)	25 x 23	30.00	40.00	18.00
3i	White; pink ears; large black eyes; green nose; blue heart/green arrow (front); blue daisy (back)	25 x 23	30.00	40.00	18.00
3j	White; yellow ears; large black eyes; orange nose; blue/green notes (front) red/blue notes (back)	25 x 23	30.00	40.00	18.00
3k	White; yellow ears; large black eyes; orange nose; green daisy front; green heart/blue arrow back	25 x 23	30.00	40.00	18.00
3l	White; yellow ears; large black eyes; blue nose; red L (front); orange L (back)	25 x 23	30.00	40.00	18.00
3m	White; yellow ears; large black eyes; orange nose; orange daisy (front); orange/blue notes (back)	25 x 23	30.00	40.00	18.00
3n	White; yellow ears; large black eyes; red nose; red/yellow daisy (front); red/green daisy (back)	25 x 23	30.00	40.00	18.00

174

Narrow-Eared Rabbit (left), Wide-Eared Rabbit (right)

Wide-Eared Rabbit

Backstamp: Unmarked

No.	Description	Size	U.S. $	Can. $	U.K. £
4a	White; green ears; blue nose; red/green flower (front); red heart/blue arrow (back)	25 x 20	30.00	40.00	18.00
4b	White; green ears; red nose; red heart/green arrow (front); blue heart/ green arrow (back)	25 x 20	30.00	40.00	18.00
4c	White; pink ears; black nose; orange daisy (front); orange L (back)	25 x 20	30.00	40.00	18.00
4d	White; pink ears; black nose; red L-plate (front and back)	25 x 20	30.00	40.00	18.00
4e	White; pink ears; green nose; blue daisy (front); red notes (back)	25 x 20	30.00	40.00	18.00
4f	White; yellow ears; blue/green notes (front); green heart/blue arrow (back)	25 x 20	30.00	40.00	18.00
4g	White; yellow ears; red heart/blue arrow (front and back)	25 x 20	30.00	40.00	18.00
4h	White; yellow ears; blue heart/red arrow (front); red daisy (back)	25 x 20	30.00	40.00	18.00

SERIES C: DOG, DONKEY, FAWN AND PELICAN
1957-1958

| Pelican | Fawn | Dog | Donkey |

Dog

Backstamp: Unmarked

No.	Description	Size	U.S. $	Can. $	U.K. £
1a	White; blue ears; small black/blue eyes; blue collar	28 x 15	35.00	45.00	22.00
1b	White; blue/green ears; small black/blue eyes; orange flowers; blue collar	28 x 15	35.00	45.00	22.00
1c	White; green ears; large black/blue eyes; red/green collar	28 x 15	35.00	45.00	22.00
1d	White; green ears; small black/blue eyes; orange/red flowers; no collar	28 x 15	35.00	45.00	22.00
1e	White; green ears; small black/blue eyes; red/green collar	28 x 15	35.00	45.00	22.00
1f	White; pink ears; small black/blue eyes; orange/pink collar	28 x 15	35.00	45.00	22.00
1g	White; yellow ears; small black/blue eyes; orange/yellow collar	28 x 15	35.00	45.00	22.00

Donkey

Backstamp: Unmarked

No.	Description	Size	U.S. $	Can. $	U.K. £
2a	White; green ears; large black/blue eyes; pink/blue garland	35 x 20	35.00	45.00	22.00
2b	White; green ears; large black/blue eyes; red flower (front)	35 x 20	35.00	45.00	22.00
2c	White; pink ears; large black/blue eyes; red flower (front)	35 x 20	35.00	45.00	22.00
2d	White; pink ears; large black/blue eyes; red/yellow flower garland	35 x 20	35.00	45.00	22.00
2e	White; pink ears; large black/yellow eyes; red/yellow garland	35 x 20	35.00	45.00	22.00
2f	White; yellow ears; large black/blue eyes; red flower (front)	35 x 20	35.00	45.00	22.00
2g	White; yellow ears; large black/blue eyes; pink/blue garland	35 x 20	35.00	45.00	22.00
2h	White; yellow ears; large black/yellow eyes; red/yellow garland	35 x 20	35.00	45.00	22.00

Fawn

Backstamp: Unmarked

No.	Description	Size	U.S. $	Can. $	U.K. £
3a	White; green ears, tail; black/blue eyes; yellow flower	28 x 20	35.00	45.00	22.00
3b	White; green ears, tail; black/yellow eyes; yellow heart; red arrow	28 x 20	35.00	45.00	22.00
3c	White; pink ears, tail; black/blue eyes; blue flowers/heart/notes	28 x 20	35.00	45.00	22.00
3d	White; pink ears; black/blue eyes; yellow flower	28 x 20	35.00	45.00	22.00
3e	White; pink ears; black/yellow eyes; yellow flower	28 x 20	35.00	45.00	22.00
3f	White; yellow ears, tail; black/blue eyes; blue flowers/heart/notes	28 x 20	35.00	45.00	22.00
3g	White; yellow ears, tail; black/yellow eyes; red flower	28 x 20	35.00	45.00	22.00

Pelican

Backstamp: Unmarked

No.	Description	Size	U.S. $	Can. $	U.K. £
4a	White; black/blue eyes; blue wings, feet, anchor	30 x 15	35.00	45.00	22.00
4b	White; black/blue eyes; green wings, feet; blue anchor	30 x 15	35.00	45.00	22.00
4c	White; black/blue eyes; pink wings, feet; blue anchor	30 x 15	35.00	45.00	22.00
4d	White; black/blue eyes; yellow wings, feet; blue anchor	30 x 15	35.00	45.00	22.00
4e	White; black/blue eyes; green wings, feet; black waistcoat; red bowtie	30 x 15	35.00	45.00	22.00
4f	White; black/blue eyes; pink wings, feet; black waistcoat; red bowtie	30 x 15	35.00	45.00	22.00
4g	White; black/blue eyes; yellow wings, feet; black waistcoat; red bowtie	30 x 15	35.00	45.00	22.00
4h	White; black/blue eyes; yellow wings, feet; blue waistcoat; red bowtie	30 x 15	35.00	45.00	22.00

NATIVITY SET

2001 - 2003

This beautiful and unusual six-piece nativity set was produced in November 2001 and cost £79.95 for the set.

| Shepherd | Angel | Mary, Joseph and Jesus | King | Wiseman | Shepherd and Sheep |

Backstamp: Gold oval "Wade"

No.	Name	Description	Size	U.S. $	Can. $	U.K. £
1	Angel	White; gold halo	150	26.00	32.00	16.00
2	Mary, Joseph, Jesus	White; gold halo	85	26.00	32.00	16.00
3	Wiseman	White; gold highlights	70	26.00	32.00	16.00
4	King	White; gold highlights	95	26.00	32.00	16.00
5	Shepherd	White; gold highlights	105	26.00	32.00	16.00
6	Shepherd and sheep	White; gold highlights	96	26.00	32.00	16.00
—	6 pce set		—	110.00	160.00	80.00

2002 - 2003

Three new models were added to the Nativity Set in late 2002, the issue price £15.99 each. The Stable was issued in 2003, priced at £10.00, completing the set.

Donkey, Frankincense and Myrrh

Backstamp: Gold oval "Wade"

No.	Name	Description	Size	U.S. $	Can. $	U.K. £
1	Donkey	White; gold trim	70	26.00	32.00	16.00
2	Stable	White; gold trim	95	26.00	32.00	16.00
3	Wiseman, Frankincense	White; gold trim	95	26.00	32.00	16.00
4	Wiseman, Myrrh	White; gold trim	145	26.00	32.00	16.00

NENNIE SCOTTISH TERRIER

1996

Originally commissioned by Ms. F. Shoop (Ficol), "Nennie" was the first model in an intended series of Scottish dogs to be issued in a limited edition of 2,000, to raise funds for the STECS (Scottish Terrier Emergency Care Scheme). Unfortunately the series was cancelled and "Nennie," who was modelled on a rescued Scottish terrier, was sold by Wade Ceramics at the Wade Fair, Birmingham in April 1996, for £25.00.

Backstamp: White printed "Nennie produced exclusively for Ficol by Wade," print of 2 Scottie dogs and the edition No. in gold.

No.	Description	Size	U.S. $	Can. $	U.K. £
1	Black; grey streaks; pale blue collar; gold disc	125 x 165	60.00	90.00	45.00

POCKET PALS

SERIES ONE: ANIMALS

October 1999

Pocket Pals, which were introduced in October 1999, are produced from the same moulds as the 1960s/1980s "Happy Families." The models used are the "Mother" animals from the Cat, Dog, Elephant, Frog, Giraffe, Hippo, Mouse, Owl, Pig, and Rabbit Happy Families. The models were sold attached by double-sided tape to a card base at a cost of £5.50. For Cat model named "Tango" please see C&S Collectables page 269; for Frog model "Hopper" and Dog model "Woofit" please see *Collect It!* Magazine page 293.

Backstamp: Gold transfer print "Wade Pp" in shield

No.	Name	Description	Size	U.S. $	Can. $	U.K. £
1	Cat Slinky	Dark brown body; honey face/chest; blue eyes	45 x 35	10.00	15.00	7.00
2	Dog Waggs	White; black patches; brown eyes	55 x 35	10.00	15.00	7.00
3	Elephant Tusker	Pale pink; pink ears; blue eyes	35 x 70	10.00	15.00	7.00
4	Frog Hip Hop	Dark green; green spots; blue eyes	25 x 45	10.00	15.00	7.00
5	Giraffe Stretch	Apricot; blue eyes	60 x 45	10.00	15.00	7.00
6	Hippo Paddles	Pink; blue eyes	35 x 50	10.00	15.00	7.00
7	Mouse Cheesy	Khaki; pink ears; blue eyes; brown tail	50 x 28	10.00	15.00	7.00
8	Owl Specs	Brown; off white; yellow eyes	40 x 40	10.00	15.00	7.00
9	Pig Truffle	White; tan brown patches; blue eyes	28 x 65	10.00	15.00	7.00
10	Rabbit Bounce	White; black patches; pink ears; brown eyes	55 x 30	10.00	15.00	7.00

SERIES TWO: POCKET HORRORS

October 2001

The second set of *Pocket Pals* was introduced in 2001, and is loosely based on fictional horror characters: Jekyll and Hyde (who has two faces), Wolfy (Wolfman) and Frankie (Frankenstein). The models were sold individually at a cost of £5.95 each.

Baby Bodzilla, Frankie, Igor Jr., Jekyll, Lizzie

Hyde

Lugsi, Spooky, Where's my Mummy, Witch Hazel, Wolfy

Jekyll

Backstamp: Gold label "Wade Pp"

No.	Name	Description	Size	U.S. $	Can. $	U.K. £
1	Baby Bodzilla	Green	54	10.00	15.00	7.00
2	Frankie	Blue	65	10.00	15.00	7.00
3	Igor Jr.	Royal blue	50	10.00	15.00	7.00
4	Jekyll and Hyde	Blue-grey	56	10.00	15.00	7.00
5	Lizzie	Turquoise	50	10.00	15.00	7.00
6	Lugsi	Orange	58	10.00	15.00	7.00
7	Spooky	White	50	10.00	15.00	7.00
8	Where's my Mummy	White	50	10.00	15.00	7.00
9	Witch Hazel	Purple	60	10.00	15.00	7.00
10	Wolfy	Orange	55	10.00	15.00	7.00

POKEMON

2001

This set of *Pokemon* characters was introduced in summer 2001, and is based on characters in a children's computer game. The models were sold individually at a cost of £8.99 each.

Gengar, Jigglypuff, Pikachu, Poliwhirl, Psyduck

Backstamp: Gold transfer print "Wade" and printed "Nintendo TM © 2001"

No.	Name	Description	Size	U.S. $	Can. $	U.K. £
1	Gengar	Purple; red eyes; blue mouth	55	20.00	25.00	12.00
2	Jigglypuff	Pink; green eyes; red mouth	55	20.00	25.00	12.00
3	Pikachu	Yellow; black eyes; red cheek spots	55	20.00	25.00	12.00
4	Poliwhirl	Blue; black swirls; white hands	55	20.00	25.00	12.00
5	Psyduck	Orange; white beak, feet	55	20.00	25.00	12.00

RULE BEARTANNIA

1999-2002

This nine-piece set of "Royal Teddy Bears" was produced by Wade and issued in the United States in early 1999. They were modelled by a well-known American artist Jerome Walker. The models were later sold by Wade in the U.K. The series ended in 2002.

Queen Beatrice, Queen Mum, King Velveteen

Royal Guard

Nanny Fluffins and Baby Velveteena, Prince Tedward,
Princess Elizabeth Tedwina, Princess Plushette

Rule Beartannia Plaque

Backstamp: Printed "©Jerome Walker 1998 Wade Made in England"

No.	Name	Description	Size	U.S. $	Can. $	U.K. £
1	Princess Elizabeth Tedwina	Pale blue bonnet, dark red, pink/blue flowers; pale blue dress; pearl ribbon bow; white base	127	45.00	70.00	35.00
2	King Velveteen	Red/gold crown; red cloak; pale blue/white edged robe; gold sceptre	165	70.00	100.00	50.00
3	Queen Beatrice	Green/gold crown; pearl earrings, necklace; green/white cloak; pale blue dress; gold sceptre; gold/white orb	150	70.00	100.00	50.00
4	Queen Mum	Pink hat, handbag, dress; dark blue/white cloak; gold spectacles	120	45.00	70.00	35.00
5	Prince George Tedward	White sailor hat; dark blue/white sailor suit; gold telescope; white base	97	45.00	70.00	35.00
6	Princess Plushette	White bonnet, dark red/pink flowers; yellow dress; dark red/pink flower posy; white base	97	45.00	70.00	35.00
7	Nanny Fluffins and Baby Velveteena	Yellow hat, dark blue band; white dress, dark blue band; pale blue shawl, baby's pram, base	130	60.00	90.00	45.00
8	Royal Guard	Black helmet, shoulder epaulettes, gold trim; dark red jacket; gold trim; gold trumpet; dark blue trousers; black shoes; white base	115	55.00	80.00	40.00
9	Rule Beartannia Plaque	White; multicoloured bears; bee/honey pot print; red/black lettering	125	20.00	30.00	15.00

SHAMROCK POTTERY

1956-1984

In 1956 Wade Ireland introduced a small series of models known as the *Shamrock Pottery Series*. It consisted of the "Irish Comical Pig," "The Pink Elephant," "Shamrock Cottage," "Pixie Dish" and the "Donkey and Cart Posy Bowl." The last three models were reissued between 1977 and the early 1980s. (For "Pixie Dish" and "Shamrock Cottage" see Leprechauns and Pixies section. For "Donkey and Cart Posy Bowl," see *The Charlton Standard Catalogue of Wade, Volume Two: Decorative Ware*).

IRISH COMICAL PIG

1956-1961

The *Irish Comical Pig*, made by Wade (Ulster) Ltd., is found in several different combinations of back patterns and nose and tail colours. The original selling price was 2/6d each. The places of interest named on the back are written in black lettering.

Backstamp: Green transfer print "Shamrock Pottery Made in Ireland"

No.	Name	Description	Size	U.S. $	Can. $	U.K. £
1a	Daisy pattern	Green/orange daisy; orange nostrils; yellow tail	45 x 65	50.00	60.00	30.00
1b	Daisy pattern	Green/orange daisy; yellow nostrils, tail	45 x 65	50.00	60.00	30.00
1c	Daisy pattern	Green/orange daisy; green nostrils, tail	45 x 65	50.00	60.00	30.00
1d	Daisy pattern	Green/orange daisy; yellow nostrils; orange tail	45 x 65	50.00	60.00	30.00
1e	Loop pattern	Orange loops; green stars, lines; brown eyes; green nostrils, tail	45 x 65	50.00	60.00	30.00
1f	Shamrocks	Black; green nostrils, tail, shamrocks	45 x 65	50.00	60.00	30.00
1g	Shamrocks	White; green nostrils, tail, shamrocks	45 x 65	50.00	60.00	30.00

TOWN NAMES

No.	Name	Description	U.S. $	Can. $	U.K. £
1h	Canterbury	Green nostrils, tail; black lettering	50.00	60.00	40.00
1i	Eastbourne	Green nostrils; yellow tail; black lettering	50.00	60.00	40.00
1j	Henley on Thames	Green nostrils; yellow tail; black lettering	50.00	60.00	40.00
1k	Holy Island	Black pig; gold decal Holy Island	50.00	60.00	40.00
1l	Hunstanton	Green nostrils; yellow tail; black lettering	50.00	60.00	40.00
1m	Isle of Wight	Green nostrils; yellow tail; black lettering	50.00	60.00	40.00
1n	Llandudno	Green nostrils; yellow tail; black lettering	50.00	60.00	40.00
1o	Old Smithy Godshill	Green nostrils, tail; black lettering	50.00	60.00	40.00
1p	Penmaenmawr	Green nostrils yellow tail; black lettering	50.00	60.00	40.00
1q	Sandown	Green nostrils, tail; black lettering	50.00	60.00	40.00
1r	Stratford-Upon-Avon	Green nostrils, tail; black lettering	50.00	60.00	40.00
1s	Stratford-Upon-Avon	Green nostrils; yellow tail; black lettering	50.00	60.00	40.00
1t	Windermere	Green nostrils; yellow tail; black lettering	50.00	60.00	40.00
1u	York	Green nostrils; yellow tail; black lettering	50.00	60.00	40.00

PINK ELEPHANT

1956-1961

The *Pink Elephant*, made by Wade (Ulster) Ltd., is found with several different slogans on its back associated with the consumption of too much alcohol. Some have names of places of interest. Originally, these models sold for 2/6d each.

Backstamp: Green transfer print "Shamrock Pottery Made in Ireland"

No.	Description	Size	U.S. $	Can. $	U.K. £
1a	Bournemouth; pink; orange nostrils, tail	40 x 80	60.00	80.00	40.00
1b	Devils Bridge; pink; green nostrils, tail	40 x 80	60.00	80.00	40.00
1c	Henley on Thames; pink; green nostrils, tail	40 x 80	60.00	80.00	40.00
1d	Isle of Wight; pink; orange nostrils, tail	40 x 80	60.00	80.00	40.00
1e	Never Again; pink; green nostrils, tail	40 x 80	60.00	80.00	40.00
1f	Never Again; pink; orange nostrils, tail	40 x 80	60.00	80.00	40.00
1g	Never Mix Em! pink; green nostrils, tail	40 x 80	60.00	80.00	40.00
1h	Oh! My Head; pink; green nostrils, tail	40 x 80	60.00	80.00	40.00
1i	Old Smithy Godshill pink; green nostrils, tail	40 x 80	60.00	80.00	40.00
1j	Pale pink; green nostrils, tail (no lettering)	40 x 80	60.00	80.00	40.00
1k	Ramsgate; pink; orange nostrils, tail	40 x 80	60.00	80.00	40.00
1l	Salisbury; pink; green nostrils, tail	40 x 80	60.00	80.00	40.00
1m	Stick to Water; pink; green nostrils, tail	40 x 80	60.00	80.00	40.00

SNIPPETS

1956-1957

Snippets models are thin, flat outlines of a figure with a rectangular porcelain box on the back, which enables the model to stand. It was a new idea by Wade, one which was not very successful at the time. Only two sets of three models were produced. Because of this and the fact that they are easily broken, these models are rare.

Set One was a set of three 15th, 16th and 17th century sailing ships, modelled as an outline of the ships and enameled in bright colours. The three ships are in graduated sizes.

SET ONE: SAILING SHIPS

1956

Backstamp: A. Black transfer "Wade Snippet No. 1 Mayflower Carried 102 Pilgrims to North America 1620 Real Porcelain Made In England" (1)
B. Black transfer "Wade Snippet No. 2 Santa Maria Flag ship of Columbus 1492 Real Porcelain Made In England" (2)
C. Black transfer "Wade Snippet No. 3 Revenge Flag ship of Sir Richard Grenville 1591 Real Porcelain Made in England" (3)

No.	Name	Description	Size	U.S. $	Can. $	U.K. £
1	The Mayflower	Brown; yellow sails; red flags; blue/white waves	58 x 60	75.00	90.00	45.00
2	The Santa Maria	Brown; green sails; red/yellow flags; blue/white waves	45 x 50	75.00	90.00	45.00
3	The Revenge	Brown; red sails; yellow flags; blue/white waves	35 x 45	75.00	90.00	45.00
—	3 pce set	Boxed	—	185.00	250.00	125.00

SET TWO: HANSEL AND GRETEL

1957

Set Two comprises three characters from the fairy tale, *Hansel and Gretel*.

Backstamp: **A.** Black transfer "Wade Snippet No. 4 Hansel Real Porcelain Made in England" (4a, 4b)
  B. Black transfer "Wade Snippet No. 5 Gretel Real Porcelain Made in England" (5)
  C. Black transfer "Wade Snippet No. 6 Gingy Real Porcelain Made in England" (6)

No.	Name	Description	Size	U.S. $	Can. $	U.K. £
1a	Hansel	Yellow stockings; grey-blue trousers, jacket; red shirt, toadstools	64 x 42	200.00	250.00	125.00
1b	Hansel	Green stockings; grey-blue trousers, jacket; red shirt, toadstools	64 x 42	200.00	250.00	125.00
2	Gretel	Yellow pigtail, apron; blue shoe; green grass; red toadstools	56 x 42	200.00	250.00	125.00
3	Gingy the Bear	Brown/beige; red toadstools	32 x 20	200.00	250.00	125.00
—	3 pce set	Boxed	—	450.00	650.00	325.00

THE TORTOISE FAMILY

1958-1988

Wade's first tortoise, the "Large (Father)," was issued in January 1958, and it proved so popular that the following January Wade introduced two more, the "Medium (Mother)" and "Small (Baby)," which were sold as a boxed pair and named "Baby Tortoises.". These three models were so successful that they were produced almost continuously for the next thirty years. Considered by Wade as their best-selling line, this family of tortoises is in plentiful supply. The original price for the "Large (Father)" was 4/6d the pair of "Medium (Mother)" and "Small (Baby)" cost 4/9d.

In 1973 the "Jumbo" tortoise was added to the family. It was modelled differently from the other tortoises, however, and resembles a turtle. Because it was not in production for as long as the rest of the *Tortoise Family*, it is harder to find. The "Large (Father)" and the "Jumbo" tortoises are the only ones in this series to have lift-off shells. The numbers 1 through 8 were embossed on the bases of model 3, which refer to the production tool used to press the model. Production tools usually lasted for one to three years before having to be replaced; therefore, the models with the lowest numbers should be the oldest.

Version One: Recessed Back   Version Two: Full Back

Baby, Mother and Father

Jumbo Tortoise

Backstamp: A. Embossed "Wade Porcelain Made in England No. 3" (1, 2, 3)
B. Embossed "Wade Made in England" (4)

No.	Name	Description	Size	U.S. $	Can. $	U.K. £
1a	Small (Baby)	Brown/blue	25 x 45	10.00	12.00	6.00
1b	Small (Baby)	Green/blue	25 x 45	35.00	40.00	20.00
1c	Small (Baby)	Green	25 x 45	35.00	40.00	20.00
2a	Medium (Mother)	Brown/blue	35 x 75	15.00	16.00	8.00
2b	Medium (Mother)	Green/blue	35 x 75	35.00	40.00	20.00
2c	Medium (Mother)	Green	35 x 75	35.00	40.00	20.00
3a	Large (Father, Type 1)	Beige/blue	50 x 105	30.00	36.00	18.00
3b	Large (Father, Type 2)	Brown/blue	50 x 105	28.00	36.00	18.00
3c	Large (Father)	Green/blue	50 x 105	50.00	60.00	30.00
3d	Large (Father)	Green	50 x 105	50.00	60.00	30.00
4	Jumbo	Beige/blue	65 x 150	90.00	110.00	55.00

The Tortoise Family Derivatives
1958-1984

The *Tortoise Ash Bowls* are large and round, with a scintillite, high-gloss finish. An embossed reptile-skin design covers the inside, and a model from the *Tortoise Family* set is fixed to the inside curve of the bowl. The ash bowl with the "Medium (Mother)" tortoise was issued in January 1958 for 12/6d. The ash bowl with the "Small (Baby)" tortoise was produced from 1975 to 1984.

Ash Bowls

Backstamp: A. Impressed "Wade Porcelain Made in England" (1a, 1b)
B. Large embossed "Wade Made in England" (2a, 2b)

No.	Description	Size	U.S. $	Can. $	U.K. £
1a	Ash bowl with medium (Mother) tortoise; brown/blue	55 x 183	65.00	80.00	40.00
1b	Ash bowl with medium (Mother) tortoise; green/blue	55 x 183	65.00	80.00	40.00
2a	Ash bowl with small (Baby) tortoise; brown/blue	45 x 145	45.00	60.00	30.00
2b	Ash bowl with small (Baby) tortoise; green/blue	45 x 145	45.00	60.00	30.00

The Tortoise Family Derivatives (cont.)
1976

The round tortoise ash bowls were such a successful line that Wade introduced a new oblong bowl in 1976. This bowl had small rounded feet and was embossed with a reptile-skin design and finished with a high-gloss finish. A second version with a flat base has been found. The "Medium (Mother)" tortoise figure was used on this bowl.

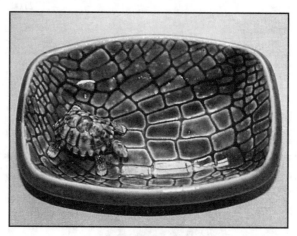

Footed Oblong Bowl

Backstamp: Large embossed "Wade Made in England"

No.	Description	Size	U.S. $	Can. $	U.K. £
1	Medium (Mother) tortoise; beige/blue	150 x 100	65.00	80.00	40.00

Souvenir Tortoises

Wade retooled the "Medium (Mother)" tortoise from the *Tortoise Family* series by cutting a recess in the back of the model and inserting the name of a British colony resort in embossed letters in the top shell.

Backstamp: Embossed "Wade Porcelain Made in England"

No.	Name	Description	Size	U.S. $	Can. $	U.K. £
1	Bahamas	Bahamas on shell; brown; blue markings	35 x 75	75.00	90.00	45.00
2	Bermuda	Bermuda on shell; brown; blue markings	35 x 75	75.00	90.00	45.00
3	Bermuda Triangle	Bermuda Triangle on shell; brown; blue markings	35 x 75	75.00	90.00	45.00
4	Devil's Hole, Bermuda	Devils Hole, Bermuda on shell; brown; blue markings	35 x 75	75.00	90.00	45.00

Note: See page 291 for a commissioned set of tortoises for *Ciba Geigy* that is another derivative of the *Tortoise Family*.

TREASURES SET

1957-1959

The *Treasures* set was the first in an intended series, but unfortunately for collectors, no more sets were put into production. It consists of a set of five white elephants in varying sizes, with bright pink blankets decorated with orange, yellow, blue and green flowers. Early advertising material calls the set *Elephant Chains* and *Elephant Train*. The original price for a box of five elephants was 10/6d.

Backstamp: Blue transfer "Wade England"

No.	Name	Description	Size	U.S. $	Can. $	U.K. £
1	Elephant, large	White; pink blanket; howdah and mahout; blue turban	47 x 63	120.00	160.00	80.00
2	Elephant, medium	White; pink blanket; gold tassel	35 x 57	110.00	140.00	70.00
3	Elephant, small	White; pink blanket; gold tassel	28 x 54	100.00	150.00	60.00
4	Elephant, tiny	White; pink blanket; gold tassel	24 x 45	100.00	150.00	60.00
5	Elephant, miniature	White; pink blanket; gold tassel	20 x 39	100.00	150.00	60.00
—	5 pce set	Boxed	—	650.00	800.00	350.00

Treasures Elephant Derivative Whimtray

1957-1959

This unusual model of the *Treasure Set* miniature elephant attached to a Whimtray is the only example known to date.

Backstamp: Embossed "Whimtrays Wade Porcelain Made in England"

No.	Name	Description	Size	U.S. $	Can. $	U.K. £
1	Elephant, miniature	Blue-grey; pink/blue blanket; yellow tray	40 x 75	100.00	150.00	60.00

VARIOUS NOVELTY MODELS

1955-1960

This set of five models was advertised as "Various Novelty Models" in late 1955. Although Wade advertisements suggest that they were in production for five years, they are hard to find and are considered rare.

Backstamp: **A.** Embossed "Wade" (1, 2)
B. Embossed "Wade Ireland" (on 2b Dustbin Cat)
C. Black and gold label "Wade England" (3, 4, 5)
D. Unmarked (3, 4, 5)

No.	Name	Description	Size	U.S. $	Can. $	U.K. £
1	Bernie and Poo	One white/brown; one white/blue	55 x 75	145.00	180.00	90.00
2a	Dustbin Cat	White cat; beige dustbin	45 x 25	140.00	200.00	100.00
2b	Dustbin Cat	White cat; grey dustbin	45 x 25	140.00	200.00	100.00
3	Jonah in the Whale	Blue jacket; white whale	40 x 40	1,300.00	1,600.00	800.00
4	Jumbo Jim	Blue hat, tears	45 x 25	165.00	200.00	100.00
5a	Kitten on the Keys	Grey cat; white blue spotted shirt; white trousers	30 x 35	210.00	260.00	130.00
5b	Kitten on the Keys	White cat	30 x 35	210.00	260.00	130.00

Jumbo Jim Derivative Calendar

A model of *Jumbo Jim* has been found attached to a Bakelite perpetual calendar.

Backstamp: Unknown

No.	Name	Description	Size	U.S. $	Can. $	U.K. £
1	Jumbo Jim Calendar	White; blue hat, tears; brown Bakelite calendar	50 x 100	200.00	250.00	125.00

WATER LIFE COLLECTION
1997

Alligator, Goldfish, Whale

Backstamp: Black printed (on Whale) and red printed (on goldfish and alligator) "Wade Made in England"

No.	Name	Description	Size	U.S. $	Can. $	U.K. £
1	Alligator	Green	25 x 65	16.00	25.00	10.00
2	Goldfish	Orange fish; blue-grey, orange streaked water	50 x 40	16.00	25.00	10.00
3	Whale	Light blue whale; blue waves	47 x 70	16.00	25.00	10.00

Hermit Crab, Octopus, Seahorse

Backstamp: Gold "Wade England" between two gold lines

No.	Name	Description	Size	U.S. $	Can. $	U.K. £
4	Hermit Crab	Orange crab; grey-blue waves	30	16.00	25.00	10.00
5	Octopus	Grey octopus; sea green-blue waves	50	16.00	25.00	10.00
6	Seahorse	Beige seahorse; dark blue waves	30	16.00	25.00	10.00

ZOO MAZING

Hip-Hippos

2002

Hip-Hippos were produced as a retail line of five models, plus four being produced as show specials, for a total of nine pieces. The hippos were produced in various poses and have names such as "Born to be Cool" and "Born to be Loved." The first five models, "Big Brother," "Cool," "Friends," "Loved" and "Wild," were launched at the Birmingham Trade Show in February 2002, and were available from retailers from March 2002.

The four show specials, "Sleepy," "Naughty," "Slide" and "Daydreamer," were available in April, July and September at various U.K. and U.S.A. Wade Shows. They were also available on-line and from the Wade Retail Shop in September 2003, at the U.K. and U.S.A. prices listed below (which included postage).

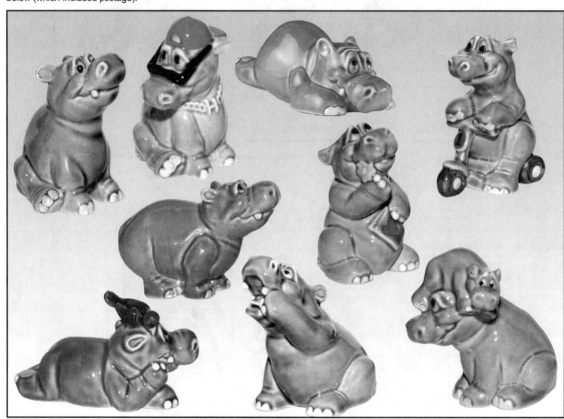

First row: "Naughty," "Cool," "Slide," "Wild"
Second row: "Daydreamer," "Loved"
Third row: "Friends," "Sleepy, " "Big Brother"

Backstamp: Printed "Hip Hippos Wade" [with name of model]

No.	Name	Description	Issue - Price	Size	U.S. $	Can. $	U.K. £
1	Born to be a Big Brother	Grey; white toenails		70 x 50	33.00	40.00	20.00
2	Born to be Cool	Grey; red cap; black sunglasses		70 x 50	33.00	40.00	20.00
3	Born to be a Daydreamer	Grey; white toenails		55 x 80	33.00	40.00	20.00
4	Born to be Friends	Grey; black bird		55 x 90	33.00	40.00	20.00
5	Born to be Loved	Grey; red heart; white toenails		70 x 45	33.00	40.00	20.00
6	Born to be Naughty	Grey; white toenails		65 x 50	33.00	40.00	20.00
7	Born to be Sleepy	Grey; white toenails		70 x 55	33.00	40.00	20.00
8	Born to Slide	Grey; white toenails		35 x 90	33.00	40.00	20.00
9	Born to be Wild	Grey; white toe nails; red/black number "1"; brown wheels		80 x 70	33.00	40.00	20.00

CIRCUS SET

2003

The Circus Set was produced as a retail line by Wade and was available from the Wade Shop and through retail outlets. The set consists of seven figures, all of which were individually boxed. A Circus Ring display base was produced for this set. Models would be purchased individually at £15.00 each, and £10.00 for the display stand. In September 2003, the cost for the complete set is advertised at $115.00. The words WADES CIRCUS are embossed on the base edge.

Backstamp: Red "Wade" logo

No.	Name	Description	Size	U.S. $	Can. $	U.K. £
1	Bear	Brown, red hat; yellow waistcoat; multicoloured drum base	74	25.00	30.00	15.00
2	Clown	Green suit, hat; blue car	60	25.00	30.00	15.00
3	Elephant	Grey; yellow, green blanket; multicoloured drum base	60	25.00	30.00	15.00
4	Lion	Honey; brown mane; multicoloured drum base	58	25.00	30.00	15.00
5	Pony	White; brown mane; blue saddle; multicoloured drum base	58	25.00	30.00	15.00
6	Ringmaster	Black coat, top hat, boots; red waistcoat; white pants; yellow bow tie; multicoloured drum base	70	25.00	30.00	15.00
7	Strongman	Brown hair; white/brown spotted leotard; tan shoes; multicoloured drum base	70	25.00	30.00	15.00
8	Display stand	White; multicoloured design around edge; red lettering "Wades Circus"	180	16.00	20.00	10.00

BETTY BOOP

Top of the World

2003

Produced as a Wade retail line in conjunction with C&S Collectables, who own the UK License for Betty Boop, this model is of Betty Boop seated on top of the world. Issued in a limited edition of 2000, the issue price was £55.00, with a 10% discount to Wade Club members.

A colourway version, with the countries in gold, was issued in a limited edition of twenty pieces. These models were available only as prizes in Bran Tub draws at various Wade events during the year.

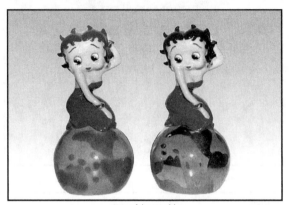

Top of the World

Backstamp: Printed "Betty Boop Top of the World 2000 Limited edition" with "Wade" logo

No.	Name	Description	Issued - Price	Size	U.S. $	Can. $	U.K. £
1	Betty Boop Top / World	Red dress; black hair; blue globe; green countries	2000 - £55	150	90.00	110.00	55.00
2	Betty Boop Top / World	Red dress; black hair; blue globe; gold countries	20 - Prizes	150		Rare	

FAIRS AND EVENTS

ALTON TOWERS FAIR

1998

Wade held their Extravaganza in a marquee at Alton Towers, a theme park in Staffordshire, England, on November 22nd, 1998.

Bears Just Want to Have Fun (1998)

Once Upon a Time Money Box (1998)

Panda Bear Plaque (1998)

Backstamp: Bears Just Want to Have Fun: "Bears Just Want To Have Fun Limited Edition of 500 Wade" with Alton Towers logo
Once Upon a Time Money Box: "Once Upon a Time-Wade England 1998 Limited Edition of 120"
Panda Bear Plaque: "Wade England Extravaganza 1998"

Date	Name	Colourways	Issue - Price	Size	U.S. $	Can. $	U.K. £
1998	Bears Just Want to Have Fun	Amber; dark blue dungarees; yellow shirt; pale blue shoes	500 - £25.00	145	65.00	80.00	40.00
1998	Once Upon a Time Money Box	Papa: Dark blue robe; brown slippers Boy: Light blue pyjamas	120 - £150.00	157	300.00	380.00	190.00
1998	Panda Bear Plaque	Black /white panda; white plaque; red lettering	— / £20.00	195	50.00	60.00	30.00

CIRCUS POODLE

1998

A special limited edition of 100 each of the Tom Smith's Circus Poodle, with a pink or gold skirt, or an all-over white glaze, were given as prizes in the Wade Bran Tub draw at the show.

Please note that models with red and green skirts exist, but these were not produced by Wade.

Backstamp: Embossed "Wade England"

Date	Name	Colourways	Size	U.S. $	Can. $	U.K. £
1998	Poodle	White	43	40.00	50.00	25.00
1998	Poodle	White; gold skirt	43	40.00	50.00	25.00
1998	Poodle	White; pink skirt	43	40.00	50.00	25.00

ARUNDEL SWAP MEETS
1997-2000

Arundel Duck (1997)

Arundel Bunny (1998)

Teddy Bear Plaque (1998)

Arundel Chick (1999)

Puppy Love "Steino" (1999)

Arundel Cat (2000)

Backstamp: **Arundel Bunny:** Embossed "Wade England" and printed "The Official International Wade Collectors Club the Arundel Bunny July 1998" with OIWCC logo
Arundel Cat: Large embossed "Wade"
Arundel Chick: Printed "The Arundel Chick Arundel 1999" with the O.I.W.C.C. logo
Arundel Duck: OIWCC logo and "The Arundel Duck August 1997"
Arundel Salmon: Red printed "Wade Made in England"
Clowns: Red printed "Wade Made in England"
Puppy Love "Steino": Black paw print with black/red lettering "Puppy L♥ve By Wade Puppy L♥ve Limited Edition 500 1999 Steino"
Teddy Bear Plaque: Gold printed "Wade England Swap Meet 1998"

Date	Name	Colourway	Issue - Price	Size	U.S. $	Can. $	U.K. £
1997	Arundel Duck	Creamy white	100 - £20.00	95	325.00	400.00	200.00
1997	Arundel Duck	Dull yellow	1400 - £15.00	95	95.00	130.00	65.00
1998	Arundel Bunny	Honey; green ears; brown eyes	1400 - £25.00	110	55.00	70.00	35.00
1998	Arundel Bunny	White; blue ears; black eyes	100 - £25.00	110	260.00	320.00	160.00
1998	Teddy Bear Plaque	Caramel bear, plaque	1500 - £20.00	195	35.00	55.00	28.00
1999	Arundel Chick	Honey	900 - £15.00	78	50.00	70.00	35.00
1999	Arundel Chick	White	900 - £15.00	78	245.00	300.00	150.00
1999	Puppy Love "Steino"	White/brown; blue ball	500 - £20.00	70	40.00	55.00	28.00
2000	Arundel Cat	Honey	900 - £15.00	108	45.00	65.00	32.00
2000	Arundel Cat	White	100 - £15.00	108	165.00	200.00	100.00
2000	Arundel Salmon, (EW) (RRC)	Pink	1500 - Free	30 x 30	15.00	20.00	10.00
2000	Clown, singing	Pearlised; black hat, shoes	250 - £35.00 pr	120	33.00	40.00	20.00
2000	Clown, banjo	Pearlised; black hat, shoes	250 - £35.00 pr	120	33.00	40.00	20.00

Note: EW: *English Whimsies*; RRC: Red Rose Canada; WL: *Whimsie-land*

ARUNDEL COLLECTORS MEET

2001

The Arundel Swap Meet was renamed Arundel Collectors Meet in 2001.

At the 2001 Collectors Meet, Wade Ceramics offered a 'mystery parcel' (Goodie Bags) which was guaranteed to contain models up to the value of £70.00. Fifty bags contained a special gold edition of the Cuties, either Clarence the Cow, or Sumo the Elephant, each issued in an edition of 25 pieces. The bags were sold at £50.00 each. The 'mystery parcels' were also available at the April and October 2001 Trentham Gardens Fairs. Those bags contained a special gold edition of one the following: Hector the Owl, Major the Lion, Pedro the Donkey or Poppy the Pig, from the Cuties series. The regular issue of those models was available on-line and from the Wade Factory Shop in September 2003, at the U.K. and U.S.A. prices listed.

Arundel Puppy (2001)

Clarence the Cow (2001)

Sumo the Elephant (2001)

Otter (2001)

Clarence the Cow - gold edition (2001)

Sumo the Elephant - gold edition (2001)

Backstamp: **Arundel Puppy:** Printed "Collectors Meet 2001" with printed red and white "Wade" decal
Clarence the Cow / Sumo the Elephant: Printed red and white "Wade" decal
Otto: Embossed "Wade England"
Gold models: Printed red or gold "Wade" logo

Date	Name	Colourway	Issue - Price	Size	U.S. $	Can. $	U.K. £
2001	Arundel Puppy	Honey	900 - £20.00	75 x 60	50.00	62.00	31.00
2001	Arundel Puppy	White	100 - £20.00	75 x 60	165.00	200.00	100.00
2001	Clarence the Cow	White; black patches; blue flower	250 - £20.00	50 x 75	45.00	60.00	28.00
2001	Clarence the Cow	White; gold patches; white flower	25 - Goody bag	50 x 75	100.00	120.00	60.00
2001	Otter (WL)	Grey	2000 - Free	40 x 40	15.00	22.00	11.00
2001	Sumo the Elephant	Grey; blue balloon	250 - £20.00	50 x 75	45.00	60.00	28.00
2001	Sumo the Elephant	Grey; gold balloon	25 - Goody bag	50 x 75	100.00	120.00	60.00

ARUNDEL COLLECTORS MEET

2002-2003

The "Pony Whimsie" was formerly the Tom Smith Cracker "Family Pets" Shetland Pony. The model was complimentary with the £3.00 admission to the Collectors Meet.

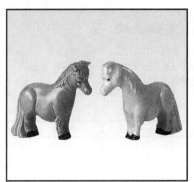
Arundel Pony (honey and white) (2002)

Arundel Lamb (white and black) (2003)

Arundel Town Mouse [black hat /gold hat] (2002)

Swan (black, white and pearl) (2002)

Badger Whimsie (2003)

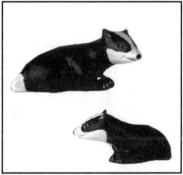
Badger Mother and Badger Baby (2003)

Bulldog Key Chain (2003)

T.Rex Moneybank (2003)

Vulcanodon Dinosaur Moneybank (2003)

Backstamp: **Arundel Pony:** Printed "Collectors Meet 2002" and "Wade" logo

Arundel Town Mouse: Printed "Arundel 7th July 2002 Arundel Town Mouse Official International Wade Collectors Club Centre 200 Limited Edition" with "C&S" and "Wade" logos

Badger Baby: Printed "Baby Badger July 2003 Limited Edition of 150" with red "Wade" and blue "C&S" logos

Badger Mother: Printed "Mother Badger July 2003 Limited Edition of 150" with red "Wade" and blue "C&S" logos

Badger Mother: Printed gold "Wade" logo

Badger Whimsie: Embossed "Wade England"

Lady Mouse: Printed "Arundel Lady Mouse July 2003 LTD EDT 200" with red "Wade" and blue "C&S" logos

Lamb: Printed "Collectors Meet 2003" and black "Wade" logo

Pony Whimsie: Embossed "Wade England"

Swans (pair): Printed "Pair of Swans Arundel 7th July2002, 150 pairs Limited Edition" with blue "C&S" and red "Wade" logos

Vulcanodon Dinosaur Moneybank: Printed "Dinosaur Moneybank Limited Edition of 500" with red "Wade" and blue "C&S" logos

Vulcanodon Dinosaur Moneybank: Gold "Wade" logo

2002

Date	Name	Colourway	Issue - Price	Size	U.S. $	Can. $	U.K. £
2002	Arundel Pony	Honey; brown hooves	900 - £20	80 x 125	50.00	60.00	30.00
2002	Arundel Pony	White; brown hooves	100 - £20	80 x 125		Rare	
2002	Arundel Town Mouse	White; black hat, tail, umbrella	200 - £25	90	75.00	95.00	46.00
2002	Arundel Town Mouse	White; gold hat, umbrella; black tail	20 - Prizes	90		Rare	
2002	Pony Whimsie (TS)	Honey	– / £3	25 x 30	8.00	10.00	5.00
2002	Swan	Black; orange beak	150 - £20	70 x 95	36.00	48.00	22.00
2002	Swan	Pearl lustre	20 - Prizes	70 x 95	90.00	120.00	55.00
2002	Swan	White; orange beak	150 - £20	70 x 95	36.00	48.00	22.00

2003

Date	Name	Colourway	Issue - Price	Size	U.S. $	Can. $	U.K. £
2003	Arundel Lamb	Black	100 - Prizes	60 x 90		Rare	
2003	Arundel Lamb	White; black eyes, feet	900 - £20	60 x 90	40.00	50.00	25.00
2003	Badger Baby	Black; white markings	150 - £40)	50 x 115	43.00	50.00	25.00
2003	Badger Mother	Black; white markings	150 - Pair)	90 x 130	43.00	50.00	25.00
2003	Badger Mother	Gold	20 - Prizes	90 x 130		Rare	
2003	Badger Whimsie	Grey	– / £3	25 x 30	15.00	22.00	10.00
2003	Bulldog Key chain	White; honey patches; black nose	– / £5	35	11.00	14.00	7.00
2003	Lady Mouse	White; pink ear; blue bonnet, cloak; yellow ribbon	200 - £26	80	50.00	60.00	30.00
2003	T.Rex Money Box	Beige; green base	400 - £25	125	40.00	50.00	25.00
2003	T.Rex Money Box	White; gold base	100 - £25	125	65.00	80.00	40.00
2003	Vulcanodon Dinosaur Moneybank	Blue; black eyes; mottled brown base	500 - £25	120	57.00	70.00	35.00
2003	Vulcanodon Dinosaur Moneybank	White; black eyes; mottled brown base	100 - £25	120	65.00	80.00	40.00
2003	Vulcanodon Dinosaur Moneybank	White; black eyes; gold base	20 - Prizes	120		Rare	

Note: The Arundel Town Mouse, in the gold colourway, bears the same backstamp as the regular issue. Please note that the backstamps on both Vulcanodon Dinosaur Money boxes reads "Limited Edition of 500," but the white colourway was issued in a limited edition of 100.

BIRMINGHAM FAIRS

1994-1996

Spaniel (1994)

Grey-haired Rabbit (1995)

Smiling Frog (1996)

Backstamp: All: Embossed "Wade"

Date	Name	Colourways	Issue - Price	Size	U.S. $	Can. $	U.K. £
1994	Spaniel	Honey	1000 - £12.50	75 x 60	200.00	250.00	125.00
1995	Grey-haired Rabbit	Grey-brown	1250 - £12.50	87 x 60	165.00	200.00	100.00
1996	Smiling Frog	Green	1250 - £12.50	60 x 80	80.00	100.00	50.00

COLLECT IT! FAIRS

NEWARK, 1998, STONELEIGH, 1998

Baby Bear in Pyjamas (1998)

Oops! the Bear, Style One (1998)

Travelling Frog (1998)

Backstamp: Travelling Frog: Black printed "Genuine Wade Porcelain Newark 1998"
Baby Bear in Pyjamas: Gold printed "Baby Bear Collection, Baby Bear in Pyjamas-Limited edition of 1,000 Wade England"
Oops! The Bear: Printed "Oops! The Bear Wade England Ltd. Edition 500 1998"

No.	Name	Colourway	Issue - Price	Size	U.S. $	Can. $	U.K. £
1998	Baby Bear in Pyjamas	Blue/white striped pyjamas	1000 - £25.00	153	70.00	90.00	45.00
1998	Oops! the Bear, Style One	Amber; pink plaster on knee	500 - £12.50	60	65.00	85.00	40.00
1998	Travelling Frog	Green jacket; red cravat, bag	2500 - £20.00	135	45.00	60.00	30.00

Honey Bunch Bears

Approximately 40 of each of the six Honey Bunch Bears, with the bee transfer omitted, were randomly decorated by freehand and sold at the Collect It! Fair wrapped in Christmas paper and shaped as a cracker. See also page 165.

Bear, seated (1998)

Bear, Honeypot (1998)

Bear, arms raised; Bear, sleeping (1998)

Backstamp: All: Embossed "Wade"

Date	Name	Colourways	Issue - Price	Size	U.S. $	Can. $	U.K. £
1998	Bear, arms raised	Honey, blue dungarees	40 - £25.00 set	55	45.00	60.00	30.00
1998	Bear, honey pot	Honey; gold collar, cuffs	40	57	45.00	60.00	30.00
1998	Bear, honey pot	Honey; red vest; gold honey pot	40	57	45.00	60.00	30.00
1998	Bear, seated	Honey; gold collar, cuffs	40	57	45.00	60.00	30.00
1998	Bear, seated	Honey; red/blue spots	40	57	45.00	60.00	30.00
1998	Bear, sleeping	Honey; pink night cap, collar	40	55	45.00	60.00	30.00

DUNSTABLE FAIRS

Timid Mouse (1996)

Koala Bear (1997)

Cook Catkins (1998)

British Lion (1999)

Puppy Love "Ella" (1999)

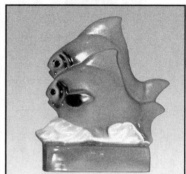
Shoal of Fish (1999)

Backstamp: **British Lion:** Printed "Wade Limited Edition of 350 ©Wade Ceramics LTD ©UKI Ceramics Limited Produced in an exclusive World-wide Edition" [name of model and UKI Ceramics tel no.]

Cook Catkins: Printed "Cook Catkins 1 of 1,500 Exclusive Edition for the Dunstable Wade Fair 1998 UKWCO2 ©UK Fairs Ltd and Wade ®Ceramics Ltd"

Cook Catkins: Printed "Wade Limited Edition of 350 ©Wade Ceramics LTD ©UKI Ceramics LTD Produced Exclusively for UKI

Puppy Love "Ella": Black paw print with black and red lettering "Puppy L♥ve By Wade Puppy L♥ve Limited Edition 500 1999 Ella"

Koala Bear: Black printed "The Koala Bear 1 of 1,500 Exclusive Edition for Dunstable Wade Fair 1997 ©UK Fairs Ltd and Wade Ceramics Ltd"

Koala Bear: Black printed "The Koala Bear 1 of 150 Exclusive Edition of Dunstable Wade Fair Special Produced Soley for Over-seas Wade Collectors ©UK Fairs Ltd & Wade Ceramics Ltd"

Seals: Printed "Wade England"

Shoal of Fish: Printed "Wade Limited Edition of 350 ©Wade Ceramics LTD ©UKI Ceramics LTD Produced Exclusively for UKI Ceramics LTD in an Exclusive World-wide Edition" [name of model and UKI tel. no.]

Timid Mouse: Embossed "Wade," black printed "Limited Edition of 1,750 Exclusively Dunstable Wade Fair 1996"

Date	Name	Colourways	Issue - Price	Size	U.S. $	Can. $	U.K. £
1996	Timid Mouse	Light brown; green/brown base	1750 - £16.00	60	75.00	90.00	45.00
1997	Koala Bear	Beige; brown tree; green leaves	1650 - £20.00	127	75.00	90.00	45.00
1998	Cook Catkins	White apron	1500 - £25.00	140	75.00	90.00	45.00
1998	Cook Catkins	White/green apron	500 - £25.00	140	75.00	90.00	45.00
1999	British Lion	Tan, streaked brown mane	340 - £30.00	160	65.00	80.00	40.00
1999	British Lion	Unknown	10 - £30.00	160		Rare	
1999	Puppy Love "Ella"	White; tan patches	500 - £20.00	70	40.00	55.00	28.00
1999	Seals (pair)	Grey/black	750 - £30.00	40 x 70	55.00	70.00	35.00
1999	Shoal of Fish	Orange; white waves; blue base	340 - £30.00	140	65.00	80.00	40.00
1999	Shoal of Fish	Unknown	10 - £30.00	140		Rare	

DUNSTABLE LEISURE CENTRE

2002-2003

After a three year absence, the Wade Fair returned to a new venue in Dunstable, Bedfordshire. In September 2002, the entrance model was the *English Whimsies* Polar Bear (#60), in a pearlised glaze. The model was complimentary with admission to the show.

In September 2003, the entrance model was the Water Snail (from the Aquarium set) renamed Pearl Snail. "Lil' Cricketer" continued the Lil' Bears Series, he was produced in a limited edition of 125, with 25 models being held for members unable to attend the show who sent a postcard with their name, to be entered in a draw. Shep the Sheepdog, the second model in the Wade Dog Series, and "Buttercup," the second model in the Ponies Series were also available at the show, priced at $20.00 each.

Lil' Witch (2002)

Polar Bear (2002)

Union Bear (2002)

Buttercup (2003)

Lil' Cricketer (2003)

Pearl Snail (2003)

Backstamp: **Polar Bear:** Embossed "Wade"
Lil Witch: Printed "Ltd Edit. 125 Lil Witch September 2002" and red "Wade" logo
Union Bear: Printed "Union Bear 125 Ltd. Edt." and red "Wade" logo

Date	Name	Colourways	Size	U.S. $	Can. $	U.K. £
2002	Lil Witch	Black cloak, hat; red hat band and ribbon; white dress	98	105.00	130.00	65.00
2002	Polar Bear (EW)	Pearlised	30 x 30	13.00	16.00	8.00
2002	Union Bear	White bear; red/white/blue Union Jack flag	78	45.00	75.00	35.00
2003	Buttercup	Amber horse; brown base	85	32.00	40.00	20.00
2003	Lil' Cricketer	White jersey with red/blue trim; blue hat; gold shin guards; green base	95	65.00	95.00	45.00
2003	Pearl Snail	Pearl	30 x 35	13.00	16.00	8.00
2003	Shep the Sheepdog	Black/white; green base	90	32.00	40.00	20.00

STAFFORD FAIR

2000

In 2000, the Spring Wade Fair (May 7th) was moved from Trentham Gardens to the Show Grounds at Stafford. There were two Wade Show specials, "Fireman Catkins" and "Millennium Catkins."

The "Millennium Teddy" was designed by Stoke-on-Trent schoolgirl Helen Bourne, it was sold at the fair by Wade Ceramics.

Fireman Catkins (2000)

Millennium Catkins (2000)

Millennium Teddy (2000)

Backstamp: **Fireman Catkins:** Printed "Fireman Catkins Exclusive Limited Edition of 250 No. 7 in the series
WADE © UKI CERAMICS LTD. © WADE CERAMICS LTD."
Millennium Catkins: Printed "Millennium Catkins Exclusive Limited Edition of 250 (No.) in the series
WADE England © UKI CERAMICS LTD. © WADE CERAMICS LTD."
Millennium Teddy: Printed "May 2000" with International Wade Club logo.

Date	Name	Colourways	Issue - Price	Size	U.S. $	Can. $	U.K. £
2000	Fireman Catkins	Dark blue uniform; yellow helmet gold nozzle, badge	250 - £38.50	128	65.00	80.00	40.00
2000	Millennium Catkins	White shirt; grey trousers; multicoloured balloons	250 - £38.50	125	65.00	80.00	40.00
2000	Millennium Teddy	Brown; white/pewter/blue numeral 2000	500 - £20.00	90	65.00	60.00	40.00

U.K. WADE COLLECTORS FAIR

(TRENTHAM GARDENS)
GENERAL ISSUES 1997-2002

Kangaroo (1997)

Rufus (1997)

Penguins (1999)

Hector the Owl (2001)   Pedro the Donkey (2001)   Major the Lion (2001)   Poppy the Pig (2001)

Roly Poly Rabbi (2000)

Owl (2001)

Lil' Devil (2001)

U.K. WADE COLLECTORS FAIR

(TRENTHAM GARDENS)
GENERAL ISSUES 1997-2002

At the April and October 2001, Trentham Gardens Fairs, Wade Ceramics offered a 'mystery parcel' (Goody Bag) which was guaranteed to contain models up to the value of £70.00. There were 50 bags offered at each show, at a cost of £50.00. Each bag contained one of the specials (from the Cuties Series) plus another Wade model. The mystery specials for the April show were either "Hector the Owl" or "Pedro the Donkey," in a special gold colourway, and for the October show, either "Major the Lion" or "Poppy the Pig." Twenty-five models each of the Wade Cuties were produced for these shows.

The entrance model for the April show was a gold *Whimsie-land* Owl, and for the October show, a pearl *Whimsie-land* Duck.

Backstamp: Australia Olympic Catkins: Unknown
  City Gent Catkins: Printed "The City Gent Catkins ® 1 of 1,500 Exclusive Limited Edition For The Trentham Gardens Wade Fair 1998 © UK Fairs LTD & Wade Ceramics LTD"
  Clown Catkins: Unknown
  Gypsy Catkins: Printed "Gypsy Catkins 1 of 1,000 Exclusive Limited Edition for the Trentham Wade Fair 1999 UKWCO3 ©UK Fairs & Wade® Ceramics Ltd"
  Hector the Owl: Printed red and white "Wade" decal
  Kangaroo: Black printed "The Kangaroo 1 of 1,500 Exclusive Limited Edition For The Trentham Gardens Wade Fair 1997 ©UK Fairs LTD & Wade Ceramics LTD"
  Kangaroo: Printed "The Kangaroo 1 of 50 Exclusive Limited Edition Trentham Gardens 1997 Wade Fair Special Produced solely for overseas Wade Collectors ©UK Fairs Ltd & Wade Ceramics Ltd"
  Lil' Devil: Printed "Lil' Devil Extravaganza Special 2001 Ltd Ed 100" with red Wade logo
  Major the Lion: Printed white "Wade" in red decal
  Penguins: Printed "Wade Made in England"
  Pedro the Donkey: Printed red and white "Wade" decal
  Poppy the Pig: Printed red and white "Wade" decal
  Quackers the Duck: Red printed "Wade Made in England"
  Roly Poly Rabbit: Red printed "Wade Made in England"
  Rufus: Printed "The Official International Wade Collectors Club Wade on Tour 1997"
  Puppy Love "Sidney": Black paw print with black and red lettering "Puppy L♥ve By Wade Puppy L♥ve Limited Edition 500 1999 Sidney"
  Travelling Badger: Printed circular "The Official International Wade Collectors Club Travelling Badger Wade on Tour 1998"

Date	Name	Colourways	Issue - Price	Size	U.S. $	Can. $	U.K. £
1997	Kangaroo	Orange-brown; green base	1650 - £18.00	127	75.00	100.00	50.00
1997	Mr. Snowman Pepper	Black hat; green striped scarf	100 - £17.50	100	12.00	16.00	8.00
1997	Mrs. Snowman Salt	Black hat; brown collar, muff	(a pair)	95	12.00	16.00	8.00
1997	Rufus	Red-brown; cobalt blue cushion	— /£15.00	65 x 84	40.00	60.00	28.00
1998	City Gent Catkins	Light grey coat; dark grey pants	1500 - £25.00	115	65.00	80.00	40.00
1998	Travelling Badger	Blue coat, hat; brown case	— /£15.00	90	35.00	50.00	25.00
1999	Gypsy Catkins	Maroon waistcoat; blue pants	1000 - £20.00	140	65.00	80.00	40.00
1999	Penguins (pair)	Black/white; yellow beaks	750 - £35.00	80/60	65.00	90.00	45.00
1999	Puppy Love "Sidney"	Tan/white; blue cushion	500 - £20.00	50	40.00	55.00	28.00
2000	Roly Poly Rabbit	Yellow dress; white apron	500 - £20.00	75	38.00	55.00	28.00
2001	Australia Olympic Catkins	Yellow/green suit; gold medal	100 - £50.00	120	105.00	130.00	65.00
2001	Clown Catkins	Red tunic, black ruffles, bobbles; white trousers; gold hat	22 - £45.00	120	105.00	130.00	65.00
2001	Duck (WL)	Pearl	— / Free	45 x 35	30.00	36.00	18.00
2001	Gypsy Catkins	Red shirt; maroon waistcoat; blue/brown check trousers;	70 - £45.00	120	105.00	130.00	65.00
2001	Hector the Owl	Tan; black mortar board cap; maroon book, gold letters	250 - £20.00	80 x 40	40.00	60.00	30.00
2001	Hector the Owl	Tan; gold mortar board hat, book	25 - Specials	80 x 40	90.00	125.00	60.00
2001	Lil' Devil	Red horns, bow; black cloak	100 - £39.50	95	160.00	200.00	100.00
2001	Major the Lion	Honey; brown mane	250 - £20.00	52 x 86	40.00	50.00	25.00
2001	Major the Lion	Honey; gold	20 - £50.00	52 x 86	130.00	160.00	80.00
2001	Owl (WL)	Gold	— /Free	35 x 25	16.00	20.00	10.00
2001	Pedro the Donkey	Brown; yellow/blue hat	250 - £20.00	57 x 70	40.00	60.00	30.00
2001	Pedro the Donkey	Brown, gold hat	25 / Specials	57 x 70	130.00	160.00	80.00
2001	Poppy the Pig	Pink; red/ yellow lollipop	250 - £20.00	58 x 74	40.00	50.00	30.00
2001	Poppy the Pig	Pink; gold lollipop	20 - £50.00	58 x 74	130.00	160.00	80.00

CHRISTMAS EXTRAVAGANZA, TRENTHAM GARDENS 1997

BADGES

Plain white ceramic plaques were decorated with multicoloured Christmas transfers, a pin was then added to the backs, converting them to badges (pins).

Backstamp: All: Printed "Wade made in England"

No.	Name	Colourways	Issue - Price	Size	U.S. $	Can. $	U.K. £
1997	Santa on roof	Red/white suit; green gloves	— /£2.00	50	5.00	7.00	4.00
1997	Santa skating	Red/white suit; blue gloves	— /£2.00	50	5.00	7.00	4.00
1997	Santa walking	Red/white suit; black boots	— /£2.00	50	5.00	7.00	4.00
1997	Santa with sack	Red/white suit; brown boots	— /£2.00	50	5.00	7.00	4.00
1997	Snowman flying	White; black hat; red/green scarf	— /£2.00	50	5.00	7.00	4.00
1997	Snowman laughing	White; black hat; red/green scarf	— /£2.00	50	5.00	7.00	4.00

CHRISTMAS DECORATIONS

White ceramic discs, tap caps and lamp pulls were decorated with Christmas transfers and coloured ribbon, converting them into tree decorations.

Tree Decoration Discs

Backstamp: All: Printed "Wade made in England"

No.	Name	Colourway	Issue - Price	Size	U.S. $	Can. $	U.K. £
1997	Tree discs	Gifts/garland transfer	— /£1.00	63	5.00	7.00	4.00
1997	Tree discs	Windows/garland transfer	— /£1.00	63	5.00	7.00	4.00

CHRISTMAS DECORATIONS

Tree Decoration Lamp Pulls

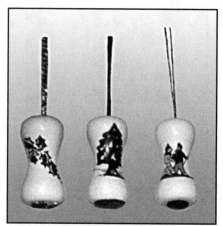

Holly, Pine Tree, Children

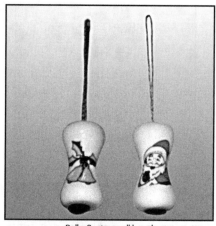

Bells, Santa, small beard

Backstamp: All: Printed "Wade made in England"

No.	Description	Colourway	Issue/Price	Size	U.S. $	Can. $	U.K. £
1997	Children	White; multicoloured print	— /£1.50	40	5.00	7.00	4.00
1997	Holly	White; green holly; red berries	— /£1.50	40	5.00	7.00	4.00
1997	Pine Tree	White; multicoloured print	— /£1.50	40	5.00	7.00	4.00
1997	Gift	White; multicoloured print	— /£1.50	40	5.00	7.00	4.00
1997	Santa, large beard	White; multicoloured print	— /£1.50	40	5.00	7.00	4.00
1997	Santa, small beard	White; red suit; green glove	— /£1.50	40	5.00	7.00	4.00

Tree Decoration Tap Caps

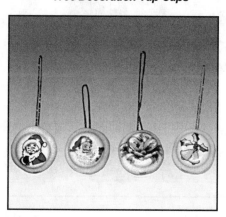

Backstamp: All: Printed "Wade made in England"

No.	Description	Colourways	Issue/Price	Size	U.S. $	Can. $	U.K. £
1997	Bells and holly	Green holly; red berries; yellow bells	— /£1.50	33	5.00	7.00	4.00
1997	Christmas crackers	White; multicoloured print	— /£1.50	33	5.00	7.00	4.00
1997	Santa, large beard	White; red suit; green gloves	— /£1.50	33	5.00	7.00	4.00
1997	Santa, small beard	White; red suit; green gloves	— /£1.50	33	5.00	7.00	4.00

FIGURES FOR THE CHRISTMAS EXTRAVAGANZA 2000

Bear Cub (2000)

Quackers the Duck, Style One (2000)

Backstamp: Bear Cub: Embossed "Wade"

Date	Name	Colourways	Issue - Price	Size	U.S. $	Can. $	U.K. £
2000	Bear Cub (EW)	Gold	1500 - Free	30 x 40	10.00	15.00	5.00
2000	Quackers the Duck, Style One	Red/white hat; blue/white scarf	500 - £20.00	70	48.00	60.00	30.00

FAMILY FAVOURITES

The Family Favourites set was still available on-line and from the Wade Factory Shop in September 2003, at the U.K. prices listed below.

Backstamp: All: Red printed "Wade Made in England"

Date	Name	Colourways	Issue - Price	Size	U.S. $	Can. $	U.K. £
2000	Boots the Rabbit	Brown rabbit; blue/white boot	—/£15.00	90 x 75	24.00	30.00	15.00
2000	Dribbles the Dog	Brown dog; white/black football	—/£15.00	70 x 90	24.00	30.00	15.00
2000	Hattie the Squirrel	Honey squirrel; grey hat	—/£15.00	85 x 70	24.00	30.00	15.00
2000	Priscilla the Pig	Pink pig; brown bed; blue blanket	—/£15.00	60 x 75	24.00	30.00	15.00
2000	Tiny the Mouse	Brown mouse; grey/platinum can	—/£15.00	95 x 40	24.00	30.00	15.00
2000	Tubby the Bear	Brown bear; blue/pewter barrel	—/£15.00	82 x 55	24.00	30.00	15.00

U.K. WADE COLLECTORS FAIR

(Kings Hall Civic Centre)

2002

The site of the Wade UK Collectors Show, formerly held at Trentham Gardens, was moved to the Kings Hall Civic Centre, Stoke-on-Trent, Staffordshire. The show was held April 21st, 2002, and there were many new models and show specials.

The Pearl Bunny, which is from the Tom Smith *Family Pets* (1988-1989) rabbit mould, was given free of charge to collectors as they entered the show. "Lil' Easter Bear," the second model in the Lil' Bears Series, was produced in a limited edition of 125. Overseas collectors who could not attend the show could send a postcard to the Wade Club to be entered into a draw for 25 of the models.

Lil' Easter Bear (2002)

Pearl Bunny (2002)

Backstamp: Lil' Easter: Printed "Ltd. Edt. 125 April 2002 Lil Easter Bear" and red "Wade" logo
Pearl Bunny: Embossed "Wade England"

Date	Name	Colourways	Issue - Price	Size	U.S. $	Can. $	U.K. £
2002	Lil' Easter Bear	Blue/white dress; blue bonnet; pink ribbon, bow; yellow chick; brown basket	125 - £45	95	105.00	140.00	65.00
2002	Pearl Bunny (TS)	Pearl	– / Free	30 x 25	13.00	16.00	8.00

PIG STYLES

Please note the name "Caesar" is wrongly spelled as "Ceaser" in Wade advertising, and on the certificate of authenticity.

| Arnie | Ceasar | Topsy-Turvey | Twirly Whirly |

Backstamp: Printed "Pig Styles 2002 Ltd Edition of 200 [name of model]" and "Wade" logo

Date	Name	Colourways	Size	U.S. $	Can. $	U.K. £
2002	Arnie	Pink; green shorts; black weights	60	40.00	50.00	25.00
2002	Ceasar	Pink; white toga; green laurel wreath	65	40.00	50.00	25.00
2002	Topsey-Turvey	Pink; yellow t-shirt; blue pants; red nose	70	40.00	50.00	25.00
2002	Twirly Whirly	Pink; blue dress	73	40.00	50.00	25.00

U.K. WADE COLLECTORS FAIR

(North Stafford Hotel)

2003

The site of the Wade UK Collectors Show, formerly held at Trentham Gardens, was moved again, this time to the North Stafford Hotel, Stoke-on-Trent, Staffordshire. The show held April 13th, 2003, offered many new models and show specials. Lil' Footballer was the fifth model in the Wade Lil' Bears series. It was produced in a limited edition of 125. Overseas collectors who could not attend the show could send a postcard to the Wade Club to be entered into a draw for 25 of the models. A set of ponies was introduced at various Wade shows throughout the year. The first model "Bluebell" was introduced at the North Stafford show. Also available at the show was the Dalmatian Key Chain, and Beau the Greyhound. The entry model was the Pearl Seahorse, originally from *English Whimsies* series, at a cost of £6.00.

Beau the Greyhound (2003)

Bluebell the Pony (2003)

Dalmatian Key Chain (2003)

Lil' Footballer Bear (2003)

Backstamp: **Beau the Greyhound:** Printed "Beau 2003" and red "Wade" logo
Bluebell: Embossed "Wade"
Brandy: Printed "Brandy 125 Limited Edition" and red "Wade" logo
Budgie: Printed "Fair Special Budgie Limited Edition 125" and red "Wade" logo
Lil' Footballer: Printed "Ltd. Edt. 125 April 2002 Lil Footballer" and red "Wade" logo
Pearl Seahorse: Embossed "Wade "

Date	Name	Colourways	Size	U.S. $	Can. $	U.K. £
2003	Beau the Greyhound	Beige; checkered blue/beige base	55 x 108	40.00	50.00	25.00
2003	Bluebell the Pony	Tan; brown base	90	40.00	50.00	25.00
2003	Brandy the St. Bernard	White; red brown markings; gold barrel; dark brown collar	70	40.00	50.00	25.00
2003	Budgie	Green wings; white body; yellow beak; brown base	68 x 91	65.00	95.00	45.00
2003	Dalmatian Key Chain	White; black markings; chrome key chain	40	11.00	14.00	7.00
2003	Lil' Footballer Bear	Brown; white shirt with blue/red stripes; black/gold ball; green base	85	50.00	60.00	30.00
2003	Pearl Seahorse (EW)	Pearl	50 x 17	13.00	16.00	8.00

Note: The Wade glaze colour for the tan pony is 'rock'.

U.S.A. WADE COLLECTORS SHOWS

1996-1999

The four U.S. Wade Collectors Shows (Seattle 1996, Oconomowoc 1997, Buffalo 1998, and San Antonio 1999) were all held in conjunction with The International Association Jim Beam Bottles Society Collectors Club.

Madison Mouse (1997)

New York Tourist (1998)

Oscar the Christmas Teddy Bear (1998)

Shelby (1999)

Rufus on Tour (1999)

Backstamp: Arthur Hare Key Ring: None
Madison Mouse: Black and red circular "The Official International Wade Collectors Club Wisconsin 1997"
New York Tourist: Printed "Buffalo Fair Special 1998" with OIWCC logo
Oscar the Christmas Teddy Bear: Printed "Oscar Special Colourway Buffalo 1998 The Official International Wade Collectors Club" with OIWCC logo
Prairie Dog: Printed "The Prairie Dog with OIWCC logo"
Puppy Love "Shelby": Black paw print with black and red lettering "Puppy L♥ve by Wade Puppy L♥ve Limited Edition 500 1999 Shelby"
Rufus on Tour: Printed "Genuine Wade Porcelain limited edition of 100"
Teddy Bear Plaque: Gold printed "Wade England Buffalo 1998"
Westie the Highland Terrier: Printed black and red "The Official International Wade Collectors Club," and black "Seattle 1996"

Date	Name	Colourways	Issue - Price	Size	U.S. $	Can. $	U.K. £
1996	Westie the West Highland Terrier	White	3000 - $20 US	75 x 78	42.00	56.00	28.00
1997	Madison Mouse	Beige; yellow cheese	—/$30 US	95 x 60	42.00	56.00	28.00
1998	Arthur Hare Key Ring	White; multicoloured transfer	—/Free	(dia.) 35	13.00	16.00	8.00
1998	New York Tourist	Blue t-shirt; black trousers	—/$24.00 US	110	40.00	60.00	30.00
1998	Oscar the Christmas Teddy Bear	Honey; green hat; brown sack; blue soldier	75 - $35 US	110	300.00	400.00	200.00
1998	Teddy Bear Plaque	Chocolate brown bear, plaque	1500 - $40 US	195	42.00	56.00	28.00
1999	Prairie Dog	Brown/white; yellow rose	500 - $20 US	120	42.00	56.00	28.00
1999	Puppy Love "Shelby"	White; brown patches	500 - $20 US	50	42.00	56.00	28.00
1999	Rufus on Tour	Beige; pearlised beige base	100 - $200 (set)	84	80.00	100.00	50.00
1999	Rufus on Tour	Grey; gold base	100 - $200 (set)	84	80.00	100.00	50.00
1999	Rufus on Tour	Honey; platinum base	100 - $200 (set)	84	80.00	100.00	50.00
1999	Rufus on Tour	Tan; copper base	100 - $200 (set)	84	80.00	100.00	50.00

KANSAS WADE SHOW

2000-2001

Cowardly Lion (2000)

Dorothy and Toto (2001)

Ozma (2001)

Backstamp: Armadillo: Embossed "Wade England"
Wizard of Oz Series: Hand written "Oz No [number of model in series]" with printed "Wade Est 1810 England"

Date	Name	Colourways	Issue - Price	Size	U.S. $	Can. $	U.K. £
2000	Armadillo (TS)	Copper lustre	915 - $10 US	25 x 45	12.00	18.00	10.00
2000	Armadillo (TS)	Light green	1000 - $10 US	25 x 45	12.00	18.00	10.00
2001	Cowardly Lion	Honey; brown mane	500 - $35 US	67	57.00	70.00	35.00
2001	Cowardly Lion	White	25 - Prizes	67		Rare	
2001	Dorothy and Toto	White/blue striped dress	500 - $70 US	60	100.00	130.00	65.00
2001	Dorothy and Toto	White	25 - Prizes	60		Rare	
2001	Ozma	Pearlised dress	500 - $50 US	65	75.00	90.00	45.00
2001	Ozma	White	25 - Prizes	65		Rare	

Circular Plaques

Attendees at the Saturday morning breakfast received a complimentary *Cowardly Lion* plaque, and those who attended the banquet received a complimentary Oz by Wade logo plaque. Ken Holmes produced the art work for the "Cowardly Lion," and "Dorothy" and "Ozma" plaques.

Cowardly Lion, Oz Logo, Dorothy and Toto, Ozma

Backstamp: Printed on the front of the plaques "Oz by Wade"

Date	Name	Colourways	Issue - Price	Size	U.S. $	Can. $	U.K. £
2001	Cowardly Lion	White; black decals, lettering	100 - Free	90	12.00	18.00	9.00
2001	Dorothy / Toto	White; black decals, lettering	100 - $10 US	90	12.00	18.00	9.00
2001	Ozma	White; black decals, lettering	100 - $10 US	90	12.00	18.00	9.00
2001	Oz Logo	White; black decals, lettering	200 - Free	90	12.00	18.00	9.00

ROSEMONT TRADE SHOW
ROSEMONT, ILLINOIS

1999

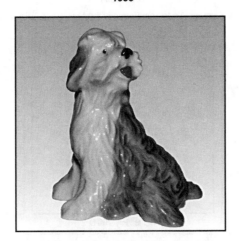

Backstamp: Black paw print with black and red lettering "Puppy L♥ve By Wade Puppy L♥ve Limited Edition 500 1999 Henry"

Date	Name	Colourways	Issue - Price	Size	U.S. $	Can. $	U.K. £
1999	Puppy Love "Henry"	White/ grey	500 - $20 US	85	45.00	55.00	28.00

MINI WADE FAIR
YORK, PENNSYLVANIA

1999

The Mini Wade Fair, organized by Pat and Gary Keenan, was held August 1999, at Harrisburg, Pennsylvania. "Jenny the Black Poodle" was complimentary with admission to fair, additional models were sold at $5.00 US.

Backstamp: Embossed "Wade England"

Date	Name	Colourways	Issue - Price	Size	U.S. $	Can. $	U.K. £
1999	Jenny the Black Poodle (RRC)	Black	—/—	40 x 45	15.00	22.00	11.00

SUMMER WADE FEST
HARRISBURG, PENNSYLVANIA

2000-2001

Organized by Pat and Gary Keenan, the Summer Wade Fest (formerly the Mini Wade Fair) is held at the Radisson Convention Centre, Camp Hill, Harrisburg, Pennsylvania.

www.collectables Plaque (2001)

Guinea Pig (2001)

Nibbles the Bunny (2001)

Little Bunnies [Lil' Bits] (2001)

Backstamp: **Arthur Hare Wizhared:** Embossed "Wade / C&S" on back rim
Cats – Thunder, Lighting, Goldie: Embossed "Wade England"
Guinea Pig: Embossed "Wade England"
Leprechaun Riding Snail: Printed "Wade"
Little Bunnies (Lil' Bits): Embossed "Wade England"
Nibbles the Bunny: Impressed "Wade"
www.cscollectablesco.uk plaque: None

Date	Name	Colourways	Issue - Price	Size	U.S. $	Can. $	U.K. £
2000	Cat/Thunder (TS/RRU)	Black	1200 - $6 US	25 x 33	12.00	18.00	10.00
2000	Cat/Lightning (TS/RRU)	White	800 - $6 US	25 x33	12.00	18.00	10.00
2000	Cat/Goldie (TS/RRU)	Gold	100 - Prizes	25 x 33	90.00	125.00	60.00
2001	Arthur Hare Wizhared	Green	250 - $10 US	43	17.00	24.00	12.00
2001	Guinea Pig (TS)	Black	500 - $7 US	20 x 30	12.00	18.00	10.00
2001	Guinea Pig (TS)	Gold	100 - Prizes	20 x 30		Rare	
2001	Guinea Pig (TS)	White	1000 - $6 US	20 x 30	12.00	18.00	10.00
2001	Leprechaun Riding Snail	Honey; brown/amber	650 - $25 US	50 x 53	35.00	52.00	28.00
2001	Little Bunnies (Lil' Bits)	Blue	450 - $8 US	22	15.00	20.00	10.00
2001	Little Bunnies (Lil' Bits)	White/pink streaks	250 - Goodie bag	22	18.00	28.00	15.00
2001	Little Bunnies (Lil' Bits)	Coronation green	450 - $8 US	22	15.00	20.00	10.00
2001	Little Bunnies (Lil' Bits)	Gold	50 - Prizes	22	90.00	125.00	60.00
2001	Little Bunnies (Lil' Bits)	Pink	450 - $8 US	22	15.00	20.00	10.00
2001	Little Bunnies (Lil' Bits)	White	450 - $8 US	22	15.00	20.00	10.00
2001	Nibbles the Bunny	Honey	135 - £20, $30 US	85	45.00	67.00	35.00
2001	Nibbles the Bunny	White	15 - £20, $30 US	85		Rare	
2001	www.cscollectables plaque	White/gold; Union Jack; blue Arthur Hare decal	100 - £10, $10 US	65 x 95	25.00	30.00	15.00

SUMMER WADE FEST
2002

American Eagle [regular and gold issues] (2002)

Leprechaun with Wheelbarrow
[regular/gold issues] (2002))

Lil' Uncle Sam (2002)

Mischief the Chimp [honey / grey issues] (2002)

Puppies [black, gold, white] (2002)

Lil' Bit Mice (2002)

SUMMER WADE FEST 2002 (cont.)

The Summer Wade Fest 2002 show was held at the Radisson Convention Centre, Camp Hill, Harrisburg, Pennsylvania. The following is a list of models which were available for the first time at this show.

American Eagle was commissioned by C&S as their special for this show. It was issued in a limited edition of 150. A limited edition of 20 models was issued with a gold base, and were given as prizes.

The Leprechaun with Wheelbarrow of Gold was commissioned by Patty Keenan, and is the second Leprechaun in the series produced for PA Wade Fest Shows. Thirty Leprechauns were produced with gold coins, of which ten were available for sale at $40.00, the others were prizes.

The Lil' Bit Mice were produced in a limited edition of 2,000 in four colourways, 500 each in blue, grey, honey and white. The set was priced at $28.00. A special limited edition of 50 mice was produced and given as prizes or auctioned. A grey Lil' Bit Mouse was also in the Goody Bag.

Two new models were issued for the June and July USA shows, "Lil' Uncle Sam," a bear wearing a red and white top hat which was the third model in Wade's Lil' Bear series. It was issued in a limited edition of 125. The second model produced for the USA shows was "Mischief the Chimp" (also known as Mischief the Monkey). Mischief was produced in a limited edition of 100, in a honey glaze, and 50 in a grey glaze. Both colourways have a July 2002 backstamp. The same models were also sold at the June West Coast Show, but bear a June 2002 backstamp. They grey models were randomly package and sold. For variations in Lil' Uncle Sam and Mischief see the West Coast USA Show, 2002.

Collectors who visited the fair on Saturday received a free black puppy (formerly the Whimsie Mongrel) with their admission. Collectors who paid in advance for the fair "Goodie Bag" (which included entrance to the fair and dinner Saturday night) received either a black or white puppy in their goodie bag. The black and white puppies were produced in a limited edition of 650 each. Gold glazed puppies which were produced in a limited edition of 100, were given in prize draws, or auctioned with the proceeds going to Parkinsons research. The remaining black and white puppies were later sold at the show for $6.00 each.

Backstamp: American Eagle: Printed "American Eagle July 2002 150 Limited Edition" with blue "C&S" and red "Wade" logos
Leprechaun with Wheelbarrow of Gold: Printed red "Wade" logo
Lil' Bit Mice: None
Lil' Uncle Sam: Printed "Lil Uncle Sam Ltd. Edit. 125 July 2002" and red "Wade" logo
Mischief the Chimp: Printed "Mischief the Chimp USA July 2002"
Puppy: Embossed "Wade England"

Date	Name	Colourways	Issue - Price	Size	U.S. $	Can. $	U.K. £
2002	American Eagle	Brown/white; yellow beak, feet; gold base	20 - Prizes	90	140.00	170.00	85.00
2002	American Eagle	Brown/white; yellow beak, feet; off-white base	150 - $38	90	45.00	55.00	28.00
2002	Leprechaun with Wheelbarrow of Gold	Greenish-blue hat, coat; honey pants, coins, base; brown wheelbarrow	350 - $28	50	30.00	45.00	22.00
2002	Leprechaun with Wheelbarrow of Gold	Greenish-blue hat, coat; honey pants, base; gold coins; brown wheelbarrow	30 - Prizes	50		Rare	
2002	Lil' Bit Mouse	Blue	500 - $7	18	10.00	14.00	7.00
2002	Lil' Bit Mouse	Gold	50 - Prizes	18	70.00	90.00	45.00
2002	Lil' Bit Mouse	Grey	500 - $7	18	10.00	14.00	7.00
2002	Lil' Bit Mouse	Honey	500 - $7	18	10.00	14.00	7.00
2002	Lil' Bit Mouse	White	500 - $7	18	10.00	14.00	7.00
2002	Lil' Uncle Sam	Brown; blue coat; white waistcoat; red pants; red/white hat	125 - $60	90	90.00	110.00	55.00
2002	Mischief the Chimp	Grey	50 - $35	80	60.00	80.00	40.00
2002	Mischief the Chimp	Honey	100 - $35	80	40.00	50.00	25.00
2002	Puppy	Black	650 - $6	35 x 35	8.00	12.00	6.00
2002	Puppy	Gold	100 - Prizes	35 x 35	30.00	35.00	18.00
2002	Puppy	White	650 - $6	35 x 35	8.00	12.00	6.00

Note: The base of the Lil' Bit Mouse is too small to hold a backstamp. The backstamp on the gold colourway Puppy is hard to see.

SUMMER WADE FEST 2003

Leprechaun on Rock [grey rock] (2003)

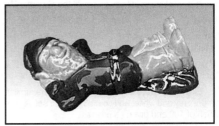

Leprechaun on Rock [gold rock] (2003)

North American Bear [dark brown and white issues] (2003)

Lil' American Footballer (2003)

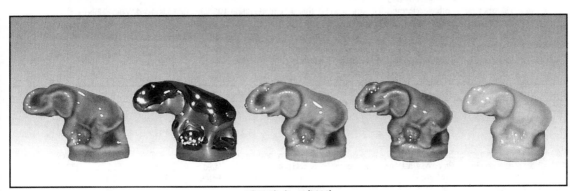

Lil' Bit Elephants (2003)

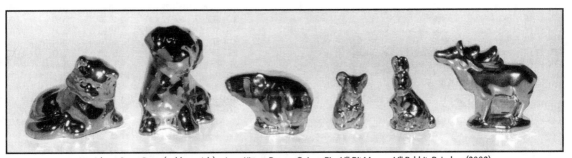

Harrisburg Straw Draw (gold specials) prizes: Kitten, Puppy, Guinea Pig, Lil' Bit Mouse, Lil' Rabbit, Reindeer (2003)

SUMMER WADE FEST 2003 (cont.)

The following is a list of models available at the Summer Wade Fest, Pennsylvania, 2003.:

"Bulgie the Frog" was issued in a limited edition 125 green, and 25 blue models. The blue models were distributed in boxes at random.

"The Lil' American Footballer," who has McWade 5 on his jersey, was produced in a limited edition of 125. A one-of-a-kind "Lil' American Footballer" was won in the Wade Bran Tub Draw.

The third Leprechaun model produced for Keenan Antiques, is the "Leprechaun on a Rock" Approximately 100 models were produced with a gold belt and gold rock. These models were available in prize draws and the silent auction.

The "Lil' Bit Elephants" were the Fair special, and are similar in style to the *English Whimsies* Elephant. They were produced as a set of four: blue, green, grey and white, and cost $32.00 per set. A grey Elephant was included in the fair package. A gold elephant was produced in a limited edition of 100 and given as prizes.

Commissioned by C&S as their special for the 2003 Summer Wade Fest, the "North American Bear" was produced in a limited edition of 150. It was modelled by Cyril Roberts. A small number of models were held back for U.K. customers. The issue price was £35.00. A limited edition of 20 white bears were given as prizes in various C&S competitions and draws.

The reindeer models are originally from the 1992-1994 *Tom Smith Snowlife Animals* set. This model is the "Reindeer," with no gap between the legs. There were 600 each white and honey coloured reindeer produced. A white or honey reindeer was included in the fair package, and a honey model was given to collectors upon admission on Saturday. The models could also be purchased for $6.00 each. A honey Reindeer with a red nose was produced in a limited edition of 70 and given as prizes, and used in the silent auction. The gold reindeer was also available in a 'Straw Draw' which cost $50.00. Gold models of the "Mongrel Puppy," "Lil' Bit Mouse," "Persian Kitten," "Lil' Bit Rabbit," and a gold "Guinea Pig," which were all previous Wade West specials, were included in the 'Straw Draw' prizes. As well as winning one of the gold models, the buy could also choose from an assortment of miscellaneous Wade models.

New colourways of the Red Rose Tea Canada models "Crocodile/Alligator," "Terrapin," and "Frog" were the prizes in the Wade Bran Rub at the Show. Tickets for the draw were purchased at $1.00 each. Every ticket won a prize.

Backstamp: Bulgie the Frog: Embossed "Wade England"
Crocodile/Alligator: Embossed "Wade England" in recessed base
Leprechaun on a Rock: Printed red "Wade England" logo
Frog: Embossed "Wade England" in recessed base
Lil' American Footballer: Printed "Lil' American Footballer Limited Edition 125 July 2003" and red "Wade" logo
Lil' Bit Elephants: Embossed "Wade Eng"
North American Bear: Printed "American Bear Limited Edition of 150 July 2003" with blue "C&S" and red "Wade" logos
North American Bear: (Special) Printed red "Wade" logo
Reindeer: Embossed "Wade Eng" on front and back rims
Terrapin: Embossed "Wade England"s in recessed base

Date	Name	Colourways	Issue - Price	Size	U.S. $	Can. $	U.K. £
2003	Bulgie the Frog	Blue	25 - $30	50 x 90	70.00	90.00	45.00
2003	Bulgie the Frog	Green	125 - $30	50 x 90	57.00	70.00	35.00
2003	Crocodile/Alligator (RR)	Honey	Unk. - Prizes	14 x 40	5.00	6.00	3.00
2003	Leprechaun on a Rock	Brown coat, hat; beige trousers, belt, boots; blue-grey rock	300 - $30	65	30.00	45.00	22.00
2003	Leprechaun on a Rock	Brown coat, hat; grey-beige trousers, boots; gold belt, rock	100 - Prizes	65	55.00	70.00	35.00
2003	Frog (RR)	Light green	Unk. - Prizes	15 x 30	5.00	6.00	3.00
2003	Lil' American Footballer	Honey; dark blue jersey with gold/red trim; white pants, helmet; pewter face, chin guard; tan football	125 - $60	80	90.00	110.00	55.00
2003	Lil' Bit Elephants	Blue	500 - $7	22 x 30	10.00	15.00	7.00
2003	Lil' Bit Elephants	Gold	100 - Prizes	22 x 30	70.00	90.00	45.00
2003	Lil' Bit Elephants	Green	500 - $7	22 x 30	10.00	15.00	7.00
2003	Lil' Bit Elephants	Grey	500 - $7	22 x 30	10.00	15.00	7.00
2003	Lil' Bit Elephants	White	500 - $7	22 x 30	10.00	15.00	7.00
2003	N. American Bear	Dark brown; black eyes, nose	150 - $35.00	70	50.00	70.00	35.00
2003	N. American Bear	White; black eyes, nose	20 - Prizes	70		Rare	
2003	Reindeer, no gap (TS)	Gold	100 - Prizes	30 x 35		Rare	
2003	Reindeer, no gap (TS)	Honey	600	30 x 35	15.00	22.00	10.00
2003	Reindeer, no gap (TS)	Honey; red nose	70 - Prizes	30 x 35		Rare	
2003	Reindeer, no gap (TS)	White	600	30 x 35	15.00	22.00	10.00
2003	Terrapin (RR)	Grey	Unk. - Prizes	10 x 40	5.00	6.00	3.00

WEST COAST WADE COLLECTORS FAIR
WASHINGTON

2002-2003

The West Coast Wade Show was organised by Reva and Michael Matthew, who commissioned a limited edition of 300 red, white and blue Eagles symbolising the colours of the American flag, issued in sets of three. A black eagle, which commemorates the September 11th, 2001, tragedy, was produced in a limited edition of 100. It was available in the Goodie Bag given to collectors who paid in advance for the fair package. Other black eagle models were given as door prizes. A special limited edition of eight gold models were given as prizes in draws. The Eagle is from the same mould as the 1984-1984 Tom Smith Cracker Survival Animals Series.

Two new models were issued for the June and the July USA Shows. "Lil' Uncle Sam," a bear wearing a blue and white top hat, was the third model in Wade's Lil' Bear Series. It was produced in a limited edition of 125. The second model produced for the USA shows was "Mischief the Chimp" (also known as "Mischief the Monkey"). Mischief was produced in a limited edition of 100 in a honey glaze, and 50 in a grey glaze. Both colourways have a June 2002 backstamp. Similar models were sold at the July Wade Fest held in Harrisburg, but those models carry a July 2002 backstamp. The grey models were randomly packed and sold.

See also 218 for colourways of "Lil' Uncle Sam" and "Mischief the Chimp."

American Patriotic Eagle (2002)

Lil' Uncle Sam (2003)

Mischief the Chimp (2002)

Backstamp: American Patriotic Eagle: Embossed "Wade England"
Lil' Uncle Sam: Printed "Lil' Uncle Sam Ltd. Edit. 125 June 2002"
Mischief the Chimp: Printed "Mischief the Chimp USA June 2002"

Date	Name	Colourways	Issue - Price	Size	U.S. $	Can. $	U.K. £
2002	American Patriotic Eagle (TS)	Black	100 - Goodie bag/ Prizes	25 x 45	15.00	22.00	12.00
2002	American Patriotic Eagle (TS)	Blue	300 - Unk.	25 x 45	15.00	22.00	12.00
2002	American Patriotic Eagle (TS)	Gold	8 - Prizes	25 x 45		Rare	
2002	American Patriotic Eagle (TS)	Red	300 - Unk	25 x 45	15.00	22.00	12.00
2002	American Patriotic Eagle (TS)	White	300 - Unk.	25 x 45	15.00	22.00	12.00
2002	Lil' Uncle Sam	Brown; red coat; white waistcoat; blue pants; blue/white hat	125 - $60	90	90.00	110.00	55.00
2002	Mischief the Chimp	Grey	50 - $35	80	60.00	80.00	40.00
2002	Mischief the Chimp	Honey	100 - $35	80	40.00	50.00	25.00

WEST COAST WADE COLLECTORS FAIR

2003

The Portland, Oregon, Airport Holiday Inn, was chosen for this years venue. The black and white Orca, also known as the Killer Whale is often seen in the oceans off the West Coast of the USA. The black, and black and white whales were produced in a limited edition of 300 each; the white whale was produced in a limited edition of 100. The black and white whale on a black base was given free of charge to collectors who stayed at the hotel, and the black whale on a blue base was in the show package. The original price of the models was $37.00 for three.

The white model was given free in the fair package, and was also sold at the fair for $15.00. These models, in grey and blue colourways, were previously used in the Great Universal Stores and Tom Smith Crackers UK promotions, and were named Baleen Whale.

Whimsical Whales (2003)

Backstamp: Embossed: "Wade England"

Date	Name	Colourways	Issue - Price	Size	U.S. $	Can. $	U.K. £
2003	Whale (TS)	Black; blue base	300 - $11	22 x 52	16.00	22.00	10.00
2003	Orca / Killer Whale (TS)	Black/white; black base	300 - $11	22 x 52	16.00	22.00	10.00
2003	Orca / Killer Whale (TS)	Black/white; blue base	300 - $11	22 x 52	16.00	22.00	10.00
2003	Whale (TS)	Gold	10 - Prizes	22 x 52		Rare	
2003	Whale (TS)	White	100 - $15	22 x 52	30.00	36.00	18.00

EVENT FIGURES

ALEXANDRA PALACE
THE TEDDY BEAR SHOW

1998

Wade Ceramics attended the Teddy Scene Event at Alexandra Palace held on October 31st - November 1st, 1998.

Backstamp: Gold printed "The Library Bear Limited edition of 500 Wade England"

Date	Name	Colourways	Issue - Price	Size	U.S. $	Can. $	U.K. £
1998	Library Bear	Amber; black/yellow hat; gold bow tie	500 - £30.00	165	120.00	150.00	75.00

ARUNDEL CHRISTMAS BONANZA

1999-2002

The Arundel Christmas Bonanza is organised jointly by Wade Ceramics and C&S Collectables. The Bonanza is held at the C&S Collectables shop (The Wade Collectors Centre, Arundel, West Sussex).

Available at the 2002 show was the third model from the Quackers series, "Quackers on his Sleigh," which was produced in a limited edition of 150. Two models commissioned by C&S were: (1) "Polar Bear Cub," issued in a limited edition of 100, with a special edition of 15 models in an all-over gold glaze being given as prizes in the Tombola; (2) "The Christmas Puppy." Seventy-five surplus models of Betty Boop's dog "Pudgy" were re-decorated to make this model.

Oops! the Bear, Style Two (1999)

Oops! the Bear, Style Three (2000)

Santa's Flight (2000)

Christmas Robin [green holly leaves] (2001)

Christmas Robin [green ivy leaves] (2001)

Christmas Robin [gold] (2001)

Quackers on Ice (2001)

Polar Bear Cub [white] (2002)

Polar Bear Cub [gold] (2002)

Christmas Puppy (2002)

Quackers on his Sleigh (2002)

Backstamp: **Christmas Puppy:** Printed "Wade" logo
Christmas Robin: Printed "Wade C&S 8th December 2001"
Oops! The Bear: "Oops! The Bear Ltd Edition of [250 (Style Two) / 300 (Style Three)] Wade England"
Polar Bear Cub (white): Printed "Wade" logo
Polar Bear Cub (gold): Printed "Wade" logo
Quackers on Ice: Printed "Wade Bonanza Arundel 2001"
Quackers on his Sleigh: Printed "Christmas Bonanza Arundel 2002" and red "Wade" logo
Santa's Flight: Printed "© 2000 C&S Collectables : with certificate of authenticity, Santa's Flight ™
Wade Christmas Bonanza 2000 250 Limited edition Wade England"

Date	Name	Colourways	Issue - Price	Size	U.S. $	Can. $	U.K. £
1999	Oops! The Bear, Style Two	Amber; creamy pink bandage on leg; brown crutch	300 - £15.00	95	57.00	70.00	35.00
2000	Oops! The Bear, Style Three	Beige bear; blue blanket	250 - £15.00	70	57.00	70.00	35.00
2000	Santa's Flight	Green body/red wings	250 - £35.00	75 x 95	70.00	100.00	50.00
2000	Santa's Flight	Green body/gold wings	10 - prizes	75 x 95	150.00	200.00	100.00
2001	Christmas Robin	White; green holly leaves	100 - £18	50	40.00	50.00	25.00
2001	Christmas Robin	Cream; green ivy leaves	100 - £18	50	40.00	50.00	25.00
2001	Christmas Robin	Gold	15 - Prizes	50		Rare	
2001	Quackers on Ice	White duck; red hat	150 - £15	75	45.00	55.00	28.00
2002	Christmas Puppy	White; black collar, markings; gold heart medallion	75 - £20	60	45.00	60.00	30.00
2002	Polar Bear Cub	Gold	15 - Prizes	42		Rare	
2002	Polar Bear Cub	White; black eyes, nose	100 - £20	42	35.00	50.00	25.00
2002	Quackers on his Sleigh	White hat; blue/white scarf; brown/silver sleigh	150 - £20	80	50.00	75.00	35.00

OLYMPIA INCENTIVE EXHIBITION

1998

The 1997 Bear Ambitions model "Admiral Sam" was reissued for the Trade Exhibition, and was handed out at random to visitors to the Wade Stand. Surplus models were placed in the Bran Tub at the San Antonio show.

Backstamp: Embossed "Wade Eng" on back rim

Date	Name	Colourways	Issue -Price	Size	U.S. $	Can. $	U.K. £
1998	Admiral Sam	Pale blue	200/—	50	70.00	90.00	45.00

RIPLEY VILLAGE FETE and
TEDDY BEARS' PICNIC
GENERAL ISSUE - 1998

The Wade Village fete and Teddy Bears' Picnic was held on Sunday June 7th, 1998, at The Castle Flatts, Ripley Castle, Warwickshire.

Backstamp: **Camping Bear:** Printed "Camping Bear 1998 The Official International Wade Collectors Club" with OIWCC logo
Teddy Bear Plaque: Gold printed "Wade England Ripley 1998"

Date	Name	Colourways	Issue - Price	Size	U.S. $	Can. $	U.K. £
1998	Camping Bear	Dark green jacket; grey trousers	2000 - £15.00	115	35.00	55.00	26.00
1998	Teddy Bear Plaque	Honey bear; white plaque	1500 - £20.00	195	45.00	55.00	28.00

Bear Ambitions, 1998

Admiral Sam and Alex the Aviator   Artistic Edward and Beatrice Ballerina   Locomotive Joe and Musical Marco

Backstamp: **Artistic Edward:** Embossed "Wade England"
All other Bear Ambition figures: Embossed "Wade Eng"

Date	Name	Colourways	Issue/Price	Size	U.S. $	Can. $	U.K. £
1998	Admiral Sam	Green	2000 - £18.00	50	10.00	15.00	6.00
1998	Alex the Aviator	Green	2000 - £18.00	45	10.00	15.00	6.00
1998	Artistic Edward	Green	2000 - £18.00	40	10.00	15.00	6.00
1998	Beatrice Ballerina	Green	2000 - £18.00	50	10.00	15.00	6.00
1998	Locomotive Joe	Green	2000 - £18.00	50	10.00	15.00	6.00
1998	Musical Marco	Green	2000 - £18.00	45	10.00	15.00	6.00

Note: For *Bear Ambitions* in different colourways, see Wade regular issue, page 151, and Tom Smith and Company, page 388.

THE OFFICIAL INTERNATIONAL WADE COLLECTORS FIGURES

MEMBERSHIP FIGURES

Starting in 1994, complimentary membership figures were given to new and renewing members. *Truly the Puppy* was available to members who had four years continuous membership in the OIWCC. First seen at the October Wade Christmas Extravaganza, the model was not available until January 2002 when membership renewals were due. The issue price was £9.99.

The membership model for 2004 was changed to celebrate the 50th anniversary of the *First Whimsies*. Wade produced a blow-up model of the Lamb from Set Two: English Animals, which was introduced in 1954.

Work's Cat Burslem (1994-95)

Christmas Puppy (1995-96)

Truly the Puppy (2002)

Blow Up Lamb (2004)

Backstamp: All: Large embossed "Wade"
Truly the Puppy: Printed 'Truly Loyalty Piece 4 Years Continuous Membership" with OIWCC Logo

Date	Name	Colourway	Size	U.S. $	Can. $	U.K. £
1994-95	Work's Cat Burslem	White; black patches	75	155.00	230.00	115.00
1995-96	Christmas Puppy	Amber	57	80.00	100.00	50.00
1996-97	Smudger	Black; grey shading	70	57.00	70.00	35.00
1997-98	Wade Baby	White vest and pants; green shoes	83	40.00	50.00	25.00
1999	Alice in Wonderland	See Membership Series, page 235				
2000	Toad of Toad Hall	See Membership Series, page 236				
2001	Cinderella in Rags	See Membership Series, page 237				
2002	Peter Pan	See Membership Series, page 238				
2002	Truly the Puppy	Honey; yellow bow, collar	60	25.00	30.00	15.00
2003	Beauty	See Membership Series, page 239				
2004	Blow Up Lamb	White; sol fawn muzzle, lower legs; grey hooves; green grass base	85	45.00	55.00	27.00

MEMBERSHIP BADGES and PLAQUES

The 2001 plaque was produced for club members and was available from the Wade booth at the Pennsylvania Wade Fest in July 2001. The plaque reads "Member of The Official International WADE Collectors Club."

Date	Name	Colourways	Size	U.S. $	Can. $	U.K. £
1996-97	OIWCC Badge	Black/gold/red/enamel	29	15.00	22.00	11.00
1997-98	OIWCC Badge	Gold/red/black/brass/enamel	25	15.00	22.00	11.00
1998-99	OIWCC Badge	Gold/red/black/brass/enamel	25	15.00	22.00	11.00
1999	OIWCC Badge	Gold/yellow; gold lettering	25	8.00	12.00	6.00
2001	OIWCC Badge	Silver/yellow/white; silver lettering	25 x 15	8.00	12.00	6.00
2002	OIWCC Badge	Silver/green/brown/enamel	35 x 25	8.00	12.00	6.00
2003	OIWCC Badge	Gold /pale green/ pink/white decoration	37	6.00	8.00	4.00
2001	Members plaque	White; black/white lettering	65 x 94	16.00	20.00	10.00

ENROL A FRIEND

In 1996 the "Enrol A Friend" scheme was introduced. Both the renewing and newly enrolled member in the OIWCC received a complimentary figure. In 1998-1999, the first 10,000 members to renew/enrol received the Blue Angelfish.

A new Enrol A Friend model named "Firm Friends" was introduced in Spring 2003, this model of a teddy bear with a rabbit was sent to new members, plus the member who recommended them to join the Wade Collectors Club.

Firm Friends

Backstamp: Embossed "Wade England"

No.	Name	Date	Colourways	Size	U.S. $	Can. $	U.K. £
1.	Seal Pup (EW, TS)	1996-97	White; blue base	17 x 30	26.00	32.00	16.00
2.	Angelfish (EW)	1998-99	Dark blue	35 x 30	26.00	32.00	16.00
3.	Ruffles the Bear	2001	Honey; red ruffles	58 x 54	26.00	32.00	16.00
4.	Firm Friends	2003	Honey; brown ears, feet pads	70	45.00	60.00	30.00

MEMBERSHIP SERIES

1995 – BIG BAD WOLF AND THE THREE LITTLE PIGS

Wade produced four models in 1995 based on the fairy tale, *The Three Little Pigs.* The first two figures produced "The Straw House Pig" and "The Wood House Pig" were issued in a limited edition of 1,250 each. Due to high demand, the production of the next two models was increased to 1,500 each.

Big Bad Wolf

Brick House Pig

Straw House Pig and Wood House Pig

Backstamp: All: Red print "Wade England" with two lines and black printed "The Official Wade International Collectors Club [name of model] 1995"

Date	Name	Colourways	Issue - Price	Size	U.S. $	Can. $	U.K. £
1995	Big Bad Wolf	Mottled-grey; white chest	1500 - £15.00	140	75.00	112.00	55.00
1995	Brick House Pig	Red-brown trousers	1500 - £15.00	130	75.00	112.00	55.00
1995	Straw House Pig	Dark blue dungarees	1250 - £15.00	125	90.00	135.00	68.00
1995	Wood House Pig	Dark green dungarees	1250 - £15.00	117	90.00	135.00	68.00

1996 – GOLDILOCKS AND THE THREE BEARS, Style Two

The first figurine in this series was *Mummy Bear,* and originally the production was intended to be 1,500 of each model but due to the increasing club membership numbers the production was increased to 2,750. For *Goldilocks and the Three Bears*, Style One, see page 58.

Mummy Bear and Daddy Bear

Baby Bear and Goldilocks

Backstamp: All: Circular black and red printed "Official International Wade Collectors Club," black printed "[name] 1996"

Date	Name	Colourways	Issue -Price	Size	U.S. $	Can. $	U.K. £
1996	Mummy Bear	Dark blue dress; white apron, cap	2750 - £15.00	102	60.00	90.00	45.00
1996	Daddy Bear	Dark blue suit; red bow tie	2750 - £15.00	105	60.00	90.00	45.00
1996	Goldilocks	Pink dress; brown chair	2750 - £15.00	85	60.00	90.00	45.00
1996	Baby Bear	Dark blue dungarees; white shirt	2750 - £15.00	60	60.00	90.00	45.00

1997 – PANTOMIME SERIES

This series was available to club members only, and limited to one per member.

Pantomime Horse and Mother Goose

Dick Whittington's Cat and Pantomime Dame

Backstamp: All: Circular black and red printed "[Name] The Official International Wade Collectors Club 1997"

Date	Name	Colourways	Issue -Price	Size	U.S. $	Can. $	U.K. £
1997	Pantomime Horse	White; brown patch	4000 - £15.00	90	40.00	50.00	25.00
1997	Mother Goose	Pale blue bonnet, bloomers	4000 - £15.00	110	40.00	50.00	25.00
1997	Dick Whittington's Cat	Light blue trousers; black boots	4000 - £15.00	110	40.00	50.00	25.00
1997	Pantomime Dame	Sea green dress; red/white bloomers; light blue hair	4000 - £15.00	110	40.00	50.00	25.00

1997 – THE CAMELOT COLLECTION

This new series of slip cast models based on the legend of King Arthur was introduced at the Wade/Jim Beam fair held in Wisconsin in July 1997. Two hundred of each figure had the C & S logo added to the Wade backstamp.

Sir Lancelot and King Arthur

The Lady of the Lake

Queen Guinivere and The Wizard Merlin

Backstamp: A. Black printed "Camelot Collection" logo and "[name] The Camelot Collection Wade"
B. Black printed "C&S logo, Camelot Collection logo" and '[name] The Camelot Collection Wade"

Date	Name	Colourways	Issue - Price	Size	U.S. $	Can. $	U.K. £
1997	King Arthur	Brown cloak; yellow crown	2000 - £20.00	108	50.00	60.00	30.00
1997	Queen Guinivere	Brown dress; dark green collar	2000 - £20.00	108	50.00	60.00	30.00
1997	Sir Lancelot	Brown cloak	2000 - £20.00	108	50.00	60.00	30.00
1997	The Wizard Merlin	Blue-grey hooded cloak	2000 - £20.00	108	50.00	60.00	30.00
1997	The Lady of the Lake	Light/dark brown robes	2000 - £20.00	83	50.00	60.00	30.00

1998 – TOY BOX SERIES

This series was created by Sue Ames, winner of a competition run by The Wade Collectors Club. The *Toy Soldier* (first in the series) was released at the Trentham Gardens Wade Fair in March 1998.

Toy Soldier and Amelia Teddy Bear   Chuckles the Clown and Emily the Doll

Backstamp: All: Printed "The Official Wade Collectors Club 1998," OIWCC logo and [name of model]

Date	Name	Colourways	Issue - Price	Size	U.S. $	Can. $	U.K. £
1998	Amelia Teddy Bear	Blue/white dress; yellow ducks	3000 - £20.00	90	50.00	60.00	30.00
1998	Chuckles the Clown	Red coat; white shirt, trousers	3000 - £20.00	115	50.00	60.00	30.00
1998	Emily the Doll	Blue dress, bonnet; maroon bow	3000 - £20.00	85	50.00	60.00	30.00
1998	Toy Soldier	Yellow jacket; blue helmet	3000 - £20.00	110	50.00	60.00	30.00

1998-99 – BRITISH MYTHS AND LEGENDS SERIES

This series released in 1998-1999 depicts characters from British Folklore. The sixth model, *King Canute,* was sent free of charge (upon application) to club members who had previously purchased a *Myths and Legends* set.

Cornish Tin Mine Pixie and Green Man   King Canute and Mermaid   Puck and St. George and the Dragon

Backstamp: All: Printed "British Myths and Legends Wade" and [name of model]

Date	Name	Colourways	Issue - Price	Size	U.S. $	Can. $	U.K. £
1998-99	Cornish Tin Mine Pixie	Brown suit; gold hammer head	2000 - £115 (set)	108	50.00	60.00	30.00
1998-99	Green Man	Green-white figure; brown tree	2000	114	50.00	60.00	30.00
1998-99	King Canute	Dark brown cloak; silver crown	2000	120	50.00	60.00	30.00
1998-99	Mermaid	Honey; green-blue tail	2000	120	50.00	60.00	30.00
1998-99	Puck	Amber body, horns; gold flute	2000	114	50.00	60.00	30.00
1998-99	St. George and and the Dragon	Brown cloak; grey armour	2000	101	50.00	60.00	30.00

1999 – ALICE IN WONDERLAND

In late 1998, the O.I.W.C.C. changed their membership renewal system so that all memberships started January 1st and ended December 31st. *Alice in Wonderland* is the first in a series of six models that members had the opportunity to purchase.

The membership model for 1999 was *Alice in Wonderland,* the first in the series. Members could purchase the other models in the series at quarterly intervals throughout the 1999 membership year. Those members having purchased the four models by February 14th, 2000, could complete their set by purchasing The Queen of Hearts. Only 1,484 Queen of Hearts models were produced, the production number being based on the number of orders received by the cut off date.

Alice and Membership Badge

Mad Hatter and White Rabbit

Cheshire Cat

Dormouse

Queen of Hearts

Backstamp: **A.** Printed "Alice in Wonderland Collection Alice 1999 Membership Piece made in England ©MacMPub 1999" with OIWCC logo
B. Printed "Alice in Wonderland Collection made in England ©MacMPub 1999" with OIWCC logo and [name of model]

Date	Name	Colourways	Issue - Price	Size	U.S. $	Can. $	U.K. £
1999	Alice	Blue dress; white pinafore	Membership	120	70.00	85.00	45.00
1999	Mad Hatter	Purple coat; red/blue trousers	2000 - £28.50	110	70.00	85.00	45.00
1999	White Rabbit	Olive green coat; yellow/red striped waistcoat	2000 - £28.50	113	70.00	85.00	45.00
1999	Dormouse	Amber; platinum teapot	2000 - £28.50	90	70.00	85.00	45.00
1999	Cheshire Cat	Brown; green eyes	2000 - £28.50	60	70.00	85.00	45.00
1999	Queen/Hearts	Red/blue/white/gold dress	2000 - £39.95	130	115.00	140.00	70.00

2000 – WIND IN THE WILLOWS

The membership model for 2000 was *Toad of Toad Hall*. Members could purchase the other models in the series at intervals throughout the year. Those members having purchased all four models by December 31st, 2000, had the opportunity to purchase "Ratty and Mole in a Rowing Boat."

Toad of Toad Hall

Ratty and Mole in a Rowing Boat

Mole, Ratty, Badger, Weasel

Backstamp: A. Printed "The Wind in the Willows Toad ©EHS"
B. Printed "The Wind in the Willows © EHS 2000" with OIWCC logo and [name of model]

Date	Name	Colourways	Issue - Price	Size	U.S. $	Can. $	U.K. £
2000	Toad of Toad Hall	Brown coat; yellow/black checked waistcoat	Membership	105	60.00	75.00	38.00
2000	Mole	Pale blue dressing gown	2000 - £25.00	108	60.00	75.00	38.00
2000	Ratty	Olive green coat; white trousers	2000 - £25.00	115	60.00	75.00	38.00
2000	Badger	Khaki coat; red waistcoat	2000 - £25.00	125	60.00	75.00	38.00
2000	Weasel	Brown satchel; red fez hat	2000 - £25.00	110	60.00	75.00	38.00
2000	Ratty and Mole in a Rowing Boat	Ratty: White suit, hat; Mole: White shirt; blue waistcoat	2000 - £39.95	85	100.00	120.00	60.00

2001 – CINDERELLA

The first figure in the series "Cinderella in Rags," was the membership model for 2001. Members could then purchase the other models in the series at intervals throughout the year. The Cinderella special, "The Fairy Godmother," (1,818 models produced) was available to all members who purchased the other four models by January 18th 2002.

The ugly sisters Clorinda and Thisbe are named after the original characters who appeared in the first Cinderella Pantomime performed in Covent Garden, London, England in 1820. Models are listed in order of issue.

Cinderella in Rags

Clorinda (Ugly Sister)

Thisbe (Ugly Sister)

Prince Charming

Cinderella, Ready for the Ball

Fairy Godmother

Backstamp: Printed "Cinderella 2001" and OIWCC logo. [name of model]

Date	Name	Colourways	Issue - Price	Size	U.S. $	Can. $	U.K. £
2001	Cinderella in Rags	Yellow dress; white/brown apron	Membership	100	57.00	70.00	35.00
2001	Clorinda	Pearl/green dress; gold highlights	2000 - £25.00	110	57.00	70.00	35.00
2001	Thisbe	Orange/pearl dress; gold highlights	2000 - £25.00	105	57.00	70.00	35.00
2001	Prince Charming	Green tunic; pearl cloak, slipper	2000 - £25.00	90	57.00	70.00	35.00
2001	Cinderella, Ready for the Ball	Pearl dress; gold bow, necklace, tiara	2000 - £25.00	100	57.00	70.00	35.00
2001	Fairy Godmother	Pearl dress; orange pumpkin	1818 - £39.95	110	80.00	100.00	50.00

2002 – PETER PAN

Peter Pan was the membership figure for 2002, and the first model in this series. The other four models were produced at intervals throughout the year, and Club members who purchased all four of the *Peter Pan* models could then order the special figure "Captain Hook and the Crocodile." The issue size of the special figure was 1,532 models, which was based on the number of orders received by February 14th, 2003.

Peter Pan

Tinkerbell

John

Wendy

Michael

Captain Hook and Crocodile

Backstamp: Captain Hook and the Crocodile: Printed "Peter Pan Collection 2002 Captain Hook Limited Edition The Official Wade Collectors Club" with red "Wade" logo

Peter Pan: Printed "Peter Pan Collection Peter Pan Membership Piece 2002" and OIWCC logo

Tinkerbell: Printed "Peter Pan Collection 2002 Limited Edition Tinkerbell Official Wade Collectors Club"

Date	Name	Colourways	Issue - Price	Size	U.S. $	Can. $	U.K. £
2002	Peter Pan	Green/brown	Membership	115	60.00	70.00	35.00
2002	Tinkerbell	Pink dress; gold thimble	— /£27.00	75	60.00	70.00	35.00
2002	John	White/blue pyjamas; black top hat	— /£27.00	85	60.00	70.00	35.00
2002	Wendy	Pearl/blue dress; brown dog	— /£27.00	95	60.00	70.00	35.00
2002	Michael	Blue nightshirt; white blanket	— /£27.00	65	60.00	70.00	35.00
2002	Captain Hook and Crocodile	Captain Hook: Blue/black coat Crocodile: Green/white	1532 /£27.00	130	120.00	150.00	75.00

2003 – BEAUTY AND THE BEAST

The membership model for 2003 was "Beauty", from *Beauty and the Beast*. The model was sent free of charge to club members in a special presentation box; a club badge was included with the model. The other models from the series could then be purchased from the club at intervals throughout the year. The special model, "Beauty and the Beast Dancing," was available to all members who purchased the other four models from the series, the edition size being based on orders received.

Beauty and Club Badge for 2003

The Beast

Beauty's Father

Enchanted Witch

Prince

Beauty and the Beast Dancing

Backstamp: Printed "Beauty & the Beast 2003 The Official International Collectors Club" with red "Wade" logo and [name of model]

Date	Name	Colourways	Issue - Price	Size	U.S. $	Can. $	U.K. £
2003	Beauty	Pearlised coat, blue trim; pink/pearl ruffled dress; brown hair; pink rose	—/£27	98	60.00	90.00	40.00
2003	The Beast	Grey; dark blue cloak; pearlised shirt; green trousers; pink rose	—/£27	112	45.00	55.00	27.00
2003	Beauty's Father	Black cloak; white pants; purple hat; green band; tan gloves, shoes; grey hair, beard	—/£27	110	45.00	55.00	27.00
2003	Enchanted Witch	Black coat, hat, grey trim; ochre green dress; brown staff, basket; pink roses	—/£27	110	45.00	55.00	27.00
2003	Prince	Black cloak, red lining; white shirt; ochre green trousers; tan boots; yellow hair	—/£27	Unknown	45.00	55.00	27.00
2003	Beauty and the Beast Dancing	Beauty: Red lustre/pearl dress, pink bow Beast: Grey; white shirt, gold epaulettes; brown lustre trousers; pearlised base	—/£27	Unknown	45.00	55.00	27.00

2004 – TONY THE TIGER AND FRIENDS

A competition was held by the Wade Collectors Club asking members for suggestions for new membership models. The winner was a series based on Kellogg's Breakfast Cereal characters. The first model in the series is the Frostie's character *Tony the Tiger* in the form of a money box. This issue price is £40.00.

Backstamp: Unknown

Date	Name	Colourways	Issue - Price	Size	U.S. $	Can. $	U.K. £
2004	Tony the Tiger Money Box	Orange head; black markings; yellow/black eyes blue nose; red tongue	— / £40.00	122	45.00	60.00	30.00

CHRISTMAS MODELS

1994-2000

Snowman (1994)

Snow Woman (1995)

Snow Children (1996)

Annabel Waiting for Christmas (1998)

Santa with Open Sack (1999)

Our Little Angel (2000)

Snowman Silent Night (2003)

Snowman Snowball Fight (2003)

CHRISTMAS MODELS (cont.)

Backstamp: Annabel Waiting for Christmas: Printed "Christmas 1998" with OIWCC logo
Our Little Angel: Printed "Christmas 2000" with OIWCC logo
Oscar the Christmas Teddy: Printed circular "The Official International Wade Collectors Club Christmas Teddy 1997" with O.I.W.C.C. logo
Santa with Open Sack: Printed Red "Christmas 1999"
Snow Children: Black printed "Christmas 1996 Wade Made in England" with two black lines
Snow Woman: Black transfer "Christmas 1995 Wade Made in England"
Snowman: Black transfer "Wade England"
Snowman Silent Night: Printed "Silent Night Christmas 2002 limited edition 500" and red "OIWCC" logo
Snowman Snowball Fight: Printed

Date	Name	Colourways	Issue - Price	Size	U.S. $	Can. $	U.K. £
1994	Snowman	Off-white/black/blue	1000/—	125	130.00	160.00	80.00
1995	Snow Woman	Off-white/dark blue/black	1500/—	127	130.00	160.00	80.00
1996	Snow Children	White/blue/brown	2500 - £15.00	120	90.00	110.00	55.00
1997	Oscar the Christmas Teddy Bear	Honey; red hat	2500 - £20.00	110	50.00	60.00	30.00
1998	Annabel Waiting For Christmas	Blue/white/red/green	2000 - £20.00	110	50.00	60.00	30.00
1999	Santa with Open Sack	Red/white/brown/yellow	1500 - £15.00	80	57.00	70.00	35.00
2000	Our Little Angel	White/yellow/gold	1000 - £20.00	90	35.00	45.00	22.00
2001	Santa's Little Helper	Olive jacket; green pants, hat	500 - £22.50	65	45.00	55.00	27.00
2002	Snowman Silent Night	White; black hat; blue/white scarf; blue carol sheet; brown robin with red/white scarf	500 - £25.00	90	45.00	55.00	30.00
2003	Snowman Snowball Fight	White; black hat; blue/red scarf; white/pearl snowballs; brown robin with green/white scarf	500 - £25.00	90	40.00	50.00	25.00

CHRISTMAS CRACKERS

SAFARI WHIMSIES 2003

Four of these models are from the 1984 *Whimsie-land* Wildlife series. The "Crocodile" is a new model, and the Giraffe is similar to the *English Whimsies* giraffe, but the front legs on this new model are bent upward. The retail price from Wade Ceramics was £20.00 per set.

Crocodile, Elephant (WL), Giraffe, Lion (WL), Panda (WL), Tiber (WL)

Backstamp: Embossed "Wade England"

No.	Name	Colourways	Size	U.S. $	Can. $	U.K. £
1	Crocodile	Light green; blue base	20 x 40			
2	Elephant (WL)	Grey; olive green base	35 x 40			
3	Giraffe	Beige	40 x 35			
4	Lion	Honey; dark brown mane; olive green base	35 x 45			
5	Panda (WL)	Black/white; blue-green base	22 x 50			
6	Tiger (WL)	Honey, brown stripes; mottled green base	22 x 50			
	Set 6 pcs	Boxed		33.00	40.00	20.00

ONE-OF-A-KIND MODELS

These one-of-a-kind models were auctioned, used as prizes, or given away at various venues. In most cases, these figures are colourways of previously issued models, and carry a backstamp naming the event at which they appeared.

Name	Date	Event	Colourway	Original Page Entry
Alice in Wonderland	2000	Trentham	Unknown	235
Alligators (Water Life)	1997	Arundel	Unknown	191
Amelia Teddy Bear	1999	San Antonio	Black; multicoloured floral body; gold eyes	234
Amelia Teddy Bear	2000	Trentham	Unknown	234
Amelia Teddy Bear	2003	Portland	Pink dress; white collar, cuffs; blue trim; blue/yellow flowers	234
Andy Capp	2000	Trentham	Black suit; yellow scarf	259
Andy Capp Money Box	2000	Trentham	Unknown	53
Annabelle Waiting Christmas	2000	Trentham	Pale blue dress; red bow, yellow cracker	242
Arundel Bunny	1999	San Antonio	Multicolourel floral body; platinum ears, tail	197
Arundel Bunny	2000	Trentham	Purple; red ears	197
Arundel Bunny	2000	Trentham	White; green patch	197
Arundel Cat	2000	Arundel	Black	197
Arundel Cat	2000	Arundel	Blue	197
Arundel Cat	2000	Arundel	Floral chintz	197
Arundel Cat	2000	Arundel	Gold	197
Arundel Cat	2000	Arundel	Pewter	197
Arundel Cat	2000	Arundel	Black	197
Arundel Cat	2000	Trentham	Honey; red collar; gold bell; black patches	197
Arundel Cat	2000	Trentham	White; black collar; silver bell; black patches	197
Arundel Chick	2000	Trentham	Red; green base	197
Arundel Duck	1997	Arundel	Blue duck; greenish base	197
Arundel Duck	1997	Arundel	Green duck; greenish base	197
Arundel Duck	1997	Arundel	Orange duck; greenish base	197
Arundel Duck	2000	Trentham	Beige/yellow; blue eyes; beige beak	197
Arundel Duck	2000	Trentham	Yellow; brown eyes, beak	197
Baby Bear in Pyjamas	2000	Trentham	Blue/white striped pyjamas, blue slippers	202
Baby Bear in Pyjamas	2000	Trentham	White/red pyjamas; red slippers; gold base	202
Bear, arms raised	2000	Trentham	Beige; blue dungarees; black buckles	151
Bear, bee on face	2001	Arundel	Honey; red spotted jacket, trousers; black/white bee on face	165
Bear, seated	2000	Trentham	Beige; blue shirt	165
Bear Money Box	2000	Trentham	Unknown	—
Bear with honey pot	2000	Trentham	Beige; black suit; pearlised collar, cuffs	165
Betty Boop Beach Belle	1998	Arundel	Black swimsuit, hair; green hat; pink towel; olive base	262
Betty Boop Beach Belle Bikini	1998	Buffalo	Black bikini with yellow spots; black hat; pink towel	—
Betty Boop Ringmaster	2000	Arundel	Red jacket, garter, shoes; black skirt, top hat; gold base	265
Betty Boop Classic Wall Plaque	1997	Arundel	White moon; pearlised dress	292
Big Bad Wolf	2000	Trentham	Brown; white face, chest, feet	232
Bookend Bear	1999	Arundel	Multicoloured chintz on a white background	—
Boots the Rabbit	2000	Trentham	Unknown	210
Brick House Pig	2000	Trentham	Unknown	232
Bulgie the Frog	2003	Harrisburg	Green; red coat with green/yellow lines; black headphones	220
Bunny Mug	1998	Buffalo	Cream bunny; red edging on clothes	—
Camping Bear	1998	Arundel	Pale blue jacket; black trousers; brown boots	228
Camping Bear	1998	Buffalo	Light green jacket; dark green trousers; pale blue boots	228
Camping Bear	2000	Trentham	Unknown	228
Cheshire Cat	2000	Trentham	Black; pink inside ears; green eyes; gold base	235
Chintz Bear	2001	Kansas City	Black; multicoloured chintz	—
Christmas Puppy	1997	Trentham	Dark brown; matt	226
Christmas Puppy	2001	Wade Fest	Matt brown	226
Christmas Teddy Bear	1997	Arundel	Brown; red/white hat; blue sack	—
Christmas Van Money Box	2000	Trentham	Unknown	—
Chuckles the Clown	1998	Arundel	Green coat; yellow spotted trousers	234
Chuckles the Clown	1998	Buffalo	Red coat, nose; yellow trousers	234
Chuckles the Clown	1998	Buffalo	Black coat, shoes, hat; yellow trousers	234
Chuckles the Clown	1999	Arundel	Yellow coat; blue trousers; green/black spotted bowtie; black hat; green/blue/red letters	234

ONE-OF-A-KIND MODELS

Daddy Bear (Arundel)

Mummy and Daddy Bears (Arundel)

Daddy Bear (Arundel)

Arundel Bunny (San Antonio)

Bookend Bear (Arundel)

Amelia Teddy Bear (San Antonio)

Chuckles the Clown (Buffalo)

Rington's Bunny Mug (Buffalo)

Emily the Doll (Arundel)

Name	Date	Event	Colourway	Original Page Entry
Chuckles the Clown	2000	Trentham	Unknown	234
Clorinda, Ugly Sister	2002	Harrisburg	Green blouse; pearl skirt with red flowers	237
Clown, banjo	2000	Arundel	Blue/red striped trousers; yellow collar, cuffs; black hat, green dots	197
Clown, banjo	2000	Trentham	Blue/red diamond trousers; blue buttons	197
Clown, banjo	2000	Trentham	Green/pink patch trousers; blue jacket	197
Clown, banjo	2000	Trentham	Grey check trousers; red buttons	197
Clown, singing	2000	Arundel	Blue/yellow bowtie; green coat; blue/red/yellow patched trousers	197
Clown, singing	2000	Trentham	Black hat; blue cuffs; black buttons	197
Clown, singing	2000	Trentham	Black hat; pink ruff, cuffs; gold buttons	197
Clown, singing	2000	Trentham	Yellow hat, ruff, cuffs; black buttons	197
Cornish Tin Mine Pixie	1997	Trentham	Green coat; brown trousers; black hat; silver buckles	234
Cornish Tin Mine Pixie	1998	Arundel	Dark green coat; brown trousers, hat; gold buckles	234
Cornish Tin Mine Pixie	1999	San Antonio	Black coat, trousers, hat, shoes; silver buckles	234
Cornish Tin Mine Pixie	2000	Trentham	Unknown	234
Daddy Bear	1997	Arundel	Dark blue jacket; green/blue striped trousers	232
Daddy Bear	1997	Arundel	Dark blue jacket; dark/light blue striped trousers	232
Daddy Bear	1997	Dunstable	Blue jacket, red spots; black trousers	232
Daddy Bear	1997	Trentham	Unknown	232
Daddy Bear	1997	Oconomowoc	Black suit	232
Daddy Bear	1997	Uxbridge	Royal blue coat; red/yellow striped trousers	232
Daddy Bear	1999	Arundel	Pale blue waistcoat; black trousers	232
Daddy Bear	1999	San Antonio	Pale blue jacket; yellow trousers	232
Daddy Bear	2000	Trentham	Unknown	232
Dick Whittington's Cat	1997	Arundel	Unknown	232
Dick Whittington's Cat	2000	Trentham	Unknown	232
Dracula	2000	Trentham	Matt black cloak, red/grey/white zigzags on cloak lining	286
Dribbles the Dog	2000	Trentham	Unknown	210
Elizabeth Tedwina	2000	Trentham	Unknown	181
Emily the Doll	1998	Arundel	Green dress, pink bands; white hat; yellow hair	234
Emily the Doll	1998	Buffalo	White dress, dark blue edging; yellow hat; brown hair	234
Emily the Doll	2000	Trentham	Unknown	234
Felicity Squirrel	1997	Arundel	Light grey	255
Felicity Squirrel	1997	Arundel	Orange	255
Fizzy the fawn	2000	Trentham	Dark brown; brown/honey base	162
Fizzy the fawn	2000	Trentham	Red brown; green/brown base	162
Glove Former, large	1998	Buffalo	Multicoloured hand; art deco design	–
Glove Former, miniature	1998	Buffalo	Hand painted yellow butterfly; orange flower	–
Glove Former, miniature	1998	Buffalo	Hand painted yellow/orange flowers	–
Goldfish (Water Life)	1997	Arundel	Orange	191
Green Man	2000	Trentham	Unknown	234
Hattie the Squirrel	2000	Trentham	Unknown	210
King Velveteen	2000	Trentham	Unknown	181
King Arthur	2000	Trentham	Cream; red cloak; gold gauntlets, base	233
Lady of the Lake	2000	Trentham	Unknown	233
Library Bear	2000	Trentham	Green hat/trousers; gold neck bow; brown book	224
Library Bear	2000	Trentham	Yellow hat/trousers; blue spotted neck bow; blue/green book	224
Lil' American Footballer	2003	Harrisburg	Honey; pale blue jersey, gold trim; pearl pants, helmet; brown football	220
Lil' Devil	2001	Trentham	Honey; black horns; red cloak	207
Long-neck Cat	2000	Trentham	Grey-blue	–
Mad Hatter	2000	Trentham	Black coat; purple trousers; yellow/black bow tie	235
Madison Mouse	2000	Trentham	Unknown	213
Merlin	2000	Trentham	Unknown	–
Mermaid	2000	Trentham	Unknown	234
Millennium Teddy	2000	Trentham	Brown; red/blue/gold numerals 2000	205
Millennium Teddy	2001	Wade Fest	Green/brown/blue/yellow numbers	205
Mischief the Chimp	2002	Harrisburg	Brown; red shirt; red/green spotted bandana; brown tool belt	218
Mother Badger	2003	Arundel	Gold	200
Mother Goose	1997	Arundel	Green bonnet, ribbon; white bloomers; red/white socks	233
Mother Goose	2000	Trentham	Unknown	233
Mummy Bear	1999	Arundel	Pale blue dress; white/black cap, apron	232

ONE-OF-A-KIND MODELS

Prince Tedward (Trentham)

Palace Guard (Trentham)

Princess Plushette

King Arthur (Trentham)

Guinevere (Trentham)

Dracula (Trentham)

Felicity Squirrel (Arundel)

Big Bad Wolf (Trentham)

Christmas Puppy (Arundel)

Name	Date	Event	Colourway	Original Page Entry
Nanny Fluffins	2000	Trentham	Unknown	181
New York Tourist	2000	Trentham	Unknown	213
Oops! The Bear, Style Three	2001	Vancouver, WA	Beige; dark green blanket	226
Oops! The Bear, Style Three	2002	Vancouver, WA	Honey; gold blanket	226
Oscar Christmas Teddy Bear	2000	Trentham	Unknown	213
Pantomime Dame	1997	Arundel	Blue dress, bag; green bow, shoes; brown hair	233
Pantomime Dame	1997	Arundel	Green dress	233
Pantomime Horse	1998	Trentham	Yellow; black stripes; green patch	233
Pantomime Horse	2000	Trentham	Unknown	233
Pantomime Horse	2002	Vancouver, WA	White; black patches, hooves, tail; yellow/red eyes; red/blue blanket	233
Pocket Pals (complete set)	2000	Trentham	Unknown	178
Prairie Dog	2000	Trentham	Unknown	213
Prince George Tedward	2000	Trentham	Blue shirt; red trousers, hat	181
Prince George Tedward	2000	Trentham	Green/white sailor suit; black shoes	181
Prince George Tedward	2000	Trentham	Red/white sailor suit	181
Princess Plushette	2000	Trentham	Rose pink dress	181
Princess Plushette	2000	Trentham	Yellow dress with red hearts	181
Priscilla Pig	2000	Trentham	Unknown	–
Priscilla the Pig	2000	Vancouver, WA	(Lavender) Light blue; multicoloured flowers	210
Puck	1998	Buffalo	White horns, hooves, blue-grey legs; gold flute	234
Puck	1999	Arundel	Gold legs, flute; black horns, hooves	234
Puck	2000	Trentham	Unknown	234
Puppy Love "Ella"	2000	Trentham	Unknown	203
Puppy Love "Shelby"	2000	Trentham	Honey	213
Puppy Love "Sidney"	2000	Trentham	Unknown	207
Queen Guinevere	2000	Trentham	Maroon/ black dress; gold hood, cloak	233
Quackers the Duck	2000	Trentham	Black/red spotted hat, blue rim	210
Quackers the Duck	2000	Trentham	Blue hat	210
Quackers the Duck	2000	Trentham	Red Santa suit; white/blue scarf	210
Queen Beatrice	2000	Trentham	Green dress; pale green cloak; green/gold crown	181
Queen Beatrice	2000	Trentham	Pink dress; red cloak; pink/gold crown	181
Ratty	2000	Trentham	Unknown	236
Roly Poly Rabbit	2000	Trentham	Pale green dress; white apron with pink flowers	207
Roly Poly Rabbit	2000	Trentham	Yellow dress with red flowers	207
Rosie the Kitten	2000	Trentham	Unknown	162
Royal Guard	2000	Trentham	Red coat; green hat, belt, boots	181
Rufus	1997	Arundel	Red-brown dog; green cushion; gold trim	207
Scottie Dog Money Box	2000	Trentham	Unknown	
Smudger	1997	Trentham	Matt black; glossy eyes	230
Snow Children	1998	Arundel	White; maroon hat, scarf; blue hat, scarf	242
St. George and the Dragon	1998	Buffalo	Brown cloak; gold armour, lance; blue-grey dragon	234
St. George and the Dragon	2000	Trentham	Unknown	234
Straw House Pig	2000	Trentham	Unknown	232
Ted "E" Bear	2001	Kansas City	Honey; dark brown marking; gold book	272
Teddy Money Box	2001	Kansas City	White; blue eyes; brown stitching	–
Tinny the Mouse	2000	Trentham	Unknown	210
Togetherness	2000	Trentham	Unknown	154
Toy Soldier	1998	Arundel	Red jacket, helmet; green trousers; pale blue plume	234
Toy Soldier	2000	Trentham	Unknown	234
Travelling Badger	2000	Trentham	Unknown	207
Travelling Badger	2002	Vancouver, WA	Purple coat. hat, gold trim; brown suitcase; green base	207
Tubby the Bear	2000	Trentham	Unknown	210
Wade Baby	2000	Trentham	Unknown	230
Welcome Home	2000	Trentham	Unknown	154
Whale (Water Life)	1997	Arundel	Unknown	191
White Rabbit	2000	Trentham	Red coat; white/brown striped waistcoat	235

DONATIONS / CHARITY / PRIZE DRAW / GOODIE BAGS
SPECIAL COLOURWAY FIGURINES

Mama Otter (gold base)

Snowy Owl (gold base)

Baby Bear Cub (gold base)

Betty Boop Ringmaster (gold base)

Poodles (Pink, white, gold skirts)

Clarence the Cow (gold hooves)

Name	Date	Event	Prize draw	Colourway	Qty	Original Entry
Arun Bear Town Crier	2001	Wade Fest	Prize draw	Green coat; black trousers	20	245
Baby Bear Cub	2001	Wade Fest	Prize draw	White; bronze base	20	244
Bear, bee on face	2001	Arundel	Tombola	Red spotted jacket, trousers	—	162
Betty Boop Ringmaster	2001	Wade Fest	Price draw	Red jacket; gold base	20	238
Circus Poodle (TS)	1997	Trentham	Bran tub	White; pink skirt	—	356
Circus Poodle (TS)	1998	Alton Towers	Bran tub	White	—	307
Circus Poodle (TS)	1998	Alton Towers	Bran tub	White; gold skirt	—	307
Clarence the Cow	2001	Wade Fest	Mystery box	White; gold hooves and patches	25	192
Lil' Devil	2001	Trentham	Raffle	Black horns, bow; red cloak	—	197
Mama Otter	2001	Wade Fest	Prize draws	Beige; bronze base	20	244
Santa's Flight	2001	Wade Fest	Prize draws	Green plane; red engine	10	243
Seals (pair)	2001	Wade Fest	Prize draws	Curved tail seal: Grey; green jersey	20	194
				Straight tail seal: Grey	20	194
Snowy Owl	2001	Wade Fest	Prize draws	Honey; bronze base	20	244
Sumo the Elephant	2001	Wade Fest	Mystery box	Grey; gold tusks, toenails, balloon	25	192
Ted "E" Bear	2001	Wade Fest	Prize draw	Honey; gold book	20	243

COMMISSIONED MODELS

AMERIWADE

UNITED CAVES OF BEARICA

2002

"Li'Bear'ty" was the first model produced for Ameriwade.

Backstamp: **A.** Printed "United Caves of Bearica Statue of Li'Bear'ty Ameriwade LE of 250" [Name of model] and red
"Wade Est. 1810 England" logo
B. Printed "United Caves of Bearica Statue of Li'Bear'ty Ameriwade LE of 25" [Name of model] and red
"Wade Est. 1810 England" logo

No.	Name	Description	Issue - Price	Size	U.S. $	Can. $	U.K. £
1	Li'Bear'ty	Brown bear; white robes; gold crown, torch	250 - $55	112	55.00	80.00	35.00
2	Li'Bear'ty	Green	25 - Prizes	112		Rare	

BEARY CHRISTMAS

2002

The second model produced for Ameriwade was Beary Christmas. Each model was issued with a hand-signed and numbered certificate of authenticity.

Backstamp: **A.** Printed "United Caves of Bearica. Beary Christmas Ameriwade LE of 250" [model number] and red "Wade" logo
B. Printed "United Caves of Bearica. Beary Christmas Ameriwade LE of 25" [model number] and red "Wade" logo

No.	Name	Description	Issue - Price	Size	U.S. $	Can. $	U.K. £
1	Beary Christmas	Honey bear; brown horns; green wreath; red lettering	250 - $49.95	70 x 35	50.00	100.00	50.00
2	Beary Christmas	White bear; brown horns; red wreath; green lettering	25 - Prizes	70 x 35		Rare	

BALDING AND MANSELL

FLINTSTONES CHRISTMAS CRACKER PREMIUMS

1965

The four prehistoric Comic Animals (based on the television series *The Flintstones*) were only used in Balding & Mansell's Christmas Crackers. The "Bluebird," "Crocodile," "Hedgehog" and "Terrapin" were reissued in 1967 and were included in the Red Rose Tea of Canada promotion. The "Hedgehog" and the "Bluebird" were also used in the 1971-1984 *English Whimsies* series. For other Christmas cracker models, see Great Universal Stores and Tom Smith and Company.

A box of *Flintstones Christmas Crackers* containing these models was auctioned in 1997 for £35.00.

The Hedgehog has been found with two different types of base. Type One, the original Red Rose Tea model, has three pads; Type Two has two pads on the base

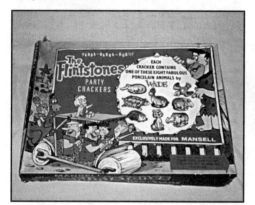

Backstamp: **A.** Embossed "Wade England" in recessed base
B. Embossed "Wade England" on rim

No.	Name	Description	Size	U.S. $	Can. $	U.K. £
1	Bluebird	Beige and blue	15 x 35	10.00	12.00	6.00
2	Bronti	Brown; beige face, feet, base; blue ears	20 x 35	20.00	25.00	12.00
3	Crocodile	Brownish-green	14 x 40	10.00	14.00	7.00
4	Dino	Beige; green eyes; black-brown base	35 x 35	20.00	25.00	12.00
5	Hedgehog, Type 1	Dark red-brown; honey face; black nose	23 x 40	5.00	6.00	3.00
6	Rhinno	Beige; blue eyes, ears	20 x 40	20.00	25.00	12.00
7	Terrapin	Beige; brown markings	10 x 40	10.00	14.00	7.00
8	Tigger	Yellow brown; black stripes, nose; brown feet	38 x 28	28.00	35.00	18.00

BJ PROMOTIONS

THE BEANO COLLECTION

1999-2000

Commissioned by BJ Promotions *Dennis the Menace* is a character from the British children's comic *The Beano*. The other models in this series are Dennis' faithful dog *Gnasher*, and *Minnie the Minx*. Each model was issued with a certificate of authenticity and the original cost of was £39.95.

Although issued in an edition of 1,500, only the first 1,000 subscribers to *Dennis the Menace* received a Beano Collection key ring

NOTE: There is no backstamp on the key ring.

Dennis the Menace and Beano Key ring

Gnasher

Minnie the Minx

Backstamp: A. Circular printed "© D.C.Thomson & Co. Ltd, 1999 Wade England Limited Edition of 1,500"
B. Circular printed "© D.C.Thomson & Co. Ltd, 1999 Wade England Limited Edition of 1,000"
C. Circular printed "© D.C.Thomson & Co. Ltd, 1999 Wade England Limited Edition of 500"

No.	Name	Date	Colourway	Issue - Price	Size	U.S. $	Can. $	U.K. £
1	Beano key ring	1999	White/black/yellow	1000 / —	dia./35	10.00	15.00	8.00
2	Dennis	1999	Black/red	1500 - £39.95	130	70.00	90.00	45.00
3	Gnasher	1999	Pink/black fur/green	1000 - £39.95	90	70.00	90.00	45.00
4	Minnie the Minx	2000	Black/red/white	500 - £39.95	135	70.00	90.00	45.00

BLYTH CERAMICS
SID THE SEXIST AND SAN THE FAT SLAG

Sid the Sexist is the first of two characters from the British comic *Viz*. *San the Fat Slag* was the second model in the *Viz* collection.

Backstamp: Printed "Wade Viz 1998 © John Brown Publishing House Viz © Blyth Ceramics Limited Edition of 1000 with Certificate of Authenticity" with name of model

No.	Name	Date	Colourway	Issue - Price	Size	U.S. $	Can. $	U.K. £
1a	Sid/Sexist	1998	Black/red; grey base	1000 - £36.00	127	35.00	50.00	25.00
1b	Sid/Sexist	2000	Black/red; platinum base	25 - Unknown	127	40.00	60.00	30.00
2a	San/Fat Slag	1998	Red/black; off-white base	1000 - £36.00	127	35.00	50.00	25.00
2b	San/Fat Slag	2000	Red/black; platinum base	25 - Unknown	127	40.00	60.00	30.00

BRIGHTON CORPORATION
BRIGHTON PAVILION

The Brighton Pavilion set consists of a circular pavilion and two oblong pavilions.

Backstamp: Unmarked

No.	Name	Date	Colourway	Size	U.S. $	Can. $	U.K. £
1	Circular Pavilion	1988	Blue/black/yellow	75 x 53	28.00	35.00	15.00
2	Oblong Pavilion	1988	Blue/black/yellow	50 x 53	28.00	35.00	15.00

BROOKE BOND OXO LTD., ENGLAND

1969-1970

After the success of the *Miniature Animals* promotion by its sister company in Canada (Red Rose Tea), Brooke Bond Oxo Ltd. of London (England) offered nine figures from the same set in its 1969 promotion of Brooke Bond Teabags. One model was included in the 36 and 72-teabag box and two models in the 144-teabag box. The first models were so popular that a further six models from Red Rose Tea were added to the series in late 1969 and early 1970, for a total of 16 models. All these figures are in the same colours as the original Red Rose Tea Canada issue. Wade later used some of them in its *English Whimsies* series. As so few of the green-tipped butterflies have been found, it is believed they were samples and not put into full production. In a late 1960s advertisement the Fantail Goldfish model is misnamed the "Angel Fish."

Backstamp: A. Embossed "Wade England"
B. Embossed "Wade" between front feet and "England" on back of model

No.	Name	Description	Size	U.S. $	Can. $	U.K. £
1	Bear Cub	Grey; beige face	30 x 40	5.00	6.00	3.00
2	Beaver	Grey-brown; honey-brown face	35 x 45	3.00	4.00	2.00
3	Bison, small	Honey; dark brown head, mane	30 x 40	5.00	6.00	3.00
4	Bushbaby	Brown; blue ears; black eyes, nose	30 x 30	3.00	4.00	2.00
5a	Butterfly	Honey; grey tips; raised circles	10 x 45	10.00	15.00	7.00
5b	Butterfly	Green/brown; green tips; raised circles	10 x 45	10.00	15.00	7.00
6	Corgi	Honey; black nose	30 x 35	7.00	10.00	5.00
7	Duck	Blue/brown; yellow beak	30 x 40	7.00	10.00	5.00
8	Fantail Goldfish	Green/yellow; blue rock	30 x 35	10.00	12.00	7.00
9	Fox	Dark brown; fawn face, chest	30 x 30	6.00	10.00	4.00
10a	Frog	Green	15 x 30	15.00	20.00	10.00
10b	Frog	Green/yellow	15 x 30	15.00	20.00	10.00
11	Otter	Beige; blue base	30 x 35	5.00	6.00	3.00
12	Owl	Dark brown; light brown chest, face	35 x 20	5.00	6.00	3.00
13	Pine Martin	Honey	30 x 30	4.00	6.00	3.00
14	Seal on Rock	Light brown; blue rock	35 x 35	12.00	10.00	7.00
14	Setter	Light brown; grey-green base	35 x 50	5.00	6.00	3.00
15	Trout	Brown; red tail; grey-green base	30 x 30	5.00	6.00	3.00

C&S COLLECTABLES DIRECT
ARTHUR HARE SERIES
Style One
1993-1997

This series of comic animals is based on the characters from the British storybook *The Adventures of Arthur Hare and the Silent Butterfly*. The figures Arthur Hare and Holly Hedgehog were modelled by Ken Holmes, and Felicity Squirrel and Edward Fox by Robert Feather.

| Edward Fox | Holly Hedgehog | Felicity Squirrel | Arthur Hare |

Backstamp: **A.** Black transfer "Arthur Hare © C&S Collectables Wade England" (1a, 1b)
B. Black transfer "Holly Hedgehog © C&S Collectables Wade England" (2)
C. Black transfer "Felicity Squirrel 1250 Limited Edition © C&S Collectables 1995 Arthur Hare Productions Wade England" between two lines (3b)
D. Printed "Felicity Squirrel 250 Limited Edition Collectors Corner © 1995 Arthur Hare Productions Wade " with two lines
E. Printed in red "Genuine Wade" (3a)
F. Black printed "Edward Fox 1000 Limited Edition © C&S Collectables 1997 Arthur Hare Productions Wade" (4)

No.	Name	Date	Description	Issue - Price	Size	U.S. $	Can. $	U.K. £
1a	Arthur Hare	1993	Blue-grey/white/red	2000 - £16.00	130	40.00	60.00	30.00
1b	Arthur Hare	1993	Fawn/white/red	200 - £25.00	130	70.00	100.00	50.00
2	Holly Hedgehog	1993	Beige/brown/grey	2000 - £19.95	95	45.00	70.00	35.00
3a	Felicity Squirrel	1993	Grey/pink/white	1250 - £25.00	105	45.00	70.00	35.00
3b	Felicity Squirrel	1996	Dark red/pink/white	200 - Unknown	105	90.00	130.00	65.00
4	Edward Fox	1997	Light orange/pink/white	1000 - £25.00	115	45.00	70.00	35.00

ARTHUR HARE SERIES
Style Two
THE VILLAGE PEOPLE COLLECTION
1997-2000

A new series of *Arthur Hare* models dressed in character clothes and modelled by freelance artist Andy Moss was introduced in December 1997. The Jesthares were issued as fair specials, the platinum version being introduced at the Brunel University, Uxbridge Show, in November 1998, and the gold version at the Alton Towers Christmas Extravaganza, November 1999. The "Harestronaut" was produced for the Wade/I.A.J.B.B.S.C. Show held in San Antonio, Texas, July 1999.

Big Chief Bravehare, Shareriff, Santhare Paws, PC Gotchare

Jesthare (gold base), Harestronaut

Harelloween, Wizhared

Backstamp: A. Printed black and red circular "© 1997 C&S Collectables Limited Edition With Certificate of Authenticity Modelled by Andy Moss Special Limited Edition (C&S) Arthur Hare™ Santhare Paws by Wade England"
B. Printed "With Certificate of Authenticity © 1998 C&S Wade England Arthur Hare The Jesthare 350 Special Edition C&S"
C. Printed "With Certificate of Authenticity. 500 Limited Edition. Harestronaut by Wade England © 1999 C&S"
D. Printed "©2000 C&S Collectables with certificate of authenticity [name of model] Wade England Modelled by Andy Moss 500 Limited Edition C&S"

No.	Name	Date	Description	Issue - Price	Size	U.S. $	Can. $	U.K. £
1	Santhare Paws	1997	Grey/red/white/brown/black	500 - £30.00	124	70.00	100.00	50.00
2	Big Chief Bravehare	1998	Red/yellow/green	500 - £33.00	115	55.00	80.00	40.00
3a	Jesthare	1998	Orange/yellow/platinum base	350 - £39.95	115	100.00	150.00	75.00
3b	Jesthare	1998	Orange/yellow/gold base	350 - £39.95	115	100.00	150.00	75.00
4	PC Gotchare	1998	Dark blue/yellow/brown	500 - £33.00	115	55.00	80.00	40.00
5	Shareriff	1998	Grey/red/yellow/blue/brown	500 - £33.00	110	55.00	80.00	40.00
6	Harestronaut	1999	Grey/silver/gold decoration; black boots; silver, silver base	500 - £39.95	115	65.00	100.00	50.00
7	Harelloween	2000	Grey/black/gold; pearlised base	500 - £39.95	110	55.00	80.00	40.00
8	Wizhared	2000	Grey/purple; pearlised base	500 - £39.95	115	55.00	80.00	40.00

THE COLLECTHARE COLLECTION
1998-1999

Backstamp: Printed "With Certificate of Authenticity. 500 Limited Edition. Arthur Hare the Collecthare by Wade England © 1998 or 1999 C&S"

No.	Name	Date	Description	Issue - Price	Size	U.S. $	Can. $	U.K. £
1	Christmas Bonanza	1998	Red shirt; *Christmas Bonanza*	400 - £39.95	120	60.00	90.00	45.00
2a	Jolly Potter	1999	Purple T shirt; *Jolly Potter*	500 - £39.95	120	60.00	90.00	45.00
2b	Wade's World	1999	Yellow T shirt; *Wade's World*	500 - £39.95	120	60.00	90.00	45.00

THE TRAVELHARE COLLECTION
1998-1999

Backstamp: Gold circular printed "© 1998 C&S Collectables Fair Special Uxbridge, Trentham Gardens, Buffalo, Arundel Swapmeet, Dunstable. Modelled by Andy Moss Special Limited Edition C&S Arthur Hare with Certificate of Authenticity by Wade England"

No.	Event	Date	Description	Issue - Price	Size	U.S. $	Can. $	U.K. £
1a	Arundel	1998	White vest, Union Jack; gold base	500 - £35.00	115	90.00	130.00	65.00
1b	Buffalo	1998	White vest, U.S.A. flag; gold base	250 - £35.00	115	100.00	150.00	75.00
1c	Dunstable	1998	Pearl lustre vest; dark green base	350 - £39.95	115	80.00	130.00	65.00
1d	Dunstable	1998	Pearl lustre vest; gold base	20/ —	115		Rare	
1e	Newark	1998	White vest; gold base; *Collect It*!	400 - £40.00	115	90.00	130.00	65.00
1f	Special Ed.	1998	Gold vest; green base	250 - £39.95	115	80.00	130.00	65.00
1g	Trentham	1998	Red vest; dark green base	250 - £35.00	115	150.00	200.00	100.00
1h	Uxbridge	1999	Yellow vest; green base	250 - £35.00	115	110.00	160.00	80.00
1i	Uxbridge	1999	Purple vest; green base	250 - £35.00	115	110.00	160.00	80.00

ARTHUR HARE TEENIES

1999-2000

The *Arthur Hare Teenies* are miniature, solid two-coloured variations of the hollow Village People Collection.

Harestronaut, Jesthare, P.C. Gotchare

Bravehare, The Shareriff

Backstamp: Embossed "Wade" on back rim

No.	Name	Date	Description	Issue - Price	Size	U.S. $	Can. $	U.K. £
1	Harestronaut	1999	Pale blue; black boots	300	58	–	–	–
2	Jesthare	1999	Grey; red costume	300	58	–	–	–
3	PC Gotchare	1999	Pale blue; dark blue uniform	300/	58	–	–	–
—	3 pce set		Boxed	£20.00 set		50.00	70.00	35.00

No.	Name	Date	Description	Issue/Price	Size	U.S. $	Can. $	U.K. £
4	Bravehare	2000	Grey; dark green shirt	250	60	50.00	70.00	35.00
5	The Shareriff	2000	Pale blue; yellow shirt	250 - £52.00/pair	60	50.00	70.00	35.00

ARTHUR HARE WIZHARED WHIMSIE

March 2001

For the green colourway of Wizhared Whimsie see Pennsylvania Wade Fest 2001, page 216.

Backstamp: Embossed "Wade / C&S" on back rim

No.	Name	Date	Description	Issue - Price	Size	U.S. $	Can.	U.K. £
1	Wizhared Whimsie	2001	Blue	1750 - £6.50	43	15.00	20.00	10.00

ANDY CAPP AND FLO

1994-1995

Andy Capp depicts the cartoon character created by Reg Smythe in 1958 for the *British* Daily Mirror. *Flo* is Andy's long-suffering wife.

Backstamp: A. Black transfer "1994 © Mirror Group Newspapers Ltd C&S Collectables Wade England" (1a, 1b)
B. Black transfer "1994 © Mirror Group Newspapers Ltd C&S Collectables Wade England Flo 1995" (2a, 2b)

No.	Name	Date	Description	Issued - Price	Size	U.S. $	Can. $	U.K. £
1a	Andy Capp	1994	Black/green/white	2000 - £12.00	75	50.00	70.00	35.00
1b	Andy Capp	1994	As above, with cigarette	100/Unknown	75	150.00	200.00	100.00
2a	Flo	1995	Green/black/white	2000 - £12.00	75	50.00	70.00	35.00
2b	Flo	1995	As above, with cigarette	100/Unknown	75	150.00	200.00	100.00

MUGS (WADE FAIR SPECIALS)

1994-1996

Although commissioned by C&S Collectables from Wade, plain white mugs were brought in from a local pottery (John Tams Ltd) and were decorated in the Wade pottery. The "Arthur Hare" mug has a rounded handle and flat base.

Arthur Hare (left); Holly Hedgehog (right)

Felicity Squirrel (left), O.I.W.C.C. logo (right)

Backstamp: A. Embossed "Made In England"   **B.** Embossed "Tams Made in England"   **C.** Unmarked

No.	Name	Date	Description	Issued	Size	U.S. $	Can. $	U.K. £
1	1st UK Wade Fair	1994	Arthur Hare	280	90	8.00	10.00	5.00
2a	2nd UK Wade Fair	1995	Holly Hedgehog	400	90	8.00	10.00	5.00
2b	3rd UK Wade Fair	1996	Felicity Squirrel	400	90	8.00	10.00	5.00
2c	4th UK Wade Fair	1996	O.I.W.C.C. logo	250	90	8.00	10.00	5.00

WHIMBLES™

1995-1997

Whimbles were first produced for the U.K. Wade Show held at Birmingham on June 11th, 1995. The first *Whimble* was of "Holly Hedgehog."

New *Whimbles* were introduced at the U.S.A. Wade Show held in Seattle, Washington, July 12-13th, 1996. The "International Wade Collectors Club logo Whimble" (a globe with WADE across it) and the house shaped "Whimble of Spooners" (the collectors shop run by C&S Collectables in Arundel,) were produced in limited editions of 1,000.

The "Seattle Space Needle," "Three Bears" and "Puss in Boots" *Whimbles* were produced in association with Collectors Corner, (Wade Watch) of Arvada, U.S.A. in a limited edition of 500. One hundred of the "Seattle Space Needle" *Whimbles* with only the Needle print and the Wade backstamp were produced for sale at the Seattle Space Needle complex. All additional Whimbles were produced in limited editions of 500.

ROUND WHIMBLES

1995-1997

Backstamp: Red transfer printed "Whimbles by Wade" with two lines

No.	Name	Description	Size	U.S. $	Can. $	U.K. £
1a	Holly Hedgehog	White; gold band; black lettering, print	27	8.00	12.00	6.00
1b	Felicity Squirrel	White; gold band; black lettering, print	27	9.00	12.00	6.00
1c	O.I.W.C.C. Logo	White; gold band; black/red lettering	27	15.00	20.00	10.00
1d	Seattle Space Needle	White; gold band; blue lettering, print	27	15.00	20.00	10.00
1e	Betty Boop	White; gold band; black lettering; black/red print	27	25.00	35.00	18.00
1f	Arthur Hare	White; gold band; red lettering; blue print	27	8.00	12.00	6.00
1g	Whimbles by Wade	White; gold band; red lettering	27	25.00	35.00	18.00
1h	The Three Bears	White; gold band; black lettering; brown print	27	9.00	12.00	6.00
1i	Arundel Castle	White; gold band; black lettering; multicoloured print of castle	27	30.00	40.00	20.00
1j	Puss in Boots	White; gold band, lettering; print of cat	27	9.00	12.00	6.00
1k	Edward Fox	White; gold band; red lettering; brown print	27	9.00	12.00	6.00
1l	Wisconsin Mouse	White; gold band; black lettering; white mouse; fawn cheese	27	15.00	20.00	10.00

HOUSE-SHAPED WHIMBLE

1996

Backstamp: Red transfer printed "Whimbles by Wade" with two lines

No.	Name	Description	Size	U.S. $	Can. $	U.K. £
1	Spooners	White; black hare; red door print; black/red lettering	27	9.00	12.00	6.00

BOXED SETS OF WHIMBLES

1996

In September 1996 the first set of specially boxed and numbered *Whimbles* were sold at the U.K. Wade Show held at Dunstable, Bedfordshire. The sets, which consisted of previously issued *Whimbles* with a new design, were issued in limited editions of 25 which sold at £15.00 for the set of four and £25.00 for the set of six.

Dunstable (left), Wisconsin (right)

Trentham Gardens

Backstamp: Red transfer printed "Whimbles by Wade" with two lines

No.	Name	Date	Description	Issue	U.S. $	Can. $	U.K. £
1	Dunstable	1996	Whimbles by Wade; Betty Boop; Arthur Hare; Spooners; Wade Club logo; Seattle Space Needle	25	80.00	100.00	50.00
2	Trentham	1996	Wade Club logo; Arthur Hare; Spooners; Edward Fox; Puss in Boots; The Three Bears	25	80.00	100.00	50.00
3	Wisconsin	—	Wisconsin Mouse; Seattle Space Needle; Arthur Hare; Edward Fox	25	45.00	60.00	30.00

BETTY BOOP

1996-2003

Originally created in 1930 by animator Grim Natwick and made famous by film producer Max Fleisher in 1931, *Betty Boop* was a popular North American cartoon character who was usually accompanied by her dog "Pudgy." King Features produced a comic strip cartoon of her in the mid-late 1930s, and her cartoons appeared on North American television in the late 1950s and 1970s. The Christmas Surprise with a gold base was sold at the Collect It! Fair in 1998. The "Southern Belle Betty Boop" (gold hat) was available only in prize draws. For variations of "Betty Boop Wall Plaque," see *Collect It!* magazine, page 292, and for a variation of Betty Boop Beach Belle see page 243.

Betty Boop (1a)

Betty Boop Christmas Surprise (2a)

Betty Boop Wall Plaque (3)

Betty Boop Beach Belle (4)

Betty Boop Halloween Trick or Treat (5a)

Betty Boop Southern Belle (6b)

Backstamps: Black printed circular "© 1996 King Features Syndicate, Inc. Fleisher Studios, Inc. [No.of Limited Edition] (C&S) Betty Boop by Wade England"

No.	Name	Date	Colourways	Issue - Price	Size	U.S. $	Can. $	U.K. £
1a	Betty Boop	1996	Red dress; white collar; green base	1500 - £35.00	95	95.00	150.00	75.00
1b	Betty Boop	1997	Blue dress; pearlised collar, base	500 - £35.00	95	110.00	170.00	85.00
2a	Christmas	1997	Red hat, dress; pearlised base	1750 - £39.95	132	120.00	170.00	85.00
2b	Christmas	1998	Red dress; gold base	250 - £39.95	132	160.00	240.00	120.00
3	Wall Plaque	1997	White dress; pearlised moon	1250 - £37.00	225	95.00	150.00	75.00
4	Beach Belle	1998	Black swimsuit with yellow spots	2000 - £41.95	145	95.00	150.00	75.00
5a	Halloween	1999	Black hat, dress, gloves, shoes	1980 - £42.00	155	150.00	200.00	100.00
5b	Halloween	1999	Platinum hat, dress, gloves shoes	20 - Charity	55	350.00	500.00	250.00
6a	Southern Belle	1999	White hat/dress; pink ribbon	500 - £35.00	80	125.00	170.00	85.00
6b	Southern Belle	1999	Blue hat; white dress; gold ribbon	100 - £35.00	80	300.00	400.00	200.00
6c	Southern Belle	1999	Gold hat, ribbon; white dress with pink flowers	20 - Prizes	80		Rare	

BETTY BOOP (2000)

In 2000, a two-piece set of Betty Boop and her dog Pudgy were issued in a limited edition of 480 pieces. An additional 20 models of Betty Boop with a gold base were used as charitable donations and prizes.

Betty Boop Liberty (7a)

Betty Boop Wall Plaque (8)

Betty Boop Springtime (11)

Betty Boop Ringmaster (9a)

Pudgy (9a)

Betty Boop Rose (10)

Backstamps: Black printed circular "© 1996 King Features Syndicate, Inc. Fleisher Studios, Inc. [No. of Limited Edition] (C&S) Betty Boop by Wade England"

No.	Name	Date	Colourway	Issue - Price	Size	U.S. $	Can. $	U.K. £
7a	Liberty (figure)	2000	Dark blue dress; platinum torch	980 - £42.00	158	150.00	200.00	100.00
7b	Liberty (figure)	2000	Dark blue dress; gold torch	20 - Charity	158	350.00	500.00	250.00
8	Liberty (plaque)	2000	Dark blue dress; pearl lustre	300 - £65.00	200	135.00	130.00	65.00
9a	Ringmaster and Pudgy	2000	Betty: Red jacket, shoes, base Pudgy: White/black	480 - £55.00	125 60	125.00	190.00	95.00
9b	Ringmaster	2000	Red jacket, shoes; gold base	20 - Charity/Prizes	125	450.00	500.00	250.00
10	Rose	2000	Pink dress	1000 - £44.00	130	150.00	200.00	100.00
11	Springtime	2000	White dress, hat; pink bows	1000 - £45.00	140	125.00	190.00	95.00
12	Whimble Rose	2000	White; multicoloured print	500 /£5.00	27	9.00	12.00	6.00

BETTY BOOP (2001)

Betty Boop Elegance, Betty Boop Queen of Hearts, and Betty Boop Valentine were modelled by Ken Holmes.

Betty Boop Graduate (13a)

Betty Boop Money Box (14)

Betty Boop Movie Queen (15)

Betty Boop St. Patrick's Day (16)

Betty Boop Superstar (17)

Betty Boop Valentine (18a)

Backstamps: A. Black printed circular "© 1996 King Features Syndicate, Inc. Fleisher Studios, Inc. [No.of Limited Edition] (C&S) Betty Boop by Wade England"
B. Printed "©2001 King Features Syndicate, Inc Fleisher Studios, Inc 750 Limited Edition [name of model] by Wade England with Certificate of Authenticity" with blue "C&S" and red "Wade" logos

No.	Name	Date	Colourway	Issue - Price	Size	U.S. $	Can. $	U.K. £
13a	Graduate, UK	2001	Black tunic; pewter tassel	500 - £55.00	130	140.00	190.00	95.00
13b	Graduate, USA	2001	Black tunic; gold tassel	500 - $78.00 (US)	130	140.00	190.00	95.00
14	Money Box	2001	Red/black/gold	500 - £49.95	115	95.00	130.00	65.00
15	Movie Queen	2001	Red dress; black/white film	250 - £99.00	230	325.00	450.00	225.00
16	St. Patrick's Day	2001	Green clothing, base; white dog	750 - £55.00	140	140.00	200.00	100.00
17	Superstar	2001	Blue dress; gold jewellery	750 - £55.00	145	140.00	190.00	95.00
18a	Valentine	2001	Black dress; red heart; pearl base	750 - £55.00	150	140.00	200.00	100.00
18b	Valentine	2001	Black dress; gold heart; pearl base	20 - Prizes	150		Rare	

BETTY BOOP (2002)

Betty Boop Christmas Morning (19)

Betty Boop Elegance (20a)

Betty Boop Halloween (21)

Betty Boop Jubilee (22)

Betty Boop Lazy Daze (23)

Betty Boop Queen of Hearts (25a)

Backstamp: Queen of Hearts: Printed "©2001 King Features Syndicate, Inc Fleisher Studios, Inc 750 Limited Edition Betty Boop Queen of Hearts by Wade England with Certificate of Authenticity" with blue "C&S" and red "Wade" logos
Printed "©2002 King Features Syndicate, Inc Fleisher Studios, Inc 750 Limited Edition [name of model] by Wade England with Certificate of Authenticity" with blue "C&S" and red "Wade" logos
Printed "©2002 King Features Syndicate, Inc. / Fleisher Studios, Inc. TM Hearst Holdings, Inc. / Fleisher Studios, Inc. Betty Boop Jubilee 2002 Premier Collection 500 limited edition with Certificate of Authenticity" with blue "C&S" and red "Wade" logos

No.	Name	Date	Colourway	Issue - Price	Size	U.S. $	Can. $	U.K. £
19a	Christmas Morning	2002	Red/white dress, hat; white dog; blue parcel; yellow ribbons	750 - £55	90	85.00	110.00	55.00
19b	Christmas Morning	2002	Red/white dress, hat; white dog; gold parcel, ribbons	20 - Prizes	90		Rare	
20a	Elegance	2002	Black dress, hair; red sash, bow	500 - £99	230	250.00	300.00	150.00
20b	Elegance	2002	Black dress, hair; gold sash, bow	20 - Prizes	230		Rare	
21a	Halloween	2002	Mauve dress; orange pumpkin with black facial markings	750 - £55	153	90.00	120.00	60.00
21b	Halloween	2002	Mauve dress; orange pumpkin with gold facial markings	20 - Prizes	153		Rare	
22a	Jubilee	2002	Red cloak; blue dress	500 - £99	230	150.00	225.00	100.00
22b	Jubilee	2002	Royal blue cloak; blue dress	25 - Prizes	230		Rare	
23a	Lazy Daze	2002	White dress; blue cushion/gold tassel	750 - £55	102	75.00	110.00	55.00
23b	Lazy Daze	2002	Gold dress; red cushion/gold tassel	20 - Prizes	102	75.00	110.00	55.00
24	Plaque	2002	White; black lettering; gold trim	1,000 - $12	65 x 100	15.00	22.00	12.00
25a	Queen of Hearts	2002	Red swimsuit, shoes; purple/gold crown	2000 - £55	135	100.00	150.00	75.00
25b	Queen of Hearts	2002	Gold swimsuit; red shoes; purple/gold crown	20 - Prizes	135		Rare	

BETTY BOOP (2003)

Betty Boop in Black

Betty Boop Rainy Days

Betty Boop Seasons Greetings

Betty Boop Sweetheart

Betty Boop Swinging 60s

Betty Boop Trick or Treat

Backstamp: Printed "©2003 King Features Syndicate, Inc Fleisher Studios, Inc 750 Limited Edition [name of model] by Wade England with Certificate of Authenticity" and blue "C&S" and red "Wade" logos

No.	Name	Date	Colourways	Issue - Price	Size	U.S. $	Can. $	U.K. £
25a	Betty in Black	2003	Black glitter dress; black hair	20 - Prizes	140		Rare	
25b	Betty in Red	2003	Red dress; black hair	750 - £55	140	100.00	120.00	60.00
26	Rainy Days	2003	Dark blue raincoat, boots; red dress white dog with yellow coat	2,000 - £55	155	90.00	110.00	55.00
27	Seasons Greetings	2003	Black dress, hair; white sleeves	750 - £55	140	80.00	100.00	50.00
27	Sweetheart	2003	Black dress; red shoes, heart; pearlised wrap; white base	750 - £55	140	85.00	110.00	55.00
28	Swinging 60s	2003	Black/white mini dress; white dog; red box	750 - £55	145	85.00	125.00	60.00
29	Trick or Treat	2003	Red dress; black hat; brown/yellow broom stick; gold moon	750 - £55	150	85.00	110.00	55.00

Note: Although only 20 models were produced of "Betty in Black," the backstamp reads "750 Limited Edition."

MR. MAGOO

1998

Backstamp: Printed "Mr Magoo Wade England ©1998 UPA Pictures, Inc. With Certificate of Authenticity 1,000 Limited Edition C&S"

No.	Name	Date	Colourways	Issue - Price	Size	U.S. $	Can. $	U.K. £
1a	Mr. Magoo	1998	Dark green coat; white base	960 - £37.00	105	65.00	110.00	55.00
1b	Mr. Magoo	1998	Dark green coat; gold base	40 - £40.00	105	140.00	200.00	100.00

GARFIELD

1999

Backstamp: Printed "With Certificate of Authenticity C&S 500 Special Edition Wade England"

No.	Name	Date	Colourways	Issue - Price	Size	U.S. $	Can. $	U.K. £
1	Garfield	1999	Orange/black/pink/yellow	500 - £35.00	70	80.00	120.00	65.00

CHARACTERS FROM CHARLIE BROWN

1999-2001

Snoopy and Woodstock

Snoopy Happy Holidays

Snoopy Hugging Woodstock

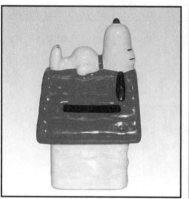

Snoopy Kennel Money Box

Charlie Brown

Linus

Backstamp: Printed "With Certificate of Authenticity C&S 500 Special Edition Wade England"

No.	Name	Date	Colourway	Issue - Price	Size	U.S. $	Can. $	U.K. £
1	Snoopy and Woodstock	1999	Snoopy: White/black/red	1000 - £38.00	65	140.00	200.00	100.00
			Woodstock: Yellow/black	(pair)	58			
2	Snoopy Happy Holidays	2000	White/green/ gold	1000 - £39.95	98	65.00	90.00	45.00
3	Snoopy Hugging Woodstock	2000	White/black/yellow	1000 - £38.0	65	80.00	100.00	50.00
4	Snoopy Kennel Money Box	2000	White/red/black	500 0 £33.00	115	65.00	90.00	45.00
5	Charlie Brown and Linus	2001	Charlie: Yellow/black/brown	500/£78.00	84	110.00	160.00	80.00
			Linus: Blue/brown/white	(pair)	70			

ORINOCO WOMBLE

1999

Orinoco is a well-known character from the British television cartoon series *The Wombles.*

Orinoco Womble (green base, left; gold base right)

Backstamp: Printed "With Certificate of Authenticity 1,000 limited edition C&S The Wombles Orinoco by Wade England. 1,000 Limited Edition, © Elisabeth Berrisford / FilmFair Ltd 1999"

No.	Name	Date	Colourways	Issue - Price	Size	U.S. $	Can. $	U.K. £
1a	Orinoco	1999	Yellow; red hat, scarf; green base	750 - £39.95	110	60.00	80.00	40.00
1b	Orinoco	1999	Yellow; red hat, scarf; gold base	250 - £39.95	110	70.00	100.00	50.00

POCKET PALS "TANGO"

1999

The mould used to make the Mother Cat in the *Happy Families Series* was also used to make "Tango." See also Pocket Pals, page 178.

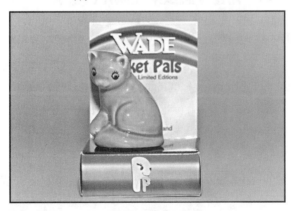

Backstamp: Gold Transfer "Wade Pp" in shield

No.	Name	Date	Colourways	Issue - Price	Size	U.S. $	Can. $	U.K. £
1	Tango	1999	Apricot; blue eyes	1000 - £6.50	45 x 35	15.00	20.00	10.00

270

ANIMALAND

2001-2002

Mama Otter, Baby Bear Cub, Snowy Owl

Elephant (4), Panda (5a), Panda (5b)

Backstamp: A. Printed "Wade's Animaland 250 Limited Edition" [name of model] with "C&S" and "Wade" logos (1, 4)
B. Printed "Wade's Animaland Otter Collectors Meet Special 12th August 2001 Limited Edition 250" with "C&S" and "Wade" Logos (2)
C. Printed "C&S 250 Limited Edition Wade's Animaland" [name of model] and "C&S" and "Wade" logo (5)

No.	Name	Date	Colourways	Issue - Price	Size	U.S. $	Can. $	U.K. £
1	Baby Bear Cub	2001	Honey/black; grey-green rock base	250 - £25.00	65 x 55	60.00	90.00	45.00
2	Mama Otter	2001	Brown; blue grey rock base	250 - £25.00	65 x 50	60.00	80.00	40.00
3	Snowy Owl	2001	White/yellow; brown log base	250 - £25.00	68 x 68	60.00	90.00	45.00
4	Elephant	2002	Honey; green grass; grey base	250 - £25.00	85 x 65	50.00	60.00	30.00
5a	Panda	2002	Black/white	250 - £25.00	60	50.00	60.00	30.00
5b	Panda	2002	White	20 - Prizes	60		Rare	

ARUN BEAR TOWN CRIER

2001

For a special colourway of the Town Crier see page 248. Note that 'Crier' is spelled incorrectly 'Cryer' in the backstamp.

Backstamp: Printed "Wade Est 1810 England Arun Bear Town Cryer Arundel Wade Collectors Meet. August 2001" with "C&S" logo

No.	Name	Date	Colourways	Issue - Price	Size	U.S. $	Can. $	U.K. £
1a	Arun Bear	2001	Brown/red/black/gold/white	250 - £35.00	65 x 50	65.00	90.00	45.00
1b	Arun Bear	2001	Brown/green/black/gold/white	20 - Prizes	65 x 50	130.00	200.00	100.00

Dinosaur Collection

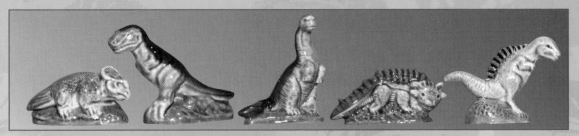

Set One: Camarasaurus, Euoplocephalus, Spinosaurus, Protoceratops, Tyrannosaurus Rex.
The huge success of "Jurassic Park" renewed interest in dinosaurs, Wade produced this set of Dinosaurs in 1993. (P. 156)

Drum Box Series

Drum Box set: Clara, Dora, Harpy, Jem, and Trunky.
This is a hard set to complete, 1957-1959 (P. 157)

Flying Birds Series

Fish Waiter

Set One: Swifts
1958-1959 (P. 159)

The **Fish Waiter** was used as
an event piece. 1998 (P. 161)

Pocket Pals

Series One – Animals

Top Row: Elephant Tusker, Cat Slinky, Pig Truffle, Giraffe Stretch, Mouse Cheesy.
Bottom Row: Dog Waggs, Rabbit Bounce, Hippo Paddles, Frog Hip Hop, Owl Specs.
Pocket Pals were new colourways of the "Mother" animals from Wade's popular **Happy Families** series. 1999 (P. 178)

Series Two – Horrors

First Row: Baby Bodzilla, Frankie, Igor Jr., Jekyll and Hyde, Lizzie
Second Row: Lugsi, Spooky, Where's my Mummy, Witch Hazel, Wolfy, 2001 (P. 179)

Rule Beartannia

Rule Beartannia set was first sold in the USA. Shown are **Rule Beartannia Plaque, Queen Beatrice, Queen Mum, King Velveteen, Nanny Fluffins with Baby Velveteena, Prince George Tedward, Princess Elizabeth Tedwina, Princess Plushette, and Royal Guard.** 2002 (P. 181)

Snippets

Set One: Santa Maria, Revenge, Mayflower, 1956 (P. 184)   Set Two: Hansel, Gretel and Gingy the Bear, 1957 (P. 185)

The Tortoise Family

Father, Mother and Baby Tortoise 1958-1988 (P. 186)   Jumbo Tortoise 1973-1988 (P. 186)

Fairs and Event Models
Arundel Swap Meets

Arundel Duck, 1997 (P. 197)

Arundel Bunny, 1998 (P. 197)

Puppy Love "Steino", 1999 (P. 197)

Arundel Cat, 2000 (P. 197)

Arundel Collectors Meet

Arundel Puppy, 2001 (P. 198)

Sumo the Elephant, 2001 (P. 198)

Arundel Pony (honey and white), 2002 (P. 199)

Swan (black, white and pearl) 2002 (P. 199)

Vulcanodon Dinosaur Moneybank, 2003 (P. 199)

T.Rex Moneybank, 2003 (P. 199)

Badger Whimsie 2003 (P. 199)

Arundel Lamb (white and black), 2003 (P. 199)

Dunstable Leisure Centre

Lil' Witch, 2002 (P. 204)

Polar Bear, 2002 (P. 204)

Buttercup, 2003 (P. 204)

Lil' Cricketer, 2003 (P. 204)

U.K. Wade Collectors Fair – Trentham Gardens

Rufus, 1997 (P. 206)

Penguins, 1999 (P. 206)

Roly Poly Rabbit, 2000 (P. 206)

Hector the Owl, 2001 (P. 206) Pedro the Donkey, 2001 (P. 206) Major the Lion, 2001 (P. 206) Poppy the Pig, 2001 (P. 206)

U.K. Wade Collectors Fair – Kings Hall Civic Centre

Arnie, Ceasar, Topsy-Turvey, Twirly Whirly, 2002 (P. 211)

U.K. Wade Collectors Fair – North Stafford Hotel

Bluebell the Pony, 2003 (P. 212)

Beau the Greyhound, 2003 (P. 212)

Lil' Footballer Bear, 2003 (P. 212)

U.S.A. Wade Collectors Shows – Jim Beam

Madison Mouse, 1997 (P. 213) New York Tourist, 1998 (P. 213)   Shelby, 1999 (P. 213)   Rufus on Tour, 1999 (P. 213)

U.S.A. Wade Collectors Shows – Kansas Wade Show

Cowardly Lion, 2001 (P. 214)   Dorothy and Toto, 2001 (P. 214)   Ozma, 2001 (P. 214)

U.S.A. Wade Collectors Shows – Summer Wade Fest

Lil' Bit Elephants, five different colourways, 2003 (P. 219)

U.S.A. Wade Collectors Shows – West Coast Wade Collectors Fair

Whimsical Whales, five different colourways, 2003 (P. 222)

Collectors Club Figures

The Camelot Collection: Sir Lancelot, Queen Guinivere, King Arthur, The Lady of the Lake, and The Wizard Merlin
1997 (P. 233)

Toy Box: Toy Soldier, Amelia Teddy Bear, Chuckles The Clown and Emily The Doll
1998 (P. 234)

British Myths and Legends: Cornish Tin Mine Pixie, Green Man, King Canute, Mermaid, Puck and St. George and The Dragon
1998-1999 (P. 234)

Alice in Wonderland: Cheshire Cat, Mad Hatter, White Rabbit, and Dormouse
1999 (P. 235)

Wade Christmas Models

Christmas issues: 1994 Snowman, 1995 Snow Woman, 1996 Snow Children, 1998 Annabel Waiting for Christmas
(P. 241)

Wade Christmas Crackers

Four of these models are from the 1984 **Whimsieland Wildlife Series**, the **Crocodile** is a new model, the **Giraffe** is a new version of the **English Whimsies Giraffe**. 2003 (P. 242)

C&S CRACKERS

October 2001

The C&S boxed set of six Christmas Crackers was produced in a limited edition of ten boxes. They contained a selection of the following Wade models: the *English Whimsies* Cow, 'Skip' the dog, a blue or green "Arthur Hare Wizhared" miniature, a "Betty Boop," "Wade Club" or a "Spooner's" whimble, a "Big Chief Bravehare Teenie", a "Miniature Teapot Key Ring," an "Arundel Otter" or the *Tiny Treasurers* 'Supergirl.' The cost of the box on the day was £29.95.

Description	U.S. $	Can. $	U.K. £
Boxed set	60.00	75.00	38.00

MINIATURE TEAPOTS

2001

Commissioned jointly by C&S and Wade Watch, U.S.A., each miniature teapot has a loop on the top so that it can be attached to a key ring. The issue price was £29.00 for the set of five teapots.

Backstamp: Transparent label with red printed "Wade England"

No.	Name	Date	Colourways	Issue	Size	U.S. $	Can. $	U.K. £
1a	Butterfly	2001	White; multicoloured chintz print	500	25 x 38	12.00	14.00	7.00
1b	Gold	2001	Gold	500	25 x 38	12.00	14.00	7.00
1c	Silver	2001	Silver	500	25 x 38	12.00	14.00	7.00
1d	Sweetpea	2001	White; multicoloured chintz print	500	25 x 38	12.00	14.00	7.00
1e	Thistle	2001	White; multicoloured chintz print	500	25 x 38	12.00	14.00	7.00

TED "E" BEAR

2001

Although named Ted "E" Bear, the backstamp incorrectly reads TEDD "E" BEAR.

Backstamp: **A.** Printed "Tedd-E-Special Edition Wade Est 1810 England C&S"
B. Printed "Tedd-E-Special Edition Wade Est 1810"

No.	Name	Date	Colourways	Issue - Price	Size	U.S. $	Can. $	U.K. £
1a	Internet Guide	2001	Honey, dark brown; *Internet Guide*	100 - £22.00	85	75.00	110.00	55.00
1b	Wade Handbook	2001	Honey; dark brown; *Wade Handbook*	100 - £22.00	85	75.00	110.00	55.00
1c	Gold book	2001	Honey/dark brown; gold book	20 - Prizes	85	100.00	150.00	75.00

THOMAS THE TANK ENGINE

STYLE TWO

2001-2002

MONEY BOX

Available by mail order and produced in a limited edition of 500, the issue price was £39.95. For *Thomas the Tank Engine*, Style One, see Storybook Figures, page 69.

Backstamp: Printed "Thomas the Tank Engine Money Bank C&S Collectables 500 Limited edition © Gullane (Thomas) Limited 2001 Wade"

No.	Name	Date	Colourways	Issue - Price	Size	U.S. $	Can.	U.K. £
1	Money Box	2001	Blue/black/red engine; red-brown brick walls	500 - £39.95	90 x 90	95.00	150.00	75.00

THOMAS THE TANK ENGINE MINIATURES

2002

The engines "Thomas" and "Percy" were modelled by Simon Millard, and "Henry" and "James" by Cyril Roberts.

Henry the Engine

James the Engine

Percy the Engine

Thomas the Tank Engine

Fat Controller

Backstamp: Printed blue "C&S" and red "Wade" logos, "©Gullane (Thomas) Limited 2002"

No.	Name	Date	Colourways	Issue - Price	Size	U.S. $	Can.	U.K. £
1	Fat Controller	2002	Black coat, hat, boots, base; yellow waistcoat; grey trousers; green base	500 - £29.95	62	65.00	80.00	40.00
2	Fat Controller	2002	Black coat, hat, boots; grey trousers; yellow waistcoat; gold base	20 - Prizes	62		Rare	
3	Henry Engine	2002	Green/black/red/grey/yellow	500 - £30	50 x 100	65.00	75.00	37.50
4	James Engine	2002	Red/black/yellow/grey	500 - £30	50 x 90	65.00	75.00	37.50
5	Percy Engine	2002	Green/black/red/grey/yellow	500 - £30	50 x 76	65.00	75.00	37.50
6	Thomas the Tank Engine	2002	Blue/black/red/grey/yellow	500 - £30	50 x 76	65.00	75.00	37.50

WEST "E" AND SCOTTIE

2001

Scottie (1a) and West "E" (1b)

West "E" (1c)

Backstamp: **A.** Printed "C&S West "E" Special Edition by Wade England"
B. Red Printed "Wade" in oval

No.	Name	Date	Colourways	Issue - Price	Size	U.S. $	Can. $	U.K. £
1a	Scottie	2001	Black; brown eyes, nose	100 - £22.50	85	60.00	80.00	40.00
1b	West "E"	2001	White; black eyes, nose	100 - £22.50	85	75.00	110.00	55.00
1c	West "E"	2001	Platinum	20 - Prizes	85	140.00	190.00	95.00

AQUALAND

2002-2003

Dolphin

Seahorse

Backstamp: A. Printed "Wade's Aqualand No. 1 Dolphin 250 Limited Edition" with blue "C&S" and red "Wade" logos
B. Printed "Limited Edt 250 Seahorse" and red "Wade" logo

No.	Name	Date	Colourways	Issue - Price	Size	U.S. $	Can. $	U.K. £
1a	Dolphin	2002	Grey; pearl white waves	250 - £27.50	85	40.00	60.00	30.00
1b	Dolphin	2002	White lustre; blue waves	20 - Prizes	85		Rare	
2a	Seahorse	2003	Honey; white spots; pearlised fin; honey base	250 - £27.50	78	40.00	60.00	30.00
2b	Seahorse	2003	Honey; white spots; pearlised fin; gold base	20 - Prizes	78		Rare	

DONKEY

2002

The Donkey was modelled by Simon Millard. It was produced in a limited edition of 100, and was introduced at the Kings Hall Wade Show, April 2002.

Backstamp: Printed "C&S Wade Official Collectors Centre"

No.	Name	Date	Colourways	Issue - Price	Size	U.S. $	Can. $	U.K. £
1	Donkey	2002	Honey; black eyes	100 - £22.00	78 x 88	60.00	90.00	40.00

FANTASYLAND

2002

The "Mermaid" and "Pegasus" were modelled by Ken Holmes, and the "Pixie on a Mushroom" by Cyril Roberts. The "Pegasus" model with the gold base was produced to mark the 10th Anniversry of C&S Collectables.

Mermaid (brown chest); Mermaid (gold chest); Pixie on a Mushroom (brown base) Pixie on a Mushroom (gold base)

Pegasus (gold base); Pegasus (blue base)

Backstamp: Printed "Wades Fantasy Land [name of model, limited edition number and number in series]" with blue "C&S" and red "Wade" logos

No.	Name	Date	Colourways	Issue - Price	Size	U.S. $	Can. $	U.K. £
1a	Mermaid	2002	Yellow hair; blue tail; brown chest	250 - £29.95	70	65.00	80.00	40.00
1b	Mermaid	2002	Yellow hair; blue tail; gold chest	20 - Prizes	70		Rare	
2a	Pegasus	2002	White; black hooves; blue base	250 - £29.95	85	65.00	80.00	40.00
2b	Pegasus	2002	Pearlised white; black hooves; gold base	20 - Prizes	85		Rare	
3a	Pixie on a Mushroom	2002	Red coat, hat; grey pants; green boots; beige/brown mushroom	250 - £29.95	75	65.00	80.00	40.00
3b	Pixie on a Mushroom	2002	Red coat, hat; grey pants; green boots; gold mushroom	20 - Prizes	75		Rare	

INTERNET EVENT

2001 - 2003

Frost "E" [white]

Donk"E" [pearl]

Rud"E" [white]

Victor"E" [blue]

Brand"E" [brown/white]

Budg"E" [blue]

Backstamp: **Brand"E":** Printed "Ewade Exclusive Brand"E" Lim Edt 125" with blue "C&S" and red "Wade" logo
Brand"E": Printed gold "Wade" logo
Budg"E": Printed "Budg"E" Limited Ed 125 Wade Exclusive" and red "Wade" logo
Budg"E": Printed gold "Wade" logo
Frost"E": Printed "Frost"E" Special Edition C&S Wade"
Victor"E": Printed "Victor"E" Bear 125 Ltd. Edt." and "Wade" logo
Donk"E": Printed "Official Collectors Centre" with "C&S" and "Wade" logos
Donk"E": Printed "Wade England"
Elephant: Printed "C&S" logo
Victor "E" Bear: Printed "Victor "E" Bear 125 Ltd. Edt." and "Wade" logo

No.	Name	Date	Colourways	Issue - Price	Size	U.S. $	Can. $	U.K. £
1a	Frost "E"	2001	White snowman; blue scarf	150 - £22.50	85	75.00	100.00	50.00
1b	Frost "E"	2001	Pearlised snowman; blue scarf	20 - prizes	85	200.00	300.00	150.00
2	Plaque	2001	White; multicoloured transfer print; blue lettering	100 - £10	65 x 100	15.00	22.00	12.00
3a	Donk"E"	2002	Light grey; black eyes	125 - £22.50	78 x 88	75.00	100.00	50.00
3b	Donk"E"	2002	Pearl	20 - Prizes	78 x 88		Rare	
4	Elephant	2002	White; gold base	20 - £45.00	85 x 65		Rare	
5a	Rud"E"	2002	Honey; dark brown antlers, red nose	150 - £25.00	80	50.00	75.00	38.00
5b	Rud"E"	2002	White; gold antlers; red nose	20 - Prizes	80		Rare	
6	Victor"E" Bear	2002	Blue bear; red/white/blue USA flag	125 - £25	78	45.00	75.00	35.00
7a	Brand"E" the St. Bernard	2003	White with brown markings; pewter barrel, collar	125 - £25	70	35.00	45.00	25.00
7b	Brand"E" the St. Bernard	2003	Pear; gold barrel, collar	20 - Prizes	70		Rare	
8a	Budg"E"	2003	Blue wings, body; white face, chest; yellow beak, feet; grey base	125 - £25.00	68 x 91	65.00	95.00	45.00
8b	Budg"E"	2003	Pearl white; gold beak, feet, base	20 - Prizes	68 x 91		Rare	

BEARS WITH FLAGS

2002-2003

In October 2002, due to demand from Canadian collectors, C&S recoloured the Victor "E" Bear yellow, and renamed it "Maple the Canadian Bear." It was produced in a limited edition of 125 and cost £25.00.

In March 2003, a limited edition of 28 bears in a black colourway was produced for the Canadian on-line Wademad group. The cost was also £25.00.

Two special colourways of green bears with either the USA or UK flags were produced in a limited edition of 15 each. These were available as prizes throughout 2003.

Maple the Canadian Bear (yellow) (2002)

Maple the Canadian Bear (black) (2003)

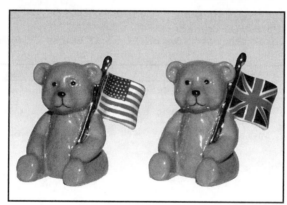

Victory "E" Bear (USA left, UK right)

Backstamp: Maple the Canadian Bear: Printed "Maple Bear 125 Ltd. Edit." and "Wade" logo
Maple the Canadian Bear: Printed gold "WADE" logo

No.	Name	Date	Colourways	Issue - Price	Size	U.S. $	Can. $	U.K. £
1a	Maple the Canadian Bear	2002	Yellow bear; red/white Canadian flag	125 - £25	78	90.00	110.00	55.00
1b	Maple the Canadian Bear	2003	Black bear; red/white Canadian flag	28 - £25	78	90.00	110.00	55.00
1c	Union Bear	2003	Green bear; red/white/blue USA flag	15 - Prizes	78		Rare	
1d	Victor "E" Bear	2003	Green bear; red/white/blue UK flag	15 - Prizes	78		Rare	

WINTER WONDERLAND

2002

A new series by Wade for C&S is called *Winter Wonderland*. The first model in the series is named "Polar Bearcubs on Ice." It was modelled by Cyril Roberts and produced in a limited edition of 250. A limited edition of 20 models with a silver ice block was produced and used in prize draws and competitions.

The second model in the series is "Polar Bear Mother and Cubs," to be issued at the Wade Christmas Bonanza, in Arundel, December 2003.

Polar Bearcubs on Ice (1a)

Polar Bearcubs on Ice (1b)

Mother Polar Bear * Cub on Ice

Backstamp: A. Printed "Wade's Winter Wonderland Polar Bear Cubs on Ice Wade Christmas Bonanza December 2002" with blue "C&S" and red "OIWCC" logo (1a, b)

B. Printed "Wade's Winter Wonderland Mother Polar Bear & Cub on Ice" with blue "C&S Made in England" and red "OIWCC" logos

No.	Name	Date	Colourways	Issue - Price	Size	U.S. $	Can. $	U.K. £
1a	Polar Bearcubs on Ice	2002	White; pink inner ears, paw pads; pearl ice block	250 - Unknown	90 x 100	35.00	45.00	25.00
1b	Polar Bearcubs on Ice	2002	White; pink inner ears, paw pads; silver ice block	20 - Unknown	90 x 100		Rare	
2	Mother Polar Bear and Cub on Ice	2003	White, pale blue ice	250 - Unknown	Unknown	35.00	45.00	25.00

BRITISH HERITAGE COLLECTION

2003

This is the first model in an intended series named "British Heritage." It was produced in a limited edition of 250 and cost £22.00.

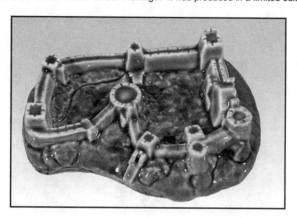

Backstamp: Printed "British Heritage Collection Arundel Castle Limited edition of 500" with blue "C&S" and red "Wade" logos

No.	Name	Date	Colourways	Issue - Price	Size	U.S. $	Can. $	U.K. £
1	Arundel Castle	2003	Grey castle; green base	250 - £22	30 x 80	40.00	60.00	30.00

BUDGIE WHIMSIES

2003

Produced in a limited edition of 500, the budgies were issued in four colourways, priced at £22.00 for the set. For the 'pink' colourway see Wade Watch.

Backstamp: Embossed "Wade C/S"

No.	Name	Date	Colourways	Issue - Price	Size	U.S. $	Can. $	U.K. £
1a	Budgie Whimsie	2003	Blue	500	50			
1b	Budgie Whimsie	2003	Green	500	50			
1c	Budgie Whimsie	2003	Honey	500	50			
1d	Budgie Whimsie	2003	White	500	50			
	Set					36.00	44.00	22.00

A boxed set of six budgies in a special edition of two was offered as prizes in the C&S prize draw at the 2003 Harrisburg, PA, Wade Fest.

Backstamp: Embossed "Wade C/S"

No.	Name	Date	Colourways	Size	U.S. $	Can. $	U.K. £
1a	Budgie Whimsie	2003	Blue	50			
1b	Budgie Whimsie	2003	Green	50			
1c	Budgie Whimsie	2003	Honey	50			
1d	Budgie Whimsie	2003	Pink	50			
1e	Budgie Whimsie	2003	White	50			
1f	Budgie Whimsie	2003	White; gold base	50			
	Boxed set of six					Rare	

CADBURY
CHUCKLEBEANS AND EGGCUPS
2002

Wade produced these eggcups and Chucklebeans for Cadbury World in November 2002. Originally available only from Cadbury World Shop, in early 2003 they were available through the Wade Collectors Club.

Backstamp: **Chucklebean:** Embossed "Wade England"
Chuckle Egg Cup: Printed "Made Exclusively for Cadbury World by Wade Est 1810 England"

No.	Name	Colourways	Size	U.S. $	Can. $	U.K. £
1a	Chucklebean	Beige; black shoes	40	3.00	4.00	2.00
1b	Chucklebean	Beige; green shoes	40	3.00	4.00	2.00
1c	Chucklebean	Beige; yellow shoes	40	3.00	4.00	2.00
2a	Chucklebean Egg Cup	Beige; black shoes	60	10.00	12.00	6.00
2b	Chucklebean Egg Cup	Beige; green shoes	60	10.00	12.00	6.00
2c	Chucklebean Egg Cup	Beige; yellow shoes	60	10.00	12.00	6.00

CAMTRAK
CHILDHOOD FAVOURITES SERIES
1995-1997

DOUGAL
1995

Dougal, a cartoon dog from the British children's television series, *The Magic Roundabout,* was the first model of this series, produced for Camtrak of Nottingham, England. It was issued in a limited edition of 2,000 figures. The first 220 models were fired twice, leaving the model with a dark mushroom-coloured face, and is known as the brown-faced Dougal. The other 1,780 models were fired once only and have a lighter, pale ivory face. The original price, direct from Camtrak, was £27.50.

Backstamp: Transfer print "Camtrak's Childhood Favourites No.1 Dougal by Wade © Serge Danot/AB Productions SA 1995 Licensed by Link Licensing Ltd."

No.	Name	Date	Description	Issue - Price	Size	U.S. $	Can. $	U.K. £
1a	Dougal	1995	Mushroom face	220 - £27.50	84 x 155	80.00	90.00	45.00
1b	Dougal	1995	Pale ivory face	1780 - £27.50	84 x 155	100.00	120.00	60.00

RUPERT BEAR

Rupert Bear, created by Mary Tourtel, featured in a British daily newspaper and children's books from the 1950s to the present.

Backstamp: Printed "Camtrak's Childhood Favourites by Wade No 2 Rupert © 1996 Express Newspapers plc Licensed by A.H.E/Nelvana"

No.	Name	Date	Colourways	Issue - Price	Size	U.S. $	Can. $	U.K. £
1a	Ruper Bear	1996	Red jacket; yellow/black trousers, scarf; green base	900 - £30.00	130	115.00	140.00	70.00
1b	Ruper Bear	1996	Red jacket; yellow/black trousers, scarf; gold base	100 - Unknown	130	270.00	330.00	165.00

CHILDHOOD FAVOURITES DISPLAY PLAQUE

Backstamp: A. Printed "Camtrak's Childhood Favourites A Series Display Plaque 1997 by Wade"
    B. Gold printed limited edition of 120 with Official International Wade Club logo

No.	Name	Date	Colourways	Issue - Price	Size	U.S. $	Can. $	U.K. £
1a	Plaque	1997	Brown/white; brown knobs	880 - £11.00	70	50.00	60.00	30.00
1b	Plaque	1997	Brown/white; gold knobs	20 - £16.00	70	60.00	70.00	35.00

DRACULA

Wade produced *Dracula* in conjunction with *Nexus* a subsidiary name used by Camtrak, as *Dracula* was deemed too much of a contrast to Camtrak's cute *Childhood Favourites* series. The original cost was £85.00 for club members and £90.00 for non-members.

Dracula

Dracula in Gift Box

Backstamp: Gold printed "Wade Nexus Hammer 40 Years Dracula"

No.	Name	Date	Colourways	Issue	Size	U.S. $	Can. $	U.K. £
1a	Dracula	1997	Black hair, cloak; red lining (gloss)	1250	254	130.00	160.00	80.00
1b	Dracula	1997	Black hair, cloak; red lining (matt)	1250	254	130.00	160.00	80.00

PADDINGTON BEAR

Paddington Bear, created by Michael Bond, made his debut in 1958.

Paddington Bear

Paddington's Snowy Day

Backstamp: A. Printed "Camtrak's Childhood Favourites No 3 Paddington © Paddington and Company LTD 1997 Licensed by Copyrights Wade Made in England"
B. Printed "Camtrak Childhood Favourites by Wade No 7 Paddington's Snowy Day. ©Paddington and Company. Ltd 1999 Licenced by Copyrights"

No.	Name	Date	colourways	Issue - Price	Size	U.S. $	Can. $	U.K. £
1a	Paddington	1997	Blue coat; grey base	2000 - £33.00	90	80.00	100.00	50.00
1b	Paddington	1997	Blue coat; gold base	Unknown	90	250.00	300.00	150.00
2	Snowy Day	1999	Red coat; pearlised base	2000 - £38.85	100	90.00	110.00	55.00

RUPERT AND THE SNOWMAN

Rupert and the Snowman was the fourth model in Camtrak's *Childhood Favourites* series and was also the first in an intended series of *Seasonal* models. A special limited edition of 110 models was produced with a pale blue Snowman's scarf for the City of London Police Fund (CLP).

Backstamp: **A.** Printed "Camtrak's Childhood Favourites by Wade No.4 Rupert and the Snowman. Rupert Characters and ©Express Newspapers Plc 1997 Licenced by Nelvana Marketing Inc. UK representative Abbey Home Entertainment"

B. Printed "Camtrak's Childhood Favourites by Wade No.4 Rupert and the Snowman. Rupert Characters and ©Express Newspapers Plc 1997 Licenced by Nelvana Marketing Inc. UK representative Abbey Home Entertainment Limited Edition of 110 Exclusive to the CLP Fund" with print of policeman and child

No.	Date	Colourways	Issue - Price	Size	U.S. $	Can. $	U.K. £
1a	1997	Rupert: Red coat; black buttons Snowman: White; dark blue scarf	1800 - Unknown	120	90.00	135.00	65.00
1b	1997	Rupert: Red coat; gold buttons Snowman: White; dark blue scarf	100 - Unknown	120	200.00	250.00	125.00
1c	1997	Rupert: Red coat; black buttons Snowman: White; pale blue scarf	110 - Unknown	120	200.00	250.00	125.00

SOOTY AND SWEEP 5OTH ANNIVERSARY

Sooty, a teddy bear, and *Sweep,* a puppy with long ears, were hand puppets that featured on a BBC children's television program from 1950 to the 1980s.

Backstamp: Printed "Childhood Favourites by Wade [model number and name] Sooty - Sooty ™" and "© Sooty international Limited 1998 Licenced by Chatsworth enterprises Ltd 50 Golden Years" with "50 Golden Years Sooty" logo

No.	Name	Date	Description	Issue - Price	Size	U.S. $	Can. $	U.K. £
1	Sooty	1998	Amber bear; blue dungarees	2000 - £38.50	132	100.00	120.00	60.00
2a	Sweep	1998	Grey; red trousers; grey baser	200 - £38.50	136	100.00	120.00	60.00
2b	Sweep	1998	Grey; red trousers; gold base	120 - Unknown	136	160.00	200.00	100.00

TINY CLANGER

Tiny Clanger one of the "Clangers," a family of long-nosed moon creatures that appeared in a BBC children's television program. He is the eighth model in Camtrak's *Childhood Favourites* Series. This was the last model produced for Camtrak.

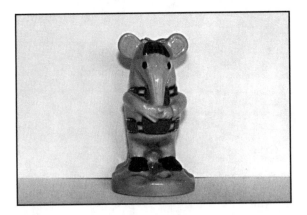

Backstamp: Printed "Camtrak's Childhood Favourites by Wade No. 8 Tiny Clanger © 1999 Oliver Postgate and Peter Firmin. Licenced by Licencing by Design Limited"

No.	Name	Date	Colourways	Issue - Price	Size	U.S. $	Can. $	U.K. £
1	Tiny Clanger	1999	Pink; Red jacket; black shoes	Unknown	110	80.00	100.00	50.00

CARRYER CRAFT OF CALIFORNIA
MINI MANSIONS
1984-1986

The beautiful Victorian houses of San Francisco survived the 1906 earthquake, but by the 1960s they had deteriorated badly. A few owners then decided to repaint their homes in the flamboyant colours of the original era, and the Painted Ladies were reborn. A Cable Car with different decals has been found: on one side of the car is a "Dewar's" decal and on the other "White Label" (the normal decals are "Fisherman's Wharf"). No information has been found to explain the change.

George Wade & Son Ltd. was commissioned by Carryer Craft of California (Iris Carryer was the elder daughter of Sir George Wade) to reproduce the Painted Ladies in porcelain. Because this short-lived series was made for export to the United States, only very limited quantities were released onto the British market.

All models are marked with "Wade England" in black on their side walls. The boxed set comprises six models, but the "Pink Lady," "Brown Lady," "White Lady" and the "Cable Car" are the most difficult to find. The original price was £10 for a box of eight models.

Original Box: Mini Mansions Set-1 San Francisco's Painted Ladies

Backstamp: Black transfer "Wade Porcelain England SF/[number of model]"

No.	Name	Description	Size	U.S. $	Can. $	U.K. £
SF/1	Pink Lady	Pink; black roof	55 x 25	90.00	110.00	55.00
SF/2	White Lady	White; grey roof	55 x 25	90.00	110.00	55.00
SF/3	Brown Lady	Brown; beige roof	65 x 30	90.00	110.00	55.00
SF/4a	Yellow Lady	Yellow; grey roof; black apex	63 x 30	70.00	90.00	45.00
SF/4b	Yellow Lady	Yellow; grey roof; blue apex	63 x 30	70.00	90.00	45.00
SF/5	Blue Lady	Blue; grey roof	70 x 38	70.00	90.00	45.00
SF/6a	Cable Car	Blue/green; red front; Fisherman's Wharf	20 x 38	120.00	150.00	75.00
SF/6b	Cable Car	Blue/green; yellow front; Dewar's White Label	20 x 38	130.00	160.00	80.00

CERAMICA

Ceramica is a museum in Burslem, Stoke-on-Trent, set in the historic Old Town Hall. The museum has many stunning displays of local pottery produced by such famous manufacturers as Moorcroft, Royal Doulton and Wade.

I'M ON MY WAY

1999

Backstamp: Printed "Wish You Were Here Collection I'm On My Way CERAMICA Limited Ed 750 With Certificate Wade England"

No.	Name	Date	Description	Issue - Price	Size	U.S. $	Can. $	U.K. £
1	I'm On My Way	1999	Green shirt; blue trousers	750 - £29.00	130	65.00	80.00	40.00

BORN FREE

2003

This model, issued in a limited edition of 250, depicts 'Elsa' the lioness and her cub. Elsa was the star of the 1966 book *Born Free* by Joy Adamson, and a film of the same name. A true life story written by Joy Adamson. In the film version, Joy Adamson was played by English actress Virginia McKenna.

Backstamp: Printed "Designed and made by Wade England exclusively for Ceramica "Born Free" Limited Edition of 250"

No.	Name	Date	Description	Issue - Price	Size	U.S. $	Can. $	U.K. £
1	Born Free	2003	Honey; brown tail tip; green base	250 - £25.00	68 x 119	75.00	90.00	45.00

CIBA GEIGY
SLOW FE AND SLOW K

In 1969, George Wade was commissioned by the British drug company Ciba Geigy to produce models of tortoises with the words *Slow Fe* and *Slow K* on their backs. These models were presented to general practitioners by Ciba Geigy sales representatives as a promotional novelty to assist in marketing their iron and potassium preparations, Slow Fe (slow-release iron) and Slow K (slow-release potassium). Wade retooled the "Medium (Mother)" tortoise from the *Tortoise Family* by embossing either the name Slow Fe or Slow K in the top shell. See also page 188.

Slow Fe

Slow K

Backstamp: Embossed "Wade Porcelain Made in England"

No.	Name	Date	Description	Issue	Size	U.S. $	Can. $	U.K. £
1	Slow Fe	1969	Brown; blue markings	10,000	35 x 75	75.00	90.00	45.00
2	Slow K	1969	Brown; blue markings	10,000	35 x 75	75.00	90.00	45.00

COLLECT IT! MAGAZINE

1997 - 2000

BETTY BOOP

Betty Boop Classic Wall Plaque

Betty Boop Liberty Wall Plaque

Backstamp: Unknown

No.	Name	Date	Colourways	Issue - Price	Size	U.S. $	Can. $	U.K. £
1	Classic Plaque	1998	Red dress; grey base	1250 - £41.95	225	100.00	170.00	85.00
2	Liberty Plaque	2000	Red dress; gold crown, torch, book	250 - £65.00	220	135.00	190.00	95.00

COLLECT IT! FAIRIES

Backstamp: **A.** Black Printed "Collectania Made Exclusively for Collect it! By Wade Limited edition of 2,500"
B. Black Printed "Collectus Made Exclusively for Collect it! By Wade Limited edition of 2,500"
C. Black Printed "Collecteenie Made Exclusively for Collect it! By Wade Limited edition of 1,500"

No.	Name	Date	Colourways	Issue - Price	Size	U.S. $	Can. $	U.K. £
1	Collectania	1998	Purple/yellow/pearl	2500 - £39.95	110	75.00	95.00	48.00
2	Collectus	1998	White/purple/pearl	2500 - £39.95	105	75.00	95.00	48.00
3	Collecteenie	1999	Red/blue/pearl	2500 - £39.95	65	75.00	95.00	48.00

COLLECT IT! HONEY BEAR CUB

A special colourway *English Whimsie* Bear Cub was given free with the October issue of *Collect It!* magazine. Some models have a thicker glaze than others producing a darker honey colour. For the gold colourway see Wade Christmas Extravaganza Figures, page 200.

Backstamp: Embossed "Wade" between front feet and "England" on back of model

No.	Name	Date	Description	Size	U.S. $	Can. $	U.K. £
1a	Bear Cub	2000	Dark honey	40	10.00	12.00	6.00
1b	Bear Cub	2000	Light honey	40	10.00	12.00	6.00

POCKET PALS "HOPPER" THE FROG and "WOOFIT" THE DOG

A special colourway Pocket Pal Frog named *Hopper* was given free with the November 1999 issue of *Collect It!* magazine. The frog was attached to the front cover of the magazine and was only available through Smith's the British Bookstore to subscribers of *Collect it!* In the same issue was an offer for a special colourway of the Wade Pocket Pal dog named *Woofit*. The original cost of *Woofit* was £5.95. See also Pocket Pals, page 178.

Backstamp: Gold transfer print "Wade Pp" in shield

No.	Name	Date	Colourways	Issue/Price	Size	U.S. $	Can. $	U.K. £
1	Hopper	1999	Green/blue/pink	Complimentary	25	25.00	30.00	15.00
2	Woofit	1999	Honey/dark brown	— / £5.95	55	25.00	30.00	15.00

294

THE COLLECTOR
IN THE FOREST DEEP

Backstamp: A. Printed "In The Forest Deep Series [name of model] for The Collector London Limited Edition of 1000 Wade"
B. Printed "In The Forest Deep Series Santa Hedgehog for The Collector London Limited Edition of 2000 Wade"

No.	Name	Date	Description	Issue - Price	Size	U.S. $	Can. $	U.K. £
1	Morris Mole	1997	Grey/buff mole	1000 - £39.95	105	80.00	100.00	50.00
2	Oswald Owl	1997	Dark/light brown owl	1000 - £39.95	113	80.00	100.00	50.00
3	Santa Hedgehog	1997	Brown hedgehog; red/white Santa suite	2000 - £39.95	132	80.00	100.00	50.00
4	Bertram Badger	1998	Black/white badger; black coat	1000 - £39.95	135	80.00	100.00	50.00
5	Tailwarmer Squirrel	1998	Brown squirrel; blue/green striped tailwarmer	1000 - £39.95	110	80.00	100.00	50.00
6	Huntsman Fox	1999	Red brown fox; red waistcoat; white shirt, jodhpurs	1000 - £39.95	115	80.00	100.00	50.00
7	Gentleman Rabbit	1999	Beige rabbit; light grey suit	1000 - £39.95	115	80.00	100.00	50.00

COTSWOLD COLLECTABLES

TUFTY AND HIS FURRYFOLK FRIENDS

1998-1999

"Tufty the Red Squirrel" is a character created by Elsie Mills, M.B.E. in her storybooks of *Tufty and his Furryfolk Friends*. Commissioned by Stuart Mitchell and Caroline Murray, of Cotswold Collectables, Tufty was first introduced in 1998. A model with a gold base was released in 1999 at the *Collect It!* fair held in Wembley, U.K.

Note: A Belisha Beacon is a bright yellow lighted globe on top of a black and white striped pole and mounted at British zebra crossings (road crossings).

Backstamp: Circular printed "©Tufty and his Furryfolk Friends by Cotswold Collectables 1998 Wade 'Tufty' ©RoSPA Enterprises Ltd. Limited Edition 1,500"

No.	Name	Date	Description	Issue - Price	Size	U.S. $	Can. $	U.K. £
1a	Tufty	1998	Dark blue jacket; grey base	1500 - £39.95	140	70.00	90.00	45.00
1b	Tufty	1999	Dark blue jacket; gold base	150 - £37.00	140	130.00	160.00	80.00

CRICKET DESIGN INCORPORATED
(CDI IMPORTS)

ANIMAL FAMILIES

Cricket Design Incorporated is an import company in Costa Mesa, California. They imported a number of previously issued Wade models to be sold in the U.S.A. The sets were given new names and packaging: Wade's Nursery Favourites became "Fairytale Friends;" the Cat and Puppy Dish set became "Pups in a Basket;" Dogs and Puppies became "Doggy Family;" Happy Families became "Happy Family;" and the Tortoise Family became "Turtle Family."

The English issues of these models ended in the early 1980s, it is estimated that a limited number of surplus models were distributed to CDI for sale in the USA during the early 1980s. All the models are in the same colourways as the original issues.

Although the Whoppas were advertised under their original Wade England name, no evidence has been seen to indicate which, if any, models were issued. The author would welcome any information on this issue.

Not all models from the original Wade series were issued. The CDI name is given with Wade's original name in parenthesis.

DOGGY FAMILY

C.1980

Only three sets of the original series of five were issued: Alsatian (renamed German Shepherd), Cairn and Red Setter (renamed Irish Setter). The Mother and Pups were issued in two separate boxes in the U.K., but were packaged in one box for CDI.

Cairn Terriers

German Shepherds

Irish Setters

Backstamp: Label "Genuine Wade Porcelain Made in England"

No.	Name	Colourways	Size	U.S. $	Can. $	U.K. £
1	Cairn Terrier Mother	Honey brown; brown ears, nose	65 x 70	35.00	45/00	20.00
2	Pup, lying	Honey brown; brown ears, nose	35 x 50	16.00	20.00	10.00
3	Pup, standing	Honey brown; brown ears, nose	40 x 50	16.00	20.00	10.00
4	German Shepherd Mother	Brown/honey brown	60 x 75	35.00	45.00	20.00
5	Pup, lying	Brown/honey brown	35 x 45	16.00	20.00	10.00
6	Pup, sitting	Brown/honey brown	40 x 45	16.00	20.00	10.00
7	Irish Setter Mother	Red-brown	60 x 75	35.00	45.00	20.00
8	Pup, lying, facing left	Red-brown	40 x 45	16.00	20.00	10.00
9	Pup, lying, facing right	Red-brown	40 x 45	16.00	20.00	10.00

FAIRYTALE FRIENDS

C.1980

These models are the original U.K. large size Nursery Favourites. All 20 of the English series were issued under the name Fairytale Friends. The majority of the models were advertised with the original Wade England names and set number, but with the 'Little,' 'Wee' or 'Old,' etc. removed. Little Boy Blue was advertised as "Blue Boy." The models were issued in Happy Family style boxes.

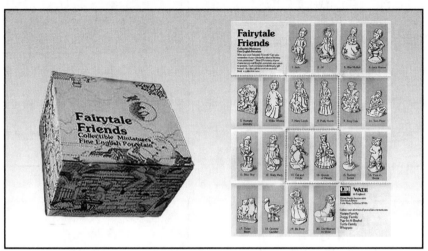

Cricket Design Incorporated packaging, and advertisement for Fairytale Friends

Backstamp: Embossed "Wade England"

No.	Name	Colourways	Size	U.S. $	Can. $	U.K. £
1	Jack	Brown hair, waistcoat; green trousers	75 x 30	45.00	55.00	28.00
2	Jill	Green dress, bonnet	75 x 40	45.00	55.00	28.00
3	Miss Muffett	Grey-green dress; yellow hair	60 x 50	45.00	55.00	28.00
4	Jack Horner	Green jacket; yellow trousers; brown hair	70 x 40	45.00	55.00	28.00
5	Humpty Dumpty	Honey brown; green suit; red tie	65 x 43	45.00	55.00	28.00
6	Willie Winkie	Grey nightshirt; yellow hair	75 x 35	30.00	40.00	20.00
7	Mary Lamb	Blue skirt, bonnet; grey-blue jacket	75 x 40	45.00	55.00	28.00
8	Polly Kettle	Brown; pink cap, kettle	75 x 35	45.00	55.00	28.00
9	King Cole	Yellow/grey hat; blue-grey cloak	65 x 50	45.00	55.00	28.00
10	Tom Piper	Grey hat, kilt; brown jacket	65 x 55	60.00	75.00	37.00
11	Blue Boy	Blue jacket, trousers, cap	75 x 30	60.00	75.00	37.00
12	Mary Mary	Blue dress; pink shoes; yellow hair	75 x 45	60.00	75.00	37.00
13	Cat and Fiddle	Brown/grey cat; yellow fiddle	70 x 50	60.00	75.00	37.00
14	Queen of Hearts	Beige dress; pink hearts, crown	75 x 48	60.00	75.00	37.00
15	Tommy Tucker	Blue pantaloons; yellow hair	75 x 45	60.00	75.00	37.00
16	Puss in Boots	Beige; blue boots	70 x 30	70.00	85.00	45.00
17	Three Bears	Grey; green base	70 x 60	70.00	85.00	45.00
18	Goosey Gander	Beige; pink beak; blue-brown steps	66 x 55	80.00	110.00	50.00
19	Bo Peep	Beige dress, bonnet; pink ribbon	70 x 40	80.00	110.00	50.00
20	Old Woman in Shoe	Blue dress, bonnet; brown roof, door	60 x 55	80.00	110.00	50.00

HAPPY FAMILY

C.1980

These *Happy Family* models were marketed in similar boxes to the third style box used in the U.K. edition. Only four sets of the original eleven were advertised: Giraffe, Hippo, Mouse and Rabbit.

Giraffe Family

Hippo Family

Mouse Family

Rabbit Family

Backstamp: **A.** Embossed "Wade England"

B. Black transfer "Wade Made in England" (some with cricket in large C)

No.	Name	Colourways	Size	U.S. $	Can. $	U.K. £
1	Giraffe Mother	Beige; turquoise eyelids; dark grey horns	60 x 45	45.00	55.00	28.00
2	Baby, upright	Beige; turquoise eyelids; dark grey horns	40 x 28	25.00	30.00	15.00
3	Baby, lying	Beige; turquoise eyelids; dark grey horns	15 x 30	25.00	30.00	15.00
4	Hippo Mother	Smokey blue; brown eyes	35 x 50	45.00	55.00	28.00
5	Baby, eyes open	Smokey blue; brown eyes	28 x 25	25.00	30.00	15.00
6	Baby, eyes closed	Smokey blue	20 x 25	25.00	30.00	15.00
7	Mouse Mother	White; grey patch; pink ears, tail	50 x 28	45.00	55.00	28.00
8	Baby, eyes closed	White; grey patch; pink ears, tail	28 x 28	25.00	30.00	15.00
9	Baby, eyes open	White; grey patch; pink ears, tail	25 x 30	25.00	30.00	15.00
10	Rabbit Mother	White; blue patches	55 x 30	45.00	55.00	28.00
11	Baby, sitting	White; blue patches	34 x 28	25.00	30.00	15.00
12	Baby, standing	White; blue patches	30 x 35	25.00	30.00	15.00

PUP-IN-A-BASKET

C.1980

Only five of the original ten puppy dishes were issued by CDI: the two Cairn Terriers, the Alsatian (renamed German Shepherd for the American market), and one Red Setter pup, which was renamed Irish Setter. Some of the poses are listed differently in the CDI advertising, e.g.: the "Lying Cairn Pup" is advertised as 'sitting', and the "Sitting Alsatian" (German Shepherd) is advertised as standing, etc. This may cause some collectors to believe that they were different models in this series, which is not the case.

German Shepherd, sitting; German Shepherd, standing; Cairn Terrier, sitting; Cairn Terrier, standing

Backstamp: Embossed "Wade England"

No.	Name	Colourways	Size	U.S. $	Can. $	U.K. £
1	Cairn Terrier, sitting	Honey brown	35 x 75	28.00	40.00	20.00
2	Cairn Terrier, standing	Honey brown	40 x 75	28.00	40.00	20.00
3	German Shepherd, sitting	Brown/honey brown	35 x 75	28.00	40.00	20.00
4	German Shepherd, standing	Brown/honey brown	40 x 75	28.00	40.00	20.00
5	Irish Setter, lying, facing right	Red-brown	40 x 75	28.00	40.00	20.00

TURTLE FAMILY

C.1980

The Father Tortoise Trinket Box with the lift-off shell is advertised as "Mother" turtle, and the two smaller tortoises, which in the U.K. are known as Mother and Baby, are advertised as baby turtles.

Backstamp: Embossed "Wade Porcelain Made in England"

No.	Name	Colourways	Size	U.S. $	Can. $	U.K. £
1	Mother Turtle	Brown/blue	50 x 105	25.00	35.00	20.00
2	Baby Turtle	Brown/blue	35 x 75	15.00	20.00	10.00
3	Baby Turtle	Brown/blue	25 x 45	16.00	22.00	12.00

E. AND A. CRUMPTON

THE LONG ARM OF THE LAW

1993-1995

The Long Arm Of The Law set was commissioned and designed by Elaine and Adrian Crumpton and modeled by Ken Holmes, in a limited edition of 2,000 each. "The Burglar" was issued in June 1993, the "Policeman" followed in October, the "Barrister" in August 1994 and the "Prisoner" in June 1995. The prisoner was produced with either black or brown hair. Due to production problems the first 400 Policeman models have impressed faces; the next 1,600 have hand-painted faces. A mislaid Policeman mould resulted in the unauthorized production of a black-suited earthenware version which has an embossed Wade backstamp but was not produced by Wade Ceramics.

Painted Face (left), Impressed Face (right)

Backstamp: A. Large embossed "Wade" (1)
B. Embossed "Wade" (2a, 2b, 4a, 4b)
C. Red transfer "Wade Made in England" (3)

No.	Name	Date	Colourways	Issue	Size	U.S. $	Can. $	U.K. £
1	The Burglar	1993	Black/white	2000	85	70.00	90.00	45.00
2a	Policeman	1993	Impressed face; dark blue uniform	400	90	80.00	100.00	50.00
2b	Policeman	1993	Painted face; dark blue uniform	1600	90	70.00	90.00	45.00
3	Barrister	1994	Black gown, shoes; grey trousers	2000	80	70.00	90.00	45.00
4a	Prisoner	1995	Black hair; grey shoes	2000	70	70.00	90.00	45.00
4b	Prisoner	1995	Brown hair, shoes	2000	70	80.00	100.00	50.00
4c	Prisoner	1995	Brown hair; grey shoes	2000	70	80.00	100.00	50.00

FATHER'S COLLECTION and WADES BY PEG
Y2K PINK ELEPHANT
2000

Originally produced as an *English Whimsie* in 1973, the Y2K Pink Elephant was a joint commission by Peg and Roger Johnson (Wades by Peg) and Father's Collection (Father David Cox). The models were first available at the Kansas City Wade Show.

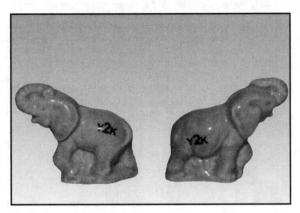

Backstamp: Embossed "Wade England" on rim

No.	Name	Date	Colourways	Issue - Price	Size	U.S. $	Can. $	U.K. £
1a	Elephant, left	2000	Pink; black decal	1500 - $10.00	35 x 45	15.00	18.00	9.00
1b	Elephant, right	2000	Pink; black decal	485 - $12.00	35 x 45	25.00	30.00	15.00

FRISCO COFFEE
ENGLISH WHIMSIES
1973-1974

During 1973-1974 Frisco Coffee (a division of Liptons Tea) of Cape Town, South Africa, distributed *Whimsie* models wrapped in cellophane packets in their boxes of Frisco Coffee. Seven models have been reported, but it is believed there may have been more. The models are the same colours as the original *English Whimsies,* and are listed in alphabetical order.

Backstamp: A. Embossed "Wade England" on rim
B. Embossed "Wade" between front feet and "England" on back of model

No.	Name	Description	Size	U.S. $	Can. $	U.K. £
1	Bear Cub	Grey; beige face	30 x 40	5.00	6.00	3.00
2	Bushbaby	Brown; blue ears; black nose	30 x 30	3.00	4.00	2.00
3	Duck	Blue/brown; yellow beak	30 x 40	7.00	10.00	5.00
4	Fawn	Brown; blue ears	30 x 30	5.00	6.00	3.00
5	Kitten, seated	Dark/light brown; pink wool	30 x 30	5.00	6.00	3.00
6	Owl	Dark/light brown	35 x 20	5.00	6.00	3.00
7	Rabbit	Beige open ears	30 x 30	5.00	6.00	3.00

G&G COLLECTABLES

HANNA-BARBERA CHARACTERS

1997

Mr. Jinks, a Hanna-Barbera cartoon character of the late 1950s-1960s, was commissioned by G & G Collectables, and was first seen at the October 1997 Dunstable Wade Show. *Pixie* and *Dixie* a pair of cartoon mice, were produced in a limited edition of 1,500 models each. The original cost was £75.00 for the pair.

Scooby-Doo

Scrappy Doo

Pixie and Dixie

Boo Boo

Yogi Bear

Huckleberry Hound and Mr. Jinks

Backstamp: Huckleberry Hound: Printed "Wade England Huckleberry Hound © 1998 H.B. Prod Inc Worldwide Edition of 1500 G & G Collectables"
Mr. Jinks: Printed "Wade England Mr. Jinks © 1997 H.B. Prod Inc G & G Collectables"
Pixie/Dixie: Printed "Wade England © 1997 H.B. Prod Inc Worldwide edition of 1,500 G & G Collectables" [name]
Scooby-Doo: Black transfer "© H/B Inc Scooby-Doo Limited Edition of 2,000 Wade England G&G Collectables"
Scrappy Doo: Transfer print "© H/B Inc Scrappy Doo Limited Edition of 2,000 Wade England G&G Collectables"
Yogi Bear / Boo Boo: Printed black "Wade England [name of model]" "©1997 H.B.Prod Inc Worldwide Edition of 1500 G & G Collectables"

No.	Name	Date	Description	Issue - Price	Size	U.S. $	Can. $	U.K. £
1	Scooby-Doo	1994	Brown; blue collar; gold medallion	2000/Unknown	115	112.00	140.00	70.00
2	Scrappy Doo	1995	Brown; blue collar;	2000 - £29.95	90	100.00	120.00	60.00
3	Mr. Jinks	1997	Orange cat; blue bow tie	1500 - £35.00	152	80.00	100.00	50.00
4	Pixie	1997	Grey mouse; red tomato	1500 - £37.50	115	65.00	80.00	40.00
5	Dixie	1997	Grey mouse; chocolate cupcake	1500 - £37.50	115	65.00	80.00	40.00
6	Boo Boo	1997	Brown bear; black waistcoat	100 - £34.00	114	70.00	80.00	40.00
7	Yogi Bear	1997	Green hat, tie; dark blue waistcoat	1500 - £34.00	130	80.00	100.00	50.00
8	Huckleberry Hound	1998	Blue hound; yellow hat; black drum base, gold lines	1500 - £38.00	135	65.00	80.00	40.00

SANTA CLAUS
1997

Santa Claus was modelled by Nigel Weaver.

Backstamp: Unknown

No.	Name	Date	Description	Issue - Price	Size	U.S. $	Can. $	U.K. £
1	Santa Claus	1997	Red/white suit; grey chimney;	1000 - £36.00	133	70.00	90.00	45.00

LITTLE RED RIDING HOOD AND THE BIG BAD WOLF

Little Red Riding Hood and the Big Bad Wolf

Backstamp: Printed "Limited Edition 1,000 ©G & G Collectables & Wade [name of model]"

No.	Name	Date	Colourways	Issue - Price	Size	U.S. $	Can. $	U.K. £
1	Big Bad Wolf	1998	Blue cape; white nightdress	1000 - £30.00	92	70.00	90.00	45.00
2	Little Red Riding Hood	1999	Red cloak; blue dress	1000 - £30.00	100	70.00	90.00	45.00

PEGGY GAMBLE (Formerly Gamble and Styles)
MR. PUNCH and JUDY

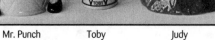

| Mr. Punch | Toby | Judy | Judy's ghost |

Backstamp: A. Black transfer outline of a corgi, "P&S" stamped on the body, "Wade" between two black lines and the issue number (1)
B. Black transfer outline of a Corgi, "P&S" stamped on the body, "Modelled by K Holmes Wade" and the issue number (2)
C. Black transfer outline of a Corgi, "PG" stamped on the body, "Modelled by Simon Millard Wade"

No.	Name	Date	Description	Issue - Price	Size	U.S. $	Can. $	U.K. £
1a	Mr. Punch	1996	Burgundy suit	1800 - £45.00	165	75.00	95.00	50.00
1b	Mr. Punch	1996	Green suit	200 - £45.00	165	200.00	300.00	145.00
2a	Judy	1997	Pale blue dress	1800 - £42.00	150	75.00	95.00	50.00
2b	Judy	1997	Green dress	200 - £45.00	150	200.00	300.00	145.00
3a	Toby	1998	Red hat	1500 - £35.00	122	75.00	95.00	50.00
3a	Toby	1998	Green hat	200 - £35.00	122	120.00	180.00	90.00
4a	Judy's Ghost	1999	Pearlised ghost; gold base	800 - £35.00	143	75.00	95.00	50.00
4b	Judy's Ghost	1999	Pearlised ghost; green base	200 - £35.00	143	95.00	140.00	70.00

GENERAL FOODS

CIRCA 1990

A planned promotion for General Foods of England that included miscellaneous animals of two or three colours and *Miniature Nursery Rhymes* characters in one-colour glazes was cancelled before it began. A number of models that had been intended for the promotion were released onto the market for a short time in late 1990. The Chimpanzee, in the olive/green-brown glaze has also been found in the USA, and may have been included in the Red Rose Decaffeinated Tea promotions.

MISCELLANEOUS ANIMALS

1990

TS: Tom Smith   EW: English Whimsies   WL: Whimsie-land series

Photograph not available
at press time

Backstamp: Embossed "Wade England"

No.	Name	Description	Size	U.S. $	Can. $	U.K. £
1	Badger (TS British Wildlife)	Light grey/white; green base	25 x 40	14.00	18.00	9.00
2	Chimpanzee (EW)	Olive/green-brown	35 x 35	14.00	18.00	9.00
3	Owl (WL)	White; orange beak; green base	35 x 25	20.00	25.00	12.00
4	Panda (WL)	Black/white	37 x 20	25.00	30.00	15.00
5	Penguin (EW, TS 1987)	Black/white; orange beak	45 x 17	20.00	25.00	12.00
6	Rabbit (EW)	White; pinky-beige; pink nose	30 x 30	20.00	25.00	12.00
7	Zebra (EW)	Black; green grass	40 x 35	65.00	80.00	40.00

MINIATURE NURSERY RHYMES

1990

These models are in an all-over solid colour.

Photograph not available
at press time

Backstamp: Embossed "Wade England"

No.	Name	Description	Size	U.S. $	Can. $	U.K. £
1	Jack	Beige	34 x 33	8.00	10.00	5.00
2	Jill	Beige	28 x 39	8.00	10.00	5.00
3	Little Bo-Peep	Green	44 x 24	20.00	25.00	12.00
4	Little Jack Horner	Beige	37 x 21	8.00	10.00	5.00
5	Little Red Riding Hood	Pink	44 x 24	20.00	25.00	12.00
6	Mother Goose	Beige	41 x 31	8.00	10.00	5.00
7	Old King Cole	Light blue	37 x 32	20.00	25.00	12.00
8	Old Woman Who Lived in a Shoe	Beige	35 x 40	8.00	10.00	5.00
9	Pied Piper	Green	46 x 28	20.00	25.00	12.00
10	Tom the Piper's Son	Blue	39 x 33	20.00	25.00	12.00
11	Wee Willie Winkie	Blue	44 x 24	20.00	25.00	12.00

GOLD STAR GIFTHOUSE
NURSERY FAVOURITES
1990-1991

Only five of the original 20 *Nursery Favourites* models were reissued for the Gold Star Gifthouse, a California Wade dealer. The Old Woman Who Lived in a Shoe and Goosey Goosey Gander are the hardest to find of the original *Nursery Favourites*, see page 62.

Backstamp: A. Embossed "Wade England 1990" (1, 2, 3)
         B. Embossed "Wade England 1991" and ink stamp "GSG" (4)
         C. Embossed "Wade England 1991" (5)

No.	Name	Description	Size	U.S. $	Can. $	U.K. £
1	Mary, Mary	Brighter than original; blue dress; yellow hair; pink shoes; green base	75 x 45	50.00	60.00	30.00
2	Polly Put the Kettle On	Same colours as original; brown; pink cap, kettle	75 x 35	50.00	60.00	30.00
3	Tom Tom the Piper's Son	Brighter than original; blue-grey kilt; yellow/honey jacket	65 x 55	50.00	60.00	30.00
4	Old Woman in a Shoe	Blue bonnet, dress; beige dog, door	60 x 55	100.00	120.00	60.00
5	Goosey Goosey Gander	Same as original; beige; pink beak	66 x 55	100.00	120.00	60.00

GRANADA TELEVISION

CORONATION STREET HOUSES

1988-1989

The *Coronation Street Houses* set was commissioned by Granada Television as a promotional item for its long-running television series, *Coronation Street*, and sold at the studio gift shop and by mail order. Only three models of the set were produced, although others were planned. The figures are very similar to the *Whimsey-on-Why* houses. They were sold on cards with details of the series printed on the back.

Backstamp: Embossed "Wade England"

No.	Name	Description	Size	U.S. $	Can. $	U.K. £
1	The Rovers Return	Brown; grey roof	45 x 48	20.00	30.00	15.00
2	No. 9 The Duckworths	Yellow/grey windows, door	45 x 33	20.00	30.00	15.00
3	Alf's Corner Shop	Brown; grey roof	45 x 33	20.00	30.00	15.00
4	Jack (Salt)	Brown hair, trousers; dark green shirt; black shoes	110	20.00	25.00	12.00
5	Vera (Pepper)	Yellow hair; red blouse; green skirt	120	20.00	25.00	12.00

GREAT UNIVERSAL STORES

For a number of years, Tom Smith and Company marketed a line of Christmas crackers through Great Universal Stores (G.U.S.).

SET ONE: SNOW LIFE

1993-1994

The Tom Smith *Snow Animals* series was reissued for G.U.S., with the addition of the Tom Smith *Survival Animals* "Whale" in grey, and the Red Rose *Miniature Nurseries* "Goosey Goosey Gander," coloured white and renamed the "Snow Goose." There are two types of the "Reindeer" model: Type 1 has a gap between the legs; Type 2 has no gap. For Type 2 see Tom Smith Crackers page 385.

Although there are ten models in this set, the box only contains eight crackers. This can cause problems for collectors wishing to complete a set and will cause a future rise in price for some figures.

Backstamp: Embossed "Wade England"

No.	Name	Description	Size	U.S. $	Can. $	U.K. £
1	Fox (WL)	Red-brown/honey	35 x 36	20.00	25.00	12.00
2	Penguin (EW)	Blue-grey	49 x 21	12.00	16.00	8.00
3	Polar Bear, head forward (EW)	White	27 x 45	12.00	16.00	8.00
4	Reindeer, Type 1 (TS)	Beige	34 x 35	18.00	22.00	11.00
5	Seal Pup (EW)	Blue-grey	26 x 39	12.00	16.00	8.00
6	Snow Goose (RR)	White	33 x 37	12.00	16.00	8.00
7	Snowshoe Hare (TS)	White	45 x 33	12.00	16.00	8.00
8	Snowy Owl (WL)	White	35 x 25	12.00	16.00	8.00
9	Walrus (EW)	Beige	34 x 36	12.00	16.00	8.00
10	Whale (Baleen TS)	Grey	22 x 52	12.00	16.00	8.00

Note: The following initials indicate the origin of the models:
TS: Tom Smith
WL: *Whimsie-land* Series
EW: *English Whimsies*
RR: Red Rose *Miniature Nurseries*

SET TWO: ENDANGERED SPECIES

1994

Backstamp: Embossed "Wade England"

No.	Name	Description	Size	U.S. $	Can. $	U.K. £
1	Cockatoo (TS)	Green	41 x 47	7.00	8.00	4.00
2	Fox (WL)	Light brown	35 x 36	20.00	25.00	12.00
3	Gorilla, standing (EW)	Brown	37 x 28	7.00	8.00	4.00
4	Koala Bear (EW)	Beige	35 x 29	8.00	10.00	5.00
5	Leopard (EW)	Honey	20 x 47	5.00	7.00	3.00
6	Orang-outan (EW)	Brown	30 x 34	7.00	8.00	4.00
7	Polar Bear, head forward (EW)	White	27 x 45	7.00	8.00	4.00
8	Rhino (EW)	Grey	25 x 43	5.00	7.00	3.00
9	Tiger (EW)	Honey	37 x 30	7.00	8.00	4.00
10	Whale (Baleen TS)	Grey	22 x 52	10.00	12.00	6.00

Note: The following initials indicate the origin of the models:
  EW: *English Whimsies*
  WL: *Whimsie-land* Series
  TS: Tom Smith

SET THREE: TALES FROM THE NURSERY

1994-1995

Also reissued for G.U.S. was the Tom Smith *Tales from the Nurseries* set. There are slight colour variations from the previous set in "Hickory Dickory Dock," "Little Bo-Peep," "Humpty Dumpty," "Queen of Hearts," "Little Jack Horner" and "Ride a Cock Horse." The remaining models are the same colour as before.

Backstamp: Embossed "Wade England"

No.	Name	Description	Size	U.S. $	Can. $	U.K. £
1	Cat and the Fiddle (RR)	Grey	47 x 33	6.00	9.00	4.00
2	Dr. Foster (RR)	Dark brown	43 x 26	6.00	9.00	4.00
3	Hickory Dickory Dock (RR)	Beige	44 x 20	6.00	9.00	4.00
4	Humpty Dumpty (RR)	Blue-grey	36 x 23	6.00	9.00	4.00
5	Little Bo-Peep (RR)	Wine	44 x 24	6.00	9.00	4.00
6	Little Boy Blue (TS)	Blue	41 x 25	6.00	9.00	4.00
7	Little Jack Horner (RR)	Honey	37 x 21	6.00	9.00	4.00
8	Queen of Hearts (RR)	Apricot	42 x 25	6.00	9.00	4.00
9	Ride a Cock Horse (TS)	Green	36 x 41	6.00	9.00	4.00
10	Tom Tom the Piper's Son (RR)	Honey	39 x 33	6.00	9.00	4.00

Note: The following initials indicate the origin of the models:
    RR: Red Rose
    TS: Tom Smith

SET FOUR: MISCELLANEOUS MODELS

Backstamp: Unknown

No.	Name	Description	Size	U.S. $	Can. $	U.K. £
1	Beaver (EW)	Dark brown	35 x 45	6.00	8.00	4.00
2	Camel (EW)	Beige	35 x 55	6.00	8.00	4.00
3	Circus lion (TS)	Honey	40 x 22	10.00	15.00	7.00
4	Giraffe (EW)	Beige	35 x 35	5.00	6.00	3.00
5	Langur, Type 2 (EW)	Dark brown	35 x 30	6.00	8.00	4.00
6	Pine marten (EW)	Honey	34 x 34	6.00	8.00	4.00
7	Pony (Shetland) (TS)	Beige	25 x 30	6.00	8.00	4.00
8	Puppy (Spaniel) (TS)	Honey	25 x 30	6.00	8.00	4.00
9	Raccoon (EW)	Light brown	25 x 35	6.00	8.00	4.00
10	Zebra (EW)	Grey	40 x 35	6.00	8.00	4.00

Note: The following initials indicate the origin of the models:
EW: *English Whimsies*
TS: Tom Smith

HARRODS OF KNIGHTSBRIDGE
DOORMAN EGG CUP, MONEY BOX, CRUET AND COOKIE JAR
1991-1996

These models were produced for Harrods of Knightsbridge. The egg cups, issued in 1991, were sold in the store at Easter, packaged with miniature chocolate eggs, and at Christmas, filled with sweets or sugared almonds. The money box, issued in 1993, originally cost £16.95. The cookie jar, released in 1996, features a younger looking doorman.

Egg Cup (left) and Money Box (right)

Pepper (left) and Salt (right)

Cookie Jar

Backstamp: Black transfer "Harrods Knightsbridge"

No.	Name	Description	Size	U.S. $	Can. $	U.K. £
1	Cookie Jar	Green cap, coat; gold buttons, trim	185	65.00	80.00	40.00
2	Egg Cup	Green cap, coat; gold buttons, trim	103 x 48	40.00	50.00	25.00
3	Money Box	Green cap, coat; gold buttons, trim	175 x 125	50.00	70.00	35.00
4	Pepper Cruet Saluting	Green cap, coat; gold buttons, trim	105	30.00	35.00	18.00
5	Salt Cruet Holding Package	Green cap, coat; gold buttons, trim	105	30.00	35.00	18.00

K.P. FOODS LTD.

K.P. FRIARS

1983

The *K.P. Friars* set was commissioned by K.P. Foods Ltd. to promote the sales of its potato crisps (chips). The first model, the "Father Abbot," was free with a given number of tokens from the packets. The remaining five models could be obtained with tokens, plus a small charge of £1.30. The offer expired November 1, 1983, and was available to U.K. collectors .

The "Father Abbot" came either in a cardboard box with a friar's design on it or in a small box with a cellophane front. The rest of the figures were issued together as a set of five, in a box with a folding cardboard lid or one with a cellophane sleeve. Although K.P. Friars was first issued as a set of five and in late 1983, as a set of six, with the inclusion of the "Father Abbot," for some reason three of the models — "Brother Crispin," "Brother Angelo" and "Brother Francis" — are the hardest to find, so have higher collector's prices. Each model stands on a square base, with the name of the friar embossed on the front.

NOTE : The origin of the two models with grey robes is unknown.

Backstamp: Embossed "Wade"

No.	Name	Description	Size	U.S. $	Can. $	U.K. £
1a	Brother Francis	Beige head, base; brown robes	42 x 20	45.00	65.00	30.00
1b	Brother Francis	Honey head, base; grey robes	42 x 20	50.00	70.00	35.00
2a	Brother Peter	Beige head, base; brown robes	40 x 18	15.00	20.00	10.00
2b	Brother Peter	Honey head, base; grey robes	40 x 18	25.00	38.00	20.00
3	Brother Angelo	Beige head, base; brown robes	48 x 20	45.00	65.00	30.00
4	Brother Benjamin	Beige head, base; brown robes	40 x 18	15.00	20.00	10.00
5	Brother Crispin	Beige head, base; brown robes	40 x 20	45.00	65.00	30.00
6	Father Abbot	Beige head, base; brown robes	45 x 18	25.00	38.00	20.00

KS WADER
TIN WOODMAN (WIZARD OF OZ)
2001

KS Wader is comprised of friends Ed and Beverly Rucker, and Brian and Judi Morris. They commissioned Wade to produce the "Tin Woodman," one of the characters from the Wizard of Oz books by Frank Baum. Modelled by Ken Holmes, in a limited edition of 500, with another 25 being decorated in an all-over white glaze. One was donated as a raffle prize for the 2001 Wade C & S Bonanza, held in Arundel on December 8th, 2001, the rest were given as prizes at Various Wade events during 2002.

The "Scarecrow" is the fifth model in the *Wizard of Oz* series. It was produced in a limited edition of 250. A special limited edition of 25 (all-white colourway) was produced and used as prizes in draws and competitions. The face, hands and ruffle on the Scarecrow are in an unglazed matt white bisque.

For the other models in the Wizard of Oz series see the Kansas City Wade Show 2001, page 214.

Tin Woodman

Scarecrow, regular issue and special issue

Backstamp: **Scarecrow:** Printed "SCARECROW SPECIAL EDITION KS WADER OZ BY WADE NO. 5 LIMITED EDITION 250" and "Wade est 1810 England" logo
           Scarecrow: Printed "SCARECROW SPECIAL EDITION KS WADER OZ BY WADE NO. 5 LIMITED EDITION 250" and "Wade est 1810 England" logo
           Tin Woodman: Hand written "Oz No 4" with printed "Wade Est 1810 England"

No.	Name	Date	Colourway	Issue - Price	Size	U.S. $	Can. $	U.K. £
1a	Tin Woodman	2001	Grey/brown/green	500 - $28.00	85	35.00	45.00	22.00
1b	Tin Woodman	2001	White	25 - Prizes	85		Rare	
2a	Scarecrow	2002	Blue suit, hat; black boots, crow; yellow base; black lettering	250 - $39.00	27 x 30	45.00	55.00	28.00
2b	Scarecrow	2002	White	25 - Prizes	27 x 30		Rare	

FANTASY SERIES

2002

Unicorns (black and white colourways)

Gargoyle

Backstamp: **Unicorn:** Printed "Wade Ltd. Edition. of 250 KSWader Fantasy Series No 1"
Unicorn: Printed in gold "Wade Special Edition of 25 KSWader Fantasy Series No 1"
Dragon: Printed "Dragon Regular Edition KSWader Fantasy Series No 2 Ltd Edt. of 250" and "Wade est 1810 England" logo
Dragon: Printed "Dragon Special Edition KSWader Fantasy Series No 2 Ltd Edt. of 25" and "Wade est 1810 England" logo
Gargoyle: Printed "Gargoyle Regular Edition KSWader Fantasy Series No 3 Ltd Edt. of 250" and "Wade est 1810 England" logo
Gargoyle: Printed "Gargoyle Special Edition KSWader Fantasy Series No 3 Ltd Edt. of 25" and "Wade est 1810 England" logo

No.	Name	Date	Colourway	Issue - Price	Size	U.S. $	Can. $	U.K. £
1a	Dragon	2002	Grey-blue; beige; pink tongue; honey rock	250 - $38	110	62.00	75.00	38.00
1b	Dragon	2002	Black; gold spines; grey rock	25 - Prizes	110	140.00	170.00	85.00
2a	Gargoyle	2002	Grey; pink tongue; inner ears	250 - $35	85	62.00	76.00	38.00
2b	Gargoyle	2002	White; pink tongue; gold base	25 - Prizes	85	140.00	170.00	85.00
3a	Unicorn	2002	White; gold horns	250 - $35	77 x 70	62.00	75.00	38.00
3b	Unicorn	2002	Black; gold horn, hooves	25 - $35	77 x 70	140.00	170.00	85.00

A HORSE OF A DIFFERENT COLOUR

2003

The first solid Whimsie produced for KS Wader, the horse was originally used for the Tom Smith Crackers, 1982-83 Farmyard Horse. It was produced in four colourways, hence the name "A Horse of a Different Colour." A limited edition of 100, in a white glaze with a gold base, was available to members of the KS mailing list, priced at $15.00, and limited one per person.

Backstamp: Embossed "Wade England"

No.	Name	Date	Colourway	Issue - Price	Size	U.S. $	Can. $	U.K. £
1a	Horse	2003	Burgundy	250 - $32.00	40 x 30	10.00	12.00	6.00
1b	Horse	2003	Cobalt blue	250 - For	40 x 30	10.00	12.00	6.00
1c	Horse	2003	Light green	250 - Set of	40 x 30	10.00	12.00	6.00
1d	Horse	2003	Orange; green base	250 - Four	40 x 30	10.00	12.00	6.00
1e	Horse	2003	White; gold base	100 - $15	40 x 30	32.00	40.00	20.00

CALVES

2003

The Calves, an Angus (black) and a Holstein (black and white) were produced in a limited edition of 125 each. The cost direct from KS Wader was $35.00 each or $68.00 for the pair.

A limited edition of 25 calves in an all-over white colourway was available for promotions and prizes. KS Wader auction one of the special white calves on e-Bay for $98.00 U.S., with the proceeds going to the American Red Cross.

Backstamp: Printed "Calf KS Wader 2003 Regular Edition of 125" and "Wade" logo
Printed "Calf KS Wader 2003 Special Edition of 25" and red "Wade" logo

No.	Name	Date	Colourway	Issue - Price	Size	U.S. $	Can. $	U.K. £
1a	Calf (Angus)	2003	Black	125 - $35	40 x 30	35.00	42.00	21.00
1b	Calf (Holstein)	2003	Black and white	125 - $35	40 x 30	35.00	42.00	21.00
1c	Calf	2003	White	25 - Prizes	40 x 30		Rare	

UNICORN BLOW-UP

2003

The Blow-up Unicorn is a larger version of the KS Waders Fantasy Series Unicorn. It was modelled by Cyril Roberts. The white and gold colourway was issued in a limited edition of 100, and issued at the 2003 Wade Fest.

KS Wader auctioned a Blow-up Unicorn in the Cobalt blue and silver colourway on e-Bay, with the proceeds of $510.00 U.S. being donated to The Children's Make a Wish Foundation.

Backstamp: Printed "Made in England Unicorn Blow-Up KS Wader Special Limited Edition of 100" and red "Wade" logo
Printed "Made in England Unicorn Blow-Up KS Wader Special Limited Edition of 20" and red "Wade" logo

No.	Name	Date	Colourway	Issue - Price	Size	U.S. $	Can. $	U.K. £
1a	Unicorn Blow-up	2003	Black; gold horn, hooves	100 - $70	90	90.00	110.00	55.00
1b	Unicorn Blow-up	2003	Cobalt blue; silver horn, hooves	20 - Prizes	90		Rare	
1c	Unicorn Blow-up	2003	White; gold horn, hooves	100 - $79	90	90.00	110.00	55.00

CHRISTMAS CAT

2003

Based on the popular 1950s Wade ABC Cats, this model is of a cat playing with a Christmas ornament. It was produced in a limited edition of 250.

Backstamp: Unknown

No.	Name	Date	Colourway	Issue - Price	Size	U.S. $	Can. $	U.K. £
1a	Christmas Cat	2003	White; red bow; green/white ornament	250 / —	50	40.00	50.00	25.00
1b	Christmas Cat	2003	Cobalt blue; gold ribbon, ball	25 - prizes	50		Rare	

PATTY KEENAN

CHRISTMAS ORNAMENTS

1994-1997

Both Wade Ceramics and Keenan Antiques sold "Santa's Train," only 500 models have a Keenan Antiques backstamp.

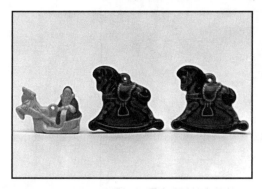

Backstamp: A. Red ink stamped "Wade made in England"
          B. Printed "Wade Ceramics"
          C. Printed "Keenan Antiques Wade England Christmas No 4" (on 500 Santa's Train models)

No.	Name	Date	Colourways	Issue - Price	Size	U.S. $	Can. $	U.K. £
1	Santa's Sleigh	1994	White/red	2000	40	25.00	40.00	20.00
2a	Rocking Horse	1995	Grey horse; dark grey mane	2000	38	25.00	40.00	20.00
2b	Rocking Horse	1996	Honey horse; dark brown mane	600	38	25.00	40.00	20.00
3	Santa's Train	1997	Grey; multicoloured prints	— / £10.50/ $17.00 (US)	35	25.00	40.00	20.00

MINIATURE TANKARD

1996

Patty Keenan commissioned a Miniature Tankard with a print of a Rocking Horse Ornament on the front for the first Wade Show held in Seattle, July 1996.

Backstamp: Red printed "Wade Made in England"

No.	Name	Date	Description	Issue	Size	U.S. $	Can. $	U.K. £
1	Tankard	1996	White; gold rim; grey print	500	31	15.00	20.00	10.00

KEY KOLLECTABLES LTD

THE STRAW FAMILY

1999-2000

Backstamp: Printed "Key Kollectables - Limited Edition of 2,000 with Certificate of Authenticity - Wade England" [name of model]

No.	Name	Date	Colourway	Issue - Price	Size	U.S. $	Can. $	U.K. £
1	Pa Straw	1999	Red/grey/black/yellow	2000 - £27.00	140	65.00	80.00	40.00
2	Ma Straw	1999	Blue/white/brown	2000 - £27.00	134	60.00	70.00	35.00
3	Teen Straw	1999	White/brown/blue vest/yellow	2000 - £27.00	120	60.00	70.00	35.00
4	Baby Straw	2000	Pink/white bib/blue/yellow	2000 - £27.00	85	60.00	70.00	35.00

HOMEPRIDE FRED
2001-2003

Fred At Your Service

Fred's Tasting Time

Fred's Christmas Surprise

Fred's Little Blue Book

Fred's Christmas Pudding

Fred's Easter Egg

Backstamp: **A.** Printed "Key Kollectables [name of model] With Signed Certificate of Authenticity This is not a Toy. © &TM Campbell Grocery Products Limited. Limited edition [edition number]" and "Wade" logo
B. Printed "Key Kollectables [name of model] With Signed Certificate of Authenticity This is not a Toy. © &TM Campbell Grocery Products Limited. Special Limited edition" and "Wade" logo
C. Printed "Key Kollectables Ltd [name of model] This is not a Toy. With Signed Certificate of Authenticity © 2003 &TM Campbell Grocery Products Limited. Limited edition 500" and "Wade" logo
D. Printed "Key Kollectables Ltd [name of model] This is not a Toy. With Signed Certificate of Authenticity Limited edition of 450/special edition of 50 © 2003 &TM Campbell Grocery Products Limited." "Wade" logo

No.	Name	Date	Colourways	Issue - Price	Size	U.S. $	Can. $	U.K. £
1	Fred at Your Service	2001	Black/white suit; blue/white cloth; white base	500 - £27.50	102	90.00	120.00	60.00
2	Fred's Tasting Time	2001	Black suit, hat; silver ladle; white base	500 - £27.50	102	90.00	120.00	60.00
3	Fred's Christmas Surprise	2002	Black suit, hat; yellow gift box, red ribbon; white base	763 - 32.50	102	90.00	120.00	60.00
4	Fred's Little Blue Book	2002	Black suit, hat; blue book; white base	750 - £30.00	102	90.00	120.00	60.00
5	Fred's Christmas Pudding	2003	Black suit, hat; brown/white pudding; white dish, base	557 - £37.50	102	90.00	120.00	60.00
6	Fred's Easter Egg	2003	Black suit, hat; blue/red egg; white base	500 - £35.00	102	90.00	120.00	60.00

HOMEPRIDE FRED BLOW-UPS

Hungry Fred

Souper Fred

Backstamp: Unknown

No.	Name	Date	Colourways	Issue - Price	Size	U.S. $	Can. $	U.K. £
1	Hungry Fred	2002	Black suit, hat; silver knife and fork	300 - £55.00	190	200.00	270.00	135.00
2a	Souper Fred	2003	Black suit, hat; blue/white soup bowl	450 - £60.00	185	125.00	170.00	85.00
2b	Souper Fred	2003	Black suit, hat; silver/white soup bowl	50 - £60.00	185		Rare	

TRAIN SETS

2001-2003

The letters on top of the carriages spell either Spring (blue) or Summer (yellow). The carriage size is 26 x 46 mm, and the engine 34 x 55 mm.

The Autumn Train set was issued in June 2002, and the Winter Train set in spring 2003. Each set has an engine with the "Wade" logo on the roof, and six carriages with lettering spelling 'autumn' or 'winter' on the roofs, and various autumn and winter theme decals on the carriages. They were produced in a limited edition of 200 each with standard lettering, and 100 sets with gold lettering.

The Christmas Train set was issued in winter 2002, and was packaged in a specially designed gift box, which included a postcard certificate.

Spring Train

Autumn Train

Winter Train

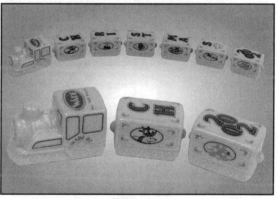

ChristmasTrain

Backstamp: **A.** Embossed "Wade England Key" also printed "Wade England" on roof
B. Embossed "Wade England Key"

No.	Name	Date	Description	Issue - Price	Size	U.S. $	Can. $	U.K. £
1a	Spring Train Set	2001	Blue; multicoloured lettering	400 - £35.00	55 x 34	65.00	80.00	40.00
1b	Spring Train Set	2001	Blue; gold lettering	100 - Unknown	55 x 34	100.00	120.00	60.00
2	Summer Train Set	2001	Yellow; multicoloured lettering	400 - £35.00	55 x 34	65.00	80.00	40.00
3a	Autumn Train Set	2002	Beige; multicoloured decals	200 - £35.00	55 x 34	57.00	70.00	35.00
3b	Autumn Train Set	2002	Beige; multicoloured decals; gold lettering	100 - £40.00	55 x 34	90.00	110.00	55.00
4	Christmas Train Set	2002	White; multicoloured decals	100 - £49.50	55 x 34	57.00	70.00	35.00
5a	Winter Train Set	2003	Cream; multicoloured decals	200 - £35.00	55 x 34	57.00	70.00	35.00
5b	Winter Train Set	2003	Cream; multicoloured decals; gold lettering	100 - £40.00	55 x 34	90.00	110.00	55.00

PEOPLE FROM WHIMSEY-ON-WHY
2003

Butcher, Vicar and Doctor

Blacksmith

Backstamp: **Blacksmith: Standard** - Printed "Wade Whimsey-On-Why Blacksmith" and red "Wade" logo;
Gold Special - Printed "Wade Whimsey-On-Why Blacksmith" and gold "Wade" logo;
Silver Special - Printed "Wade Whimsey-On-Why Blacksmith" and silver "Wade" logo
Butcher: Standard - Red "Wade" logo
Special - Gold "Wade" logo
Vicar: **Standard** - Printed "Key Kollectables Limited Edition Vicar Whimsey-On-Why" and red "Wade" logo
Special - Printed "Key Kollectables Limited Special Edition Vicar Whimsey-On-Why" and gold "Wade" logo
Doctor: Standard - Red "Wade" logo
Special - Gold "Wade" logo

No.	Name	Date	Description	Issue - Price	Size	U.S. $	Can. $	U.K. £
1a	Blacksmith	2003	Blue hat; honey apron; green trousers; gold anvil	10 - Goodie Box	70	.	Rare	
1b	Blacksmith	2003	Blue hat; honey apron; green trousers; grey anvil	250 - £29.95	70	50.00	60.00	30.00
1c	Blacksmith	2003	Blue hat; honey apron; green trousers; silver anvil	20 - £29.95	70		Rare	
2a	Butcher	2003	Yellow hat, blue band; white shirt; blue/white striped apron; pink sausages	250 - £29.95	65	50.00	70.00	35.00
2b	Butcher	2003	Yellow hat, blue band; white shirt; blue/white striped apron; gold sausages	20 - £29.95	65		Rare	
3a	Dr Healer	2003	White coat; silver stethoscope; blue trousers; ginger hair	250 - £29.95	65	50.00	60.00	30.00
3b	Dr Healer	2003	White coat; gold stethoscope; blue trousers; ginger hair	20 - Prizes	65		Rare	
4a	Vicar	2003	Black cassock; white cup/saucer	250 - £29.95	65	50.00	60.00	30.00
4b	Vicar	2003	Black cassock; gold cup/saucer	20 - £29.95	65		Rare	
4c	Vicar	2003	Burgundy cassock; white cup/saucer	10 - Prizes	65		Rare	

KING AQUARIUMS LTD.
AQUARIUM SET
1976-1980

The *Aquarium Set* was produced for King Aquariums Ltd., a British company that supplied aquarium products to pet stores, and were not on sale in gift stores. The "Bridge" is marked with "Wade England" embossed at the base of each span, whereas the other figures are marked on the back rims. For the blue colourway of the water snail / whelk see Tom Smith Crackers Sealife page 390.

Backstamp: Embossed "Wade England"

No.	Name	Description	Size	U.S. $	Can. $	U.K. £
1	Bridge	Beige; light brown base	45 x 80	110.00	140.00	70.00
2	Diver	Honey; brown base	70 x 28	40.00	50.00	25.00
3a	Lighthouse	Beige/honey; grey-green base	75 x 45	70.00	90.00	45.00
3b	Lighthouse	Honey; grey-green base	75 x 45	70.00	90.00	45.00
4	Mermaid	Beige; yellow hair; grey-green base	60 x 58	70.00	90.00	45.00
5	Seahorse	Blue/beige pattern	70 x 30	200.00	250.00	125.00
6	Water Snail/Whelk	Honey; green-grey shell	30 x 35	110.00	140.00	70.00

KEITH LANGFORD
ABSOLUTELY CRACKERS
BIRDS
November 2001

This set of Christmas crackers contains previously issued *English Whimsies, Tom Smith* or *Red Rose Tea Whimsies*, and *Whimsie-land* bird models. There are eight figures in the set, but only six crackers in a box. The issue price of the boxed crackers was £14.99.

Backstamp: Embossed "Wade England"

No.	Name	Description	Size	U.S. $	Can. $	U.K. £
1	Cockerel (WL)	Grey	50 x 35	8.00	10.00	5.00
2	Duck (WL)	Beige	45 x 35	8.00	10.00	5.00
3	Eagle (TS)	Tan	50 x 35	8.00	10.00	5.00
4	Goose (RR)	Brown	30 x 35	8.00	10.00	5.00
5	Owl (WL)	Beige	35 x 25	8.00	10.00	5.00
6	Partridge (WL)	Blue	35 x 25	8.00	10.00	5.00
7	Pelican (EW)	White	45 x 40	8.00	10.00	5.00
8	Wren (TS)	Green	33 x 24	8.00	10.00	5.00

Note: The following initials indicate the origin of the models:
EW: *English Whimsies*
RW: Red Rose Tea
TS: Tom Smith
WL: Whimsie-land

SHARON LATKA

BLACK TERRIER DOG

2000

Commissioned by Sharon Latka of Clarence, New York, this model which was originally the West Highland Terrier from the *Tom Smith Animate Crackers* set "World of Dogs," see page 383.

Backstamp: Embossed "Wade England"

No.	Name	Date	Colourway	Issue - Price	Size	U.S. $	Can. $	U.K. £
1	Terrier Dog (TS)	2000	Black	2000 - $10.00	30	15.00	18.00	9.00

LEVER REXONA
New Zealand
NURSERY RHYME MODELS

Early 1970s

Lever Rexona, makers of Signal toothpaste, offered 24 miniature *Nursery Rhyme* models as a promotion, one model per box. The same models were used in the 1972-1979 Canadian Red Rose Tea promotion.

Backstamp: Unknown

No.	Name	Description	Size	U.S. $	Can. $	U.K. £
1	Baa Baa Black Sheep	Black	25 x 30	18.00	25.00	12.00
2	Cat and the Fiddle	Beige cat; yellow fiddle	47 x 33	22.00	28.00	14.00
3	Dr. Foster	Light brown; yellow tie; blue puddle	43 x 26	10.00	12.00	6.00
4	Gingerbread Man	Red-brown; grey-green base	43 x 30	40.00	60.00	30.00
5	Goosey Gander	Honey head, neck; dark brown wings; pink beak	33 x 36	10.00	12.00	6.00
6	Hickory Dickory Dock	Red-brown/honey clock; brown mouse	44 x 20	7.00	12.00	6.00
7	House that Jack Built	Honey; red-brown roof	32 x 35	12.00	18.00	9.00
8	Humpty Dumpty	Honey; pink cheeks; blue bow tie; brown wall	36 x 23	7.00	10.00	5.00
9	Jack	Light brown; blue shirt, bucket	34 x 33	10.00	15.00	7.00
10	Jill	Yellow hair; beige dress; blue bucket	28 x 39	10.00	15.00	7.00
11	Little Bo-Peep	Light brown; blue apron; green base	44 x 24	10.00	12.00	6.00
12	Little Boy Blue	Blue hat, coat; honey trousers	41 x 25	10.00	15.00	7.00
13	Little Jack Horner	Beige; blue plum; pink cushion	37 x 21	7.00	10.00	5.00
14	Little Miss Muffett	Honey/grey dress; red-brown spider	39 x 35	10.00	15.00	7.00
15	Mother Goose	Blue hat, bodice; honey dress, goose	41 x 34	18.00	25.00	12.00
16	Old King Cole (Gap)	Beige; blue hat, hem; pink sleeves	37 x 32	10.00	15.00	7.00
17	Old Woman Who Lived in a Shoe	Honey; red-brown roof	35 x 40	10.00	15.00	7.00
18	Pied Piper	Light brown coat; green bush	46 x 28	10.00	15.00	6.00
19	Puss in Boots	Brown; blue boots; green base	43 x 20	10.00	30.00	15.00
20	Queen of Hearts	Pink hat; beige dress; two red hearts	42 x 25	15.00	20.00	10.00
21	Red Riding Hood	Beige dress; red/pink hood, cape; green base	44 x 24	10.00	15.00	6.00
22	Three Bears	Dark brown; honey base	36 x 38	30.00	40.00	20.00
23	Tom Tom the Piper's Son	Honey; blue hat, kilt; brown jacket	39 x 33	12.00	16.00	8.00
24	Wee Willie Winkie	Yellow hair, candle; beige nightshirt	44 x 24	10.00	12.00	6.00

LUX SOAP

FREE WADE MINIATURES

c.1970

This English Whimsie Mongrel was distributed free with packets of Lux with Dermasil. Lux is a brand name of Unilever, U.K. The value given is for the packaged model.

Backstamp: Embossed "Wade England"

No.	Name	Description	Size	U.S. $	Can. $	U.K. £
1	Mongrel	Dark brown; light brown	35 x 35	30.00	36.00	18.00

MEMORY JARS
YEAR OF THE RABBIT

Memory Jars commissioned a new colourway of the *English Whimsie Rabbit* to mark the last year of the Millennium (the Chinese Year of the Rabbit). Obtainable with the purchase of a limited edition Memory Jar, they were made available June 1999.

Backstamp: Embossed "Wade England" on rim

No.	Name	Date	Colourways	Issued	Size	U.S. $	Can. $	U.K. £
1a	Rabbit	1999	Blue	450	30 x 30	40.00	60.00	30.00
1b	Rabbit	1999	Gold	50	30 x 30		Rare	

NEW VICTORIA THEATRE
TOAD OF TOAD HALL

This model is a scaled-down version of the original O.I.W.C.C. "Toad of Toad Hall," and was complimentary with admission to the theatre's production of the *Wind in the Willows*.

Backstamp: Printed "New Vic Theatre Wade England"

No.	Name	Date	Description	Issue	Size	U.S. $	Can. $	U.K. £
1	Toad of Toad Hall	2000	Honey coat, cap; dark brown trousers	Free with admission	80	50.00	60.00	30.00

OUT OF THE BLUE CERAMICS
(Collectables Magazine)
COLLECT 99 BEAR

Backstamp: Black printed "Produced by Wade Ceramics England in Collaboration with Collectables Magazine"

No.	Name	Date	Colourways	Issue - Price	Size	U.S. $	Can. $	U.K. £
1	Bear	1999	Honey; blue/white lettering	500 - £25.00	105	65.00	80.00	40.00

BATMAN (LUXURY BOXED SET)

2000

This boxed set of ten Batman characters, and the Batmobile, was produced in a limited edition of 250. The issued price was £752.00

Backstamp: Printed "D.C. Comics ©1999 Produced for Out of the Blue Ceramics LTD Edition only 250 Luxury Boxed Sets Wade England"

No.	Name	Description	Size	U.S. $	Can. $	U.K. £
1	Alfred	Black suit; white base	165	–	–	–
2	Batman	Grey suit; black cloak; yellow belt; white base	180	120.00	180.00	90.00
3	Bat Mobile	Black	(length) 180	–	–	–
4	Bat Woman	Black suit, yellow belt, gloves; white base	155	–	–	–
5	Cat Woman	Black dress; white base	150	–	–	–
6	Iceman	Black/grey suit; white base	190	–	–	–
7	The Joker	Purple suit; black hat, gloves; white base	170	–	–	–
8	The Penguin	Black suit, hat; white shirt, base; grey waistband	150	–	–	–
9	Poison Ivy	Green suit; gold decoration; red hair; white base	155	–	–	–
10	The Riddler	Light green suit, hat; black cane; white base	195	–	–	–
11	Robin	Red/black suit; yellow inner cap, belt; white base	140	–	–	–
—	11 pce set	Boxed	—	1,800.00	2,700.00	1,300.00

Note: The Batman model was also available singly to subscribers of the magazine for £49.50 or non-subscribers at £85.00, it was produced in a limited edition of 1,654.

SUPERMAN

2001

There were many problems with the production of this model. The 'S' decal bubbled and had to be re-applied, plus a large number of models were stolen from the pottery. Although advertised as a limited edition of 1,938 (the date of the first *Superman* comic), due to the production problems the edition was reduced to 250. Sixty-one of these models were issued in special presentation boxes, and have an exclusive backstamp. Models purchased directly from Out of the Blue Ceramics were issued with a certificate of authenticity which was signed by both the commissioner and Wade Ceramics. The model and certificate have matching serial numbers.

Although the backstamp has the copyright date of 1999, the models were not available until 2001.

Backstamp: **A.** Black printed "DC Comics ©1999 Produced for 'Out of the Blue Ceramics' Limited Edition of only 189 pieces Wade England" with edition number
B. Exclusive: Unknown

No.	Name	Date	Description	Issue/Price	Size	U.S. $	Can. $	U.K. £
1	Superman	1998	Blue/red/yellow suit; grey rock	189/£49.50	185	150.00	275.00	125.00
2	Superman/ Presentation Box	1998	Blue/red/yellow suit; grey rock	61/£49.50	185	150.00	275.00	125.00

TINY TREASURES

SET ONE: BATMAN and SUPERMAN

Alfred, Batman, Lois Lane, Supergirl

Backstamp: Red printed "Wade Made in England" and black printed "DC Comics 1999 Wade [name of model]"

No.	Name	Date	Colourways	Issued - Price	Size	U.S. $	Can. $	U.K. £
1	Alfred	1999	Black suit; white shirt	1939 - £5.90	58	15.00	22.00	10.00
2	Batman	1999	Honey; black cloak, gloves, boots	1939 - £5.90	58	15.00	22.00	10.00
3	Lois Lane	1999	Maroon jacket; brown skirt	1938 - £5.90	58	15.00	22.00	10.00
4	Supergirl	1999	Red cloak; blue suit	1938 - £5.90	58	15.00	22.00	10.00

SET TWO: PETER PAN

Mermaid, Pirate, Peter Pan, Mrs. Darling

Backstamp: Embossed "TT 2 Wade" on the back of base

No.	Name	Date	Colourways	Issue - Price	Size	U.S. $	Can. $	U.K. £
5	Mermaid	1999	Grey-green mermaid; honey base	500 - £9.50	60	20.00	30.00	15.00
6	Mrs. Darling	1999	Grey-green dress; brown trim	500 - £9.50	67	20.00	30.00	15.00
7	Peter Pan	1999	Honey; olive suite; brown shoes	500 - £9.50	62	20.00	30.00	15.00
8	Pirate	1999	Honey; grey-green trousers	500 - £9.50	64	20.00	30.00	15.00

SET THREE: SANTA AND SNOWMAN

Backstamp: Black printed "Wade England T.T.3 [name of model]"

No.	Name	Date	Colourways	Issue - Price	Size	U.S. $	Can. $	U.K. £
9	Santa Clause	2000	Red/white suit; black belt, boots	500 - £15.00	60	50.00	60.00	30.00
10	Snowman	2000	White; blue scarf; black hat	500 - £15.00	60	50.00	60.00	30.00

PEX NYLONS

FAIRY AND CANDLE HOLDER

Circa 1952

One of the first promotional models produced by Wade was made at the Wade (Ulster) Pottery in the early 1950s for Pex Nylons. It was a model of a fairy sitting in a pink water lily, and was also produced as a candleholder, although only a very limited number of the candleholders exist. The models were issued with Wade labels; however, they are often seen unmarked because the labels have fallen off.

In the late 1950s, the surplus fairy models were sent to the George Wade Pottery, with the intention of using them in a water babies series. Because of high production costs, however, the series was never issued.

Backstamp: A. Black and gold label "Made in Ireland by Wade Co. Armagh" (1-2)
B. Unmarked (1-2)

No.	Name	Description	Size	U.S. $	Can. $	U.K. £
1a	Fairy	Blue wings; blue/pink/yellow flowers	55 x 35	500.00	600.00	300.00
1b	Fairy	Pink wings; blue/pink/yellow flowers	55 x 35	500.00	600.00	300.00
1c	Fairy	Yellow wings; blue/pink/yellow flowers	55 x 35	500.00	600.00	300.00
2	Fairy Candle Holder	Pink; green	25 x 75	600.00	750.00	375.00

POS-NER ASSOCIATES

SHERWOOD FOREST

A new colourway of Friar Tuck was issued in 1998, although it still carried the original embossed 1994 date in the backstamp. The box lid lists five figures, but the last two, Little John (as a beggar) and the Sheriff of Nottingham, have to date not been produced.

Robin Hood, Maid Marian, Friar Tuck

Backstamp A. Embossed "Mianco 89 Wade England"
B. Embossed "Mianco 90 Wade England"
C. Embossed "Wade Mianco 94"

No.	Name	Date	Colourways	Issue	Size	U.S. $	Can. $	U.K. £
1	Robin Hood	1989	Green/honey brown	5000	70 x 30	35.00	45.00	22.00
2	Maid Marian	1989	Grey-blue/brown	5000	65 x 25	35.00	45.00	22.00
3a	Friar Tuck	1994	Honey brown robes	5000	45 x 30	35.00	45.00	22.00
3b	Friar Tuck	1998	Green-blue robes	500	45 x 30	60.00	75.00	38.00

WHIMBLE FRIAR TUCK

This *Whimble* was commissioned by Pos-ner Associates through C&S Collectables and has a print of "Friar Tuck" on the front.

Backstamp: Red printed "Whimbles by Wade" with two lines

No.	Name	Date	Colourway	Size	U.S. $	Can. $	U.K. £
1	Friar Tuck	1997	White; gold band; black lettering; beige print	27	9.00	12.00	6.00

ARTHUR PRICE OF ENGLAND
THE WONDERFUL WORLD OF ANIMALS SERIES
Late 1970s-Early 1980s

Arthur Price of England commissioned an unknown quantity of Wade English Whimsie models to compliment his boxed sets of children's nursery ware of a spoon, fork and a napkin ring.

Backstamp: **A.** Embossed "Wade England" on back of model rim
B. Embossed "Wade England"

Jungle Babies

No.	Name	Description	Size	U.S. $	Can. $	U.K. £
1	Bushbaby	Brown; blue ears; black nose	30 x 30			
2	Chimp	Dark brown; light brown face, patches	35 x 35			
3	Fawn	Brown; blue ears	30 x 30			
4	Koala	Yellow-brown; black nose; green base	35 x 25			
5	Langur, Type 1	Light brown; dark brown stump	35 x 30			
6	Pine Martin	Honey brown	30 x 30			
—	Boxed Set		—	70.00	90.00	45.00

Jungle Kings

This set of Arthur Price Whimsies was titled Jungle Kings although it contained a polar bear! In the centre of the box is a silver-plated baby cup.

Jungle Babies Boxed Set with Silver-plate Baby's Cup

No.	Name	Description	Size	U.S. $	Can. $	U.K. £
1	Gorilla, standing	Grey; grey-green base	35 x 25			
2	Leopard	Yellow-brown; green base	17 x 45			
3	Lion	Brown mane; honey body	35 x 45			
4	Orang-outan	Ginger	30 x 30			
5	Polar Bear, head forward	White; blue base	30 x 30			
6	Tiger	Honey; green base	35 x 25			
—	Boxed Set		—	70.00	90.00	45.00

On the Farm

No.	Name	Description	Size	U.S. $	Can. $	U.K. £
1	Collie	Golden brown; green base	35 x 35			
2	Cow	Honey; green on base	35 x 35			
3	Horse	Dark grey; green base	45 x 35			
4	Lamb	Light beige; green base	35 x 25			
5	Pig	Beige; green base	25 x 35			
6	Ram	White; grey face; green base	30 x 30			
—	Boxed Set		—	70.00	90.00	45.00

Pets and Companions

In the boxed set illustrated are the "Donkey" and the "Cat" from the *English Whimsies* Set No 8 which was produced in 1977: therefore a date of late 1970s-early 1980s has been estimated for this series. As the models are indistinguishable from *English Whimsies* a value has been given for a boxed set only. Models are listed in alphabetical order for ease of reference.

Pets and Companions Set with Spoon, fork and napkin ring set

No.	Name	Description	Size	U.S. $	Can. $	U.K. £
1	Alsatian	Grey; tan face	30 x 40			
2	Cat	Light brown/ginger; green base	40 x 17			
3	Donkey	Light brown; green base	30 x 30			
4	Kitten, seated	Dark/light brown; pink ball of wool	30 x 30			
5	Mongrel	Dark/light brown	35 x 35			
6	Spaniel	Honey; green on base	35 x 35			
—	Boxed Set		—	70.00	90.00	45.00

R & M COLLECTABLES
BRITANNIA

Backstamp: Printed "Wade England Britannia Produced exclusively for R & M Collectables in a Limited edition of 250 to commemorate the Millennium"

No.	Name	Date	Description	Issued - Price	Size	U.S. $	Can. $	U.K. £
1	Britannia	2000	White robes; gold helmet, trident	250 - £45.00	165	105.00	130.00	65.00

R.H.M. FOODS OF ENGLAND
BISTO KIDS

The *Bisto Kids* salt and pepper cruets were marked "Wade Staffordshire" on their bases, because even though they were made in the Wade Ireland Pottery, they were intended for the British market. They were produced in November and December 1977 for Rank, Hovis & McDougall Foods Co. (R.H.M.) of England and were based on a pair of well-known characters in advertisements for Bisto Gravy Powder on British television. To receive the *Bisto Kids*, one had to mail in two tokens from the packet tops, plus a cheque for £1.95.

Backstamp: Brown transfer "Copyright RHM Foods Ltd. & Applied Creativity, Wade Staffordshire"

No.	Name	Date	Description	Size	U.S. $	Can. $	U.K. £
1	Bisto Boy	1977	Red hat; blue braces, trousers; grey jacket	110	140.00	190.00	95.00
2	Bisto Girl	1977	Yellow hair, blouse; brown hat	115	140.00	190.00	95.00
—	Set (2)			—	280.00	380.00	190.00

RED ROSE TEA (CANADA) LTD.

MINIATURE ANIMALS

FIRST ISSUE

1967-1973

In early 1967, when the sales of Red Rose Tea were in decline and the company was falling behind its competitors, it decided to start a promotional campaign to win back customers. In its campaign Wade miniature animals were used as free premiums in packages of Red Rose Tea Bags.

The first 12 promotional models were released in early 1967 and used in a trial run in Quebec, Canada, to test the public's reaction. The idea proved so successful that the series was quickly increased to 32 models in autumn 1967. The models were then offered nationally, region by region across Canada. Their popularity was so great that the promotional area and period (originally intended for two to three years) was extended to cover all of Canada for six years (from 1967 to 1973).

The models marked with "Wade England" in a recessed base were the first of this series to be produced. When the dies on five of these — the "Beaver," "Bushbaby," "Kitten," "Owl" and "Squirrel" — were retooled in 1967, the marks were placed on the back rim of the models; however the "Bear Cub," had "Wade" between the front feet and "England" on the back rim.

The "Bison" and "Hippo" are found in two sizes because, when the original dies broke, the new dies produced smaller models. In fact, there can be slight size variations in all the models listed below.

A second "Rabbit" was made with open ears because the closed ears on the first version were too difficult to fettle. The first issue "Trout" was unmarked, and the back of the base differs slightly from the second issue, which is marked "Wade England" on the back rim.

This first issue was later produced as English Whimsies, except for the "Fantail Goldfish," "Butterfly," "Frog," "Poodle," "Crocodile," "Terrapin," "Seal on Rock" and "Rabbit" with closed ears. The "Butterfly," "Frog" and "Fantail Goldfish" were also used for a Brooke Bond Tea, UK (Sister Company to Red Rose Tea) promotion and the "Crocodile" and "Terrapin" were previously used in the Balding and Mansell Flintstones Christmas Cracker set.

Due to the replacement of worn dies the hedgehog model has been found with two different types of base: Type 1 has three pads; Type 2 has two pads. The Crocodile model is found with two base variations: a recessed base and a disc base. It is not known which was produced first.

A "Trout" with a recessed base has been found in North America. A late 1960s advertisement has been seen that shows the Crocodile named as 'Alligator.' A variation in the "Bushbaby" exists where the whole of the top arm is in front of the knee, and there is no gap under the base.

The following list is in alphabetical order.

Backstamp: A. Embossed "Wade England" on rim (1, 2a, 3a, 4a, 4b, 6a, 8, 9, 11, 12, 13, 14, 16, 18a, 18b, 19a, 19b, 20, 21, 22, 23a, 24, 25a, 25b, 26, 27, 28, 29a, 31a, 32)
B. Embossed "Wade England" in recessed base (2b, 3b, 5, 6b, 7a, 7b, 10a, 10b, 15a, 15b, 17a, 17b, 19b, 23b, 29b, 30a, 30b, 30c)
C. Embossed "Wade England" on disk (10a)
D. Unmarked (31b)

No.	Name	Description	Size	U.S. $	Can. $	U.K. £
1	Alsatian	Grey; tan face	30 x 40	5.00	6.00	3.00
2a	Bear Cub	Grey; beige face	30 x 40	5.00	6.00	3.00
2b	Bear Cub (recessed base)	Grey; beige face	30 x 40	15.00	12.00	5.00
3a	Beaver	Grey-brown; honey-brown face	35 x 45	3.00	4.00	2.00
3b	Beaver (recessed base)	Grey-brown; honey-brown face	35 x 45	15.00	12.00	5.00
4a	Bison, large	Honey; dark brown head, mane	32 x 45	12.00	18.00	9.00
4b	Bison, small	Honey; dark brown head, mane	28 x 40	5.00	6.00	3.00
5	Bluebird	Beige; blue wings, head	15 x 35	10.00	12.00	6.00
6a	Bushbaby, Type 1	Brown; blue ears; black nose	30 x 30	3.00	4.00	2.00
6b	Bushbaby, Type 1 (recessed base)	Brown; blue ears; black nose	30 x 30	5.00	7.00	3.00
6c	Bushbaby, Type 2	Brown; blue ears; black nose	30 x 30	5.00	7.00	3.00
7a	Butterfly	Honey; grey tips; raised circles	10 x 45	10.00	15.00	7.00
7b	Butterfly	Olive/brown; green tips; raised circles	10 x 45	10.00	15.00	7.00
7c	Butterfly	Honey	10 x 45	10.00	15.00	7.00
8	Chimpanzee	Dark brown; light brown face, patches	35 x 35	5.00	6.00	3.00

No.	Name	Description	Size	U.S. $	Can. $	U.K. £
9	Corgi	Honey-brown; black nose	30 x 35	7.00	10.00	5.00
10a	Crocodile/Alligator	Brownish green	14 x 40	9.00	7.00	6.00
10b	Crocodile /Alligator	Brownish green	14 x 40	9.00	7.00	6.00
11	Duck	Blue/brown; yellow beak	30 x 40	7.00	10.00	5.00
12	Fantail Goldfish	Green/yellow; blue rock	30 x 35	10.00	12.00	7.00
13	Fawn	Brown; blue ears; black nose	30 x 30	5.00	6.00	3.00
14	Fox	Dark brown; fawn face, chest	30 x 30	6.00	10.00	4.00
15a	Frog	Green	15 x 30	15.00	20.00	10.00
15b	Frog	Yellow	15 x 30	15.00	20.00	10.00
16	Giraffe	Beige	35 x 35	5.00	6.00	3.00

No.	Name	Description	Size	U.S. $	Can. $	U.K. £
17a	Hedgehog, Type 1	Light brown; honey face; black nose	23 x 40	5.00	6.00	3.00
17b	Hedgehog, Type 2	Dark red brown; honey face; black nose	23 x 40	5.00	6.00	3.00
18a	Hippo, large	Honey brown	25 x 45	16.00	20.00	10.00
18b	Hippo, small	Honey brown	20 x 40	5.00	6.00	3.00
19a	Kitten, seated	Dark/light brown; pink wool	30 x 30	5.00	6.00	3.00
19b	Kitten, seated	Dark/light brown; red wool	30 x 30	10.00	8.00	4.00
20	Lion	Light brown; dark brown head, mane	35 x 45	7.00	8.00	4.00
21	Mongrel	Dark brown/light brown	35 x 35	5.00	6.00	3.00
22	Otter	Beige; blue base	30 x 35	5.00	6.00	3.00
23a	Owl	Dark/light brown	35 x 20	5.00	6.00	3.00
23b	Owl	Dark/light brown	35 x 20	15.00	12.00	8.00
24	Poodle	White; green base	40 x 45	10.00	7.00	5.00

Rabbit, closed ears   Rabbit, open ears

Embossed backstamp in
recessed base of Trout

No.	Name	Description	Size	U.S. $	Can. $	U.K. £
25a	Rabbit	Beige; closed ears	30 x 30	15.00	15.00	20.00
25b	Rabbit	Beige; ears open	30 x 30	5.00	6.00	3.00
26	Seal on Rock	Brown; blue rock	35 x 35	12.00	10.00	7.00
27	Setter	Brown; grey-green base	35 x 50	5.00	6.00	3.00
28	Spaniel	Honey brown; green on base	35 x 35	5.00	6.00	3.00
29a	Squirrel	Grey; beige; yellow acorn	35 x 30	5.00	6.00	3.00
29b	Squirrel (Recessed)	Grey; beige; yellow acorn	35 x 30	12.00	9.00	6.00
30a	Terrapin	Beige; brown markings	10 x 40	10.00	14.00	7.00
30b	Terrapin	Beige; grey markings	10 x 40	10.00	14.00	7.00
30c	Terrapin	Beige; purple-blue markings	10 x 40	10.00	14.00	7.00
31a	Trout	Brown; red tail; grey-green base	30 x 30	5.00	6.00	3.00
31b	Trout	Brown; red tail; grey-green base	30 x 30	5.00	6.00	3.00
31c	Trout (recessed base)	Brown; red tail; grey-green base	30 x 30	15.00	18.00	9.00
32a	Wild Boar	Brown; green on base	30 x 40	5.00	6.00	3.00
32b	Wild Boar	Brown	30 x 40	9.00	10.00	5.00

MINIATURE NURSERIES

SECOND ISSUE

1972-1979

A series of 24 miniature nursery rhyme characters was given away free in the second Red Rose Tea promotion. For the first two years, these models were only distributed in selected areas; it was not until 1973 that they were distributed throughout Canada.

When a new die replaces a worn one, variations in models sometimes occur, as in "The Queen of Hearts" and "Old King Cole." Models with colour variations may indicate a painters whim or that a particular glaze was temporarily out of stock. All the models are marked "Wade England" around the rim of the base.

Because over 20 million of these models are reported to have been made; only the undamaged models are worth keeping. Thin, more breakable models in mint condition are worth more than the solid, heavier models, which stand up to rough handling better. Lever Rexona of New Zealand used the same 24 models in an early 1970s promotion for Signal Toothpaste. Five of the models were released in England as a boxed set.

As the 'Queen of Hearts" with eight hearts on her dress is so rarely found, it is now believed that this model was a prototype and not put into full production.

Backstamp: Embossed "Wade England"

No.	Name	Description	Size	U.S. $	Can. $	U.K. £
1	Baa Baa Black Sheep	Black all over	23 x 30	18.00	12.00	11.00
2	Cat and the Fiddle	Beige front; grey back; yellow fiddle	47 x 33	22.00	15.00	16.00
3a	Dr. Foster	Light brown all over	43 x 26	12.00	10.00	9.00
3b	Dr. Foster	Light brown; blue puddle	43 x 26	12.00	10.00	9.00
3c	Dr. Foster	Light brown; yellow tie; blue puddle	43 x 26	12.00	6.00	12.00
3d	Dr. Foster	Brown; grey puddle	43 x 26	12.00	6.00	12.00
4	Gingerbread Man	Red-brown; grey-green base	43 x 30	40.00	30.00	30.00
5	Goosey Goosey Gander	Honey; brown wings; pink beak	33 x 36	10.00	7.00	6.00
6	Hickory Dickory Dock	Red-brown/honey brown	44 x 20	7.00	4.00	5.00
7	House that Jack Built	Honey brown; red-brown roof	32 x 35	12.00	10.00	12.00
8a	Humpty Dumpty	Honey brown; blue tie; brown wall	36 x 23	7.00	4.00	5.00
8b	Humpty Dumpty	Honey brown; brown wall	36 x 23	7.00	4.00	5.00

Backstamp: Embossed "Wade England"

No.	Name	Description	Size	U.S. $	Can. $	U.K. £
9a	Jack	Brown; blue shirt; brown bucket	34 x 33	10.00	6.00	9.00
9b	Jack	Brown; blue shirt; blue bucket	34 x 33	10.00	6.00	9.00
10	Jill	Yellow hair; beige dress; blue bucket	28 x 39	10.00	6.00	9.00
11	Little Bo-Peep	Brown; blue apron; green base	44 x 24	7.00	8.00	4.00
12	Little Boy Blue	Blue hat, coat; brown trousers	41 x 25	14.00	16.00	8.00
13	Little Jack Horner	Beige; pink cushion; blue plum	37 x 21	7.00	8.00	4.00
14	Little Miss Muffett	Honey/grey dress; red-brown spider	39 x 35	10.00	6.00	10.00
15	Little Red Riding Hood	Beige dress; red cape; green base	44 x 24	10.00	6.00	9.00
16a	Mother Goose	Brown hat; honey brown dress	41 x 31	12.00	10.00	12.00
16b	Mother Goose	Blue hat; honey brown dress	41 x 31	12.00	10.00	12.00

Backstamp: Embossed "Wade England"

No.	Name	Description	Size	U.S. $	Can. $	U.K. £
17a	Old King Cole, Type 1	Gap; brown body, shoes, pot; blue hat, cloak	37 x 32	10.00	5.00	7.00
17b	Old King Cole, Type 1	Gap; brown body, pot; blue hat, cloak, shoes	40 x 35	10.00	5.00	7.00
17c	Old King Cole, Type 2	No gap; brown body shoes, pot; blue hat	40 x 35	10.00	5.00	7.00
17d	Old King Cole, Type 2	No gap; brown body; blue hat, cloak, shoes, pot	40 x 35	10.00	5.00	7.00
18a	Old Woman Who Lived in a Shoe	Honey brown; red-brown roof	35 x 40	7.00	10.00	5.00
18b	Old Woman Who Lived in a Shoe	Honey brown	35 x 40	10.00	5.00	7.00
19a	Pied Piper	Light brown coat; green bush	46 x 28	10.00	7.00	6.00
19b	Pied Piper	Pink/brown coat; green bush	46 x 28	10.00	7.00	6.00
20	Puss in Boots	Brown; blue boots; green base	43 x 20	12.00	10.00	9.00
21a	Queen of Hearts	2 small hearts; beige dress; pink hat	42 x 25	15.00	8.00	10.00
21b	Queen of Hearts	2 large hearts; beige dress; pink hat	42 x 25	15.00	8.00	10.00
21c	Queen of Hearts	8 small hearts; beige dress; pink hat	42 x 25		Extremely rare	
22a	The Three Bears	Dark brown; honey base	36 x 38	25.00	15.00	22.00
22b	The Three Bears	Light brown; honey base	36 x 38	25.00	15.00	22.00
23a	Tom Tom the Piper's Son	Honey brown; blue tam, kilt	39 x 33	12.00	10.00	9.00
23b	Tom Tom the Piper's Son	Honey brown; brown tam, kilt	39 x 33	12.00	10.00	9.00
23c	Tom Tom the Piper's Son	Honey brown; grey tam, kilt	39 x 33	12.00	10.00	9.00
24	Wee Willie Winkie	Yellow hair; beige nightshirt	44 x 24	10.00	5.00	7.00

348

WHOPPAS
THIRD ISSUE
1981

In 1981 the English series of *Whoppas* came to an end, and the surplus stock was used for Red Rose Tea Canada premiums. To obtain a model, Canadian collectors had to mail in the tab from a box of Red Rose Tea, plus $1.00 for postage. The models in these sets were issued in numbered boxes, and all are marked "Wade England" around the rim of the base.

Numbers 1 through 5 are from Wade's *Whoppas,* Set One; 6 to 10 are from *Whoppas*, Set Two; 11 to 15 are from *Whoppas*, Set Three.

Backstamp: Embossed "Wade England"

SET ONE

No.	Name	Description	Size	U.S. $	Can. $	U.K. £
1	Polar Bear	White; grey-blue base	35 x 55	28.00	36.00	18.00
2	Hippo	Grey; green base	35 x 50	28.00	36.00	18.00
3	Brown Bear	Red-brown; brown base	35 x 45	28.00	36.00	18.00
4	Tiger	Honey brown; green base	30 x 60	28.00	36.00	18.00
5	Elephant	Grey	55 x 50	28.00	36.00	18.00

SET TWO

No.	Name	Description	Size	U.S. $	Can. $	U.K. £
6	Bison	Brown; green base	40 x 50	30.00	38.00	19.00
7	Wolf	Grey; green base	60 x 45	30.00	38.00	19.00
8	Bobcat	Light brown; dark brown spots; green base	55 x 50	30.00	38.00	19.00
9	Chipmunk	Brown; dark brown base	55 x 40	35.00	42.00	21.00
10	Raccoon	Brown; black stripes, eye patches; green base	40 x 50	35.00	42.00	21.00

SET THREE

No.	Name	Description	Size	U.S. $	Can. $	U.K. £
11	Fox	Red-brown; green on base	30 x 60	35.00	42.00	21.00
12	Badger	Brown; cream stripe; green base	35 x 45	35.00	42.00	21.00
13	Otter	Brown; blue base	30 x 55	35.00	42.00	21.00
14	Stoat	Brown; green base	35 x 55	35.00	42.00	21.00
15	Hedgehog	Brown; green base	30 x 50	35.00	42.00	21.00

MINIATURE ANIMALS

FOURTH ISSUE

1982-1984

Six animal models from the first Red Rose Tea Canada Promotion, marked RRC, were reissued some with slight colour variations, and 17 models from the 1971-1984 English *Whimsies* series were added to make this fourth promotion of 23 animals. New dies resulted in three sizes of pig.

Backstamp: Embossed "Wade England"

No.	Name	Description	Size	U.S. $	Can. $	U.K. £
1	Angelfish	Grey; dark grey stripes; blue base	35 x 30	10.00	14.00	7.00
2	Beaver (RRC)	Brown; honey brown face	35 x 45	3.00	4.00	2.00
3a	Bushbaby, Type 1 (RRC)	Beige	30 x 30	3.00	4.00	2.00
3b	Bushbaby, Type 2 (RRC)	Beige	30 x 30	5.00	7.00	3.00
4	Camel	Dark grey; green base	35 x 35	9.00	12.00	6.00
5	Collie	Honey; green base	35 x 35	10.00	12.00	6.00
6	Corgi (RRC)	Honey; black nose	30 x 35	7.00	10.00	5.00
7	Cow	Honey; green base	35 x 35	10.00	12.00	6.00
8	Fox (RRC)	Dark brown; fawn face	30 x 30	6.00	10.00	4.00

No.	Name	Description	Size	U.S. $	Can. $	U.K. £
9	Giraffe (RRC)	Beige	35 x 35	5.00	6.00	3.00
10	Gorilla, standing	Dark grey; green on base	35 x 25	6.00	9.00	4.00
11	Horse	Dark grey; green base	35 x 35	20.00	25.00	12.00
12	Lamb	Light beige; green base	30 x 25	10.00	12.00	6.00
13	Langur, Type 1	Beige; brown stump	35 x 30	5.00	8.00	4.00
14	Leopard	Honey; green base	17 x 45	8.00	12.00	6.00
15	Orang-outan	Dark brown	30 x 30	5.00	7.00	4.00

KS Wader

White Calf
(P. 317)

Christmas Cat
November 2003 (P. 318)

Dragon

Unicorn Blow Up, Cobalt Blue
(P. 317)

Horses, five different colourways
(P. 316)

Gargoyle in Grey
(P. 316)

Gargoyle in White
(P. 316)

Black and White Calves
(P. 317)

Black Calves
(P. 317)

Scarecrow
(P. 315)

Scarecrow in White
(P. 315)

Patty Keenan

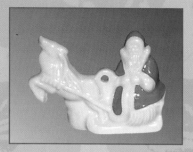

Santa on his Sleigh
Christmas tree ornament, 1994 (P. 319)

Jenny The Black Poodle
1999 (P. 215)

Leprechaun riding a Snail
2001 (P. 216)

Rocking Horse
Christmas tree ornament, 1995 – Grey, 1996 – Honey (P. 319)

Leprechaun with Wheelbarrow of Gold
Standard colourway and Gold Coin colourway, 2002 (P. 217)

Mice (Lil' Bits)
Five different colourways, 2002 (P. 217)

Little Bunnies (Lil' Bits)
Five different colourways, 2001 (P. 216)

Key Collectables

Spring Train
2001 (P. 323)

Autumn Train
2002 (P. 323)

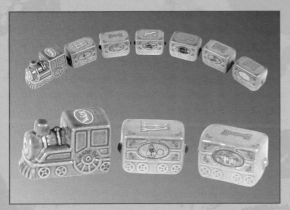

Winter Train
2003 (P. 323)

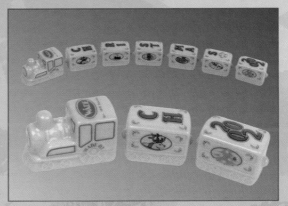

Christmas Train
2002 (P. 323)

Homepride Fred Money Box
2004

Homepride Fred
(P. 321)

Red Rose Tea (Canada) Ltd.
Miniature Nurseries

Baa Baa Black Sheep, Cat and the Fiddle, Dr. Foster, Gingerbread Man, Goosey Goosey Gander, Hickory Dickory Dock
(P. 345)

House that Jack Built, Humpty Dumpty, Jack, Jill, Little Bo-Beep, Little Boy Blue
(P. 346)

Little jack Horner, Little Miss Muffett, Little Red Riding Hood, Mother Goose, Old King Cole, Old Woman Who Lived in a Shoe
(P. 346)

Pied Piper, Puss in Boots, Queen of Hearts, The Three Bears, Tom Tom the Piper's Son, Wee Willie Winkie
(P. 347)

Red Rose Tea U.S.A. Ltd.
Miniature Animals

First Issue: Chimpanzee, Elephant, Hare, Hippo, Squirrel, Turtle, Wild Boar,
Bear Cub, Bison, Bluebird, Bushbaby, Lion, Otter, Owl, Seal on Rock, 1983-1985 (P. 352)

Second Issue: Beaver, Camel, Giraffe, Leopard, Orang-outan, Pine Marten, Polar Bear,
Gorilla, Kangaroo, Koala, Langur, Raccoon, Rhino, Tiger, Zebra, 1985-1990 (P. 353)

Fourth Issue: Kangaroo, Koala, Langur, Persian Kitten, Orang-outan, Pine Marten, Polar Bear, Pony, Raccoon,
Beaver, Cock-a-teel, Giraffe, Gorilla, Camel, Rabbit, Puppy, Tiger, Zebra, Rhino, 1992 (P. 355)

Red Rose Tea U.S.A Ltd.
Noah's Ark

Noah and his Wife with the Ark
(P. 359)

Noah and his Wife
Base Varieties – Oval and Peanut (P. 359)

Animals of the Ark
Top Row: Female Rhino, Hen, Rooster, Female Elephant, Male Elephant
Middle Row: Goose, Gander, Lioness, Lion
Bottom Row: Male Rhino, Ewe, Ram, Female Zebra, Male Zebra. 2002 (P. 359)

Tom Smith and Company Ltd.
Wildlife

Goat, Hare, Squirrel, Zebra, Bison, Collie, Duck, swimming
1986-1987 (P. 377)

Colourways

Goats in two colourways
from the **Farmyard Animals Set**, 1982-1983 (P. 374)

Swimming Duck in three colourways
Farmyard and **Wildlife Sets**, 1982-1987 (P. 374, 377)

Whelk from the **Sealife Set** 1998 (P. 390)

Koala from the **Safari Park Set**, 1976-1977 (P. 371)

West Highland Terrier from the **World of Dogs**, 1990-1991 (P. 383)

Old King Cole from the **Recoloured Models** of 1990 (P. 379)

Packaging

Early Wade model boxes were just as colourful as their contents. The lid of this 1958 Noddy set box has colourful pictures of the four models in the set.

The Happy Families Packaging went through many changes

This unusual 1981-1985 Disney's plastic Hatbox has Bambi characters illustrated on the lid, but contains the model of "Tod the Fox".

The green Hatbox has a black and white print of Bambi; the orange Hatbox has a multi-coloured print.

Box for Carryer Craft of California Printed Ladies

The Lucky Leprechauns packaging changed over the years with the first having a printed box and then a cellophane window.

Aqua-Dishes in a 1950's package

Key Kollectables package for the Seasons' Train Sets

Backstamp: Embossed "Wade England"

No.	Name	Description	Size	U.S. $	Can. $	U.K. £
16	Pelican	Honey/brown; green base	45 x 40	20.00	30.00	14.00
17a	Pig, large	Beige	27 x 44	25.00	32.00	16.00
17b	Pig, medium	Beige; green base	25 x 40	20.00	24.00	12.00
17c	Pig, small	Beige; green base	25 x 35	20.00	24.00	12.00
18	Pine Marten	Honey	30 x 30	5.00	6.00	3.00
19	Rabbit, ears open (RRC)	Beige	30 x 30	5.00	6.00	3.00
20	Rhino	Dark grey; green base	17 x 45	5.00	7.00	4.00
21	Seahorse	Honey-yellow; grey-blue base	50 x 17	20.00	30.00	14.00
22a	Turtle	Dark grey	15 x 50	10.00	15.00	7.00
22b	Turtle	Greenish-grey	15 x 50	10.00	15.00	7.00
23	Zebra	Beige	40 x 35	12.00	12.00	6.00

Note: The above pricing tables are listed in photograph order from bottom left to upper right.

352

RED ROSE TEA U.S.A. LTD. (REDCO FOODS LTD.)

1983-2002

The Canadian Red Rose Tea promotion was so successful that it was extended to the United States in 1983. Red Rose estimates that over two hundred million Wade models have been distributed in packets of Red Rose Tea in the U.S.A. and in Canada during its promotions. In many states figurine promotions overlap, with some model series still being offered in one area whilst a new series is offered in another.

A variation in the "Bushbaby" exists where the whole of the top arm is in front of the knee, and there is no gap under the base.

MINIATURE ANIMALS

FIRST ISSUE

1983-1985

In this first American series, two of the models, the "Hare" and "Squirrel," were not original *English Whimsies*, but models from the 1980-1981 Tom Smith *British Wildlife* set. All figures are in all-over, one-colour glazes, and they may vary slightly from the measurements indicated below. They are listed in alphabetical order.

Backstamp: A. Embossed "Wade England"
B. Embossed "Wade" between front feet and "England" on back of model

No.	Name	Description	Size	U.S. $	Can. $	U.K. £
1	Bear Cub (RR/EW)	Beige	30 x 40	6.00	8.00	4.00
2	Bison (RR/EW)	Dark brown	30 x 40	8.00	12.00	6.00
3	Bluebird (RR/EW)	Beige	15 x 35	8.00	12.00	6.00
4a	Bushbaby, Type 1 (RR/EW)	Beige	30 x 30	8.00	12.00	6.00
4b	Bushbaby, Type 2	Beige	30 x 30	5.00	7.00	3.00
5	Chimpanzee (RR/EW)	Honey brown	35 x 35	10.00	15.00	7.00
6	Elephant (EW)	Blue; no eyes	35 x 45	20.00	30.00	15.00
7	Hare (TS)	Dark brown	50 x 30	8.00	12.00	6.00
8	Hippo (RR/EW)	Honey	23 x 40	5.00	6.00	3.00
9	Lion, standing(RR/EW)	Honey	35 x 45	8.00	12.00	6.00
10	Otter (RR/EW)	Beige	30 x 35	8.00	10.00	5.00
11	Owl (RR/EW)	Dark brown	35 x 20	10.00	20.00	10.00
12	Seal on Rock (RR/TS)	Blue	35 x 35	8.00	10.00	5.00
13a	Squirrel (TS)	Dark blue	40 x 40	8.00	12.00	6.00
13b	Squirrel (TS)	Grey-blue/light blue	40 x 40	8.00	12.00	6.00
14	Turtle (EW)	Light grey	15 x 50	10.00	20.00	10.00
15	Wild Boar (RR/EW)	Beige	30 x 40	8.00	12.00	6.00

Note: The following initials indicate the origin of the models.
EW: *English Whimsies*
RR: Red Rose Tea
TS: Tom Smith *British Wildlife* set

SECOND ISSUE

1985-1990

All the models in this series are in all-over, one-colour glazes. Some of these figures are in the same colours used in the 1982-1984 Canada Red Rose Tea promotion. In Washington State, in early 1992 the same models were offered with Red Rose Decaffeinated tea.

Backstamp: Embossed "Wade England"

No.	Name	Description	Size	U.S. $	Can. $	U.K. £
1	Beaver (EW/RRC)	Light brown	35 x 45	5.00	7.00	6.00
2	Camel (EW/RRC)	Beige	35 x 35	6.00	8.00	4.00
3	Giraffe (EW/RRC)	Beige	35 x 35	5.00	6.00	3.00
4	Gorilla, standing (EW/RRC)	Dark brown	35 x 25	6.00	8.00	4.00
5	Kangaroo (EW)	Honey brown	45 x 25	8.00	12.00	5.00
6a	Koala (EW)	Beige	35 x 25	7.00	10.00	5.00
6b	Koala (EW)	Brown	35 x 25	7.00	10.00	5.00
7	Langur, Type 1 (EW/RRC)	Dark brown	35 x 30	5.00	7.00	5.00
8	Leopard (EW/RRC)	Honey brown	17 x 45	5.00	7.00	3.00
9	Orang-outan (EW/RRC)	Dark brown	30 x 30	5.00	8.00	4.00
10	Pine Marten (EW/RRC)	Honey brown	30 x 30	5.00	7.00	3.00
11	Polar Bear, head forward (EW/TS)	White	30 x 30	5.00	6.00	3.00
12	Raccoon (EW)	Dark brown	25 x 35	6.00	8.00	4.00
13	Rhino (EW/RRC)	Blue-grey	17 x 45	6.00	8.00	4.00
14	Tiger (EW)	Honey brown	35 x 25	5.00	6.00	3.00
15	Zebra (EW/RRC)	Grey	40 x 35	5.00	6.00	3.00

Note: The following initials indicate the origin of the models.
EW: *English Whimsies*
RRC: Red Rose Tea Canada
TS: Tom Smith

THIRD ISSUE

1990-1995

The 15 models offered in the 1985-1990 Red Rose Tea promotion were increased to 20 in late 1990, with the addition of five Tom Smith 1988-1989 models (indicated below by TS). By late 1993 in New York State, Philadelphia, Florida and in Portland, Maine, the models were no longer included free in boxes of teabags, but could be obtained by sending in the UPC code and a small shipping and handling charge. In other areas of the U.S., the 20 animal figurines were available until mid 1995.

Backstamp: Embossed "Wade England"

No.	Name	Description	Size	U.S. $	Can. $	U.K. £
1	Cock-a-teel (Cockatoo) (TS)	Green	35 x 30	6.00	9.00	4.00
2	Kitten (TS)	Grey	25 x 33	6.00	9.00	4.00
3	Pony (Shetland) (TS)	Beige	25 x 30	8.00	12.00	5.00
4	Rabbit (TS)	Dark brown	30 x 25	6.00	9.00	4.00
5	Puppy (Spaniel) (TS)	Honey brown	25 x 30	8.00	12.00	5.00

FOURTH ISSUE

1992

Red Rose U.S.A. offered these models as a mail-in offer with their packages of decaffeinated tea in early 1992. The models were obtained by mail order as the packaging method for decaffeinated tea did not allow for the inclusion of a model in the box of tea.

New dies resulted in three types of Langur: Type One (as seen on the Red Rose Tea packet) has no gap between the neck and stump; Type Two has a gap between the neck and stump, and under the left arm; Type Three has the gap between the neck and stump, but not under the left arm. The Koala has been reported in two colourways for this series, surplus models from other series may have been used to complete the order. The beige colourway of the Koala is illustrated on the Red Rose Tea packet.

Backstamp: Embossed "Wade England"

No.	Name	Description	Size	U.S. $	Can. $	U.K. £
1	Beaver (EW/RRC/RRU)	Dark brown	35 x 45	5.00	7.00	6.00
2	Camel (EW/RRC)	Dark grey	35 x 35	6.00	8.00	4.00
3	Cock-a-teel (TS)	Green	35 x 30	6.00	9.00	4.00
4	Giraffe (EW/RRC)	Beige	35 x 35	5.00	6.00	3.00
5a	Gorilla, standing (EW/RRC)	Dark brown	35 x 25	9.00	8.00	4.00
5b	Gorilla, standing (EW/RRC)	Black	35 x 25	12.00	20.00	12.00
6	Kangaroo (EW/RRU)	Honey brown	45 x 25	8.00	12.00	5.00
7	Persian kitten (TS)	Grey	25 x 33	6.00	9.00	4.00
8a	Koala (EW/RRU)	Beige	35 x 25	7.00	10.00	5.00
8b	Koala (EW/RRU)	Dark grey; beige stump	35 x 25	15.00	22.00	11.00
9a	Langur, Type 1 (EW/RRC)	Light brown; brown stump	35 x 30	8.00	10.00	5.00
9b	Langur, Type 1 (EW/RRC)	Dark brown	35 x 30	5.00	7.00	5.00
9c	Langur, Type 2 (EW/RRC)	Dark brown	35 x 30	6.00	8.00	7.00
9d	Langur, Type 3 (EW/RRC)	Brown	35 x 30	6.00	8.00	7.00
10	Leopard (EW/RRC/RRU)	Mottled olive brown	17 x 45	16.00	20.00	10.00
11	Orang-outan (EW/RRC)	Brown	30 x 30	5.00	7.00	6.00
12	Pine Marten (EW/RRC)	Honey	30 x 30	5.00	7.00	3.00
13	Polar Bear, head forward (EW/TS/RRU)	White	30 x 30	5.00	6.00	3.00
14	Pony (Shetland) (TS)	Beige	25 x 30	8.00	12.00	5.00
15	Rabbit (TS)	Dark brown	30 x 25	6.00	9.00	4.00
16	Raccoon (3W/RRU)	Brown	25 x 35	6.00	8.00	4.00
17	Rhino (E3/RRC/RRU)	Blue-grey/light grey	17 x 45	6.00	8.00	4.00
18	Puppy (Spaniel) (TS)	Honey	25 x 30	8.00	12.00	5.00
19	Tiger (EW/RRU)	Mottled olive brown	35 x 25	16.00	20.00	10.00
20	Zebra (EW/RRC/RRU)	Light grey	40 x 35	6.00	9.00	4.00

Note: 1. For an illustration of model numbers 3, 7, 14, 15 and 18 please see previous page.

2. The following initials indicate the origin of the models:
EW: *English Whimsies*; RRC: Red Rose Tea Canada; RRU: Red Rose Tea U.S.A.; TS: Tom Smith

CIRCUS ANIMALS

1993-1999

In late 1993, Red Rose offered a reissue of the most popular of the Tom Smith cracker models, *The Circus* set, originally issued in England for Tom Smith from 1978 to 1979 (indicated by the initials TS). The original moulds were used and with only a slight variation in colour from the older models. Two variations have been found in the *Circus* Tiger due to a new mould being made: the mouth of the second variation appears to be more open and there is more detailing in the fur of the throat and chest which gives it the appearance of a beard.

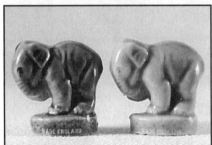

Left: Tom Smith Circus Elephant (blue
Right: Red Rose (U.S.A.) Elephant (pale blue)

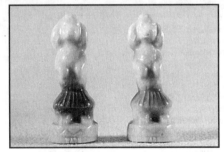

Left: Tom Smith Circus Poodle (dark blue)
Right: Red Rose (U.S.A.) Poodle (light blue)

FIFTH ISSUE

1993-1998

Backstamp: **A.** Embossed "Wade England" on back rim of base
B. Embossed "Wade Eng" on back rim of base

No.	Name	Description	Size	U.S. $	Can. $	U.K. £
1	Brown Bear (TS)	Dark brown	32 x 32	7.00	10.00	6.00
2	Chimpanzee Boy (TS)	Brown	42 x 18	7.00	10.00	6.00
3	Chimpanzee Girl (TS)	Brown	40 x 18	7.00	10.00	6.00
4	Elephant, seated (TS)	Pale blue	30 x 30	7.00	10.00	6.00
5	Elephant, standing (TS)	Pale blue	30 x 30	7.00	10.00	6.00
6	Pony (TS)	Beige	43 x 20	7.00	10.00	6.00
7	Lion (TS)	Honey brown	37 x 22	7.00	10.00	6.00
8	Poodle (TS)	White; blue skirt	43 x 17	7.00	10.00	6.00
9	Sea Lion (TS)	Light grey	43 x 30	7.00	10.00	6.00
10a	Tiger, Type 1 (TS)	Honey brown; without beard	42 x 20	7.00	10.00	6.00
10b	Tiger, Type 2 (RRU)	Honey brown; with beard	42 x 20	9.00	12.00	6.00

SIXTH ISSUE

1996-1998

Five new *Circus* models were produced for Redco Foods (Red Rose Tea U.S.A.) and were available in all U.S.A. states where Red Rose Tea is sold from July of 1996. The five new models were added to the *Circus* set which was first introduced in 1993, making a total of 15 models for this series. A brown glazed version of the "Human Cannon-ball" has been reported, the reason for the colour variation is unknown.

Large Custard Pie (left), Small Custard Pie (right)

Backstamp: Embossed "Wade England"

No.	Name	Description	Size	U.S. $	Can. $	U.K. £
11a	Clown, large custard pie, Type 1	Dark blue	40	7.00	10.00	6.00
11b	Clown, large custard pie, Type 1	Pale blue	40	7.00	10.00	6.00
11c	Clown, small custard pie, Type 2	Blue	40	7.00	10.00	6.00
12	Clown, water bucket	Light green	44	7.00	10.00	6.00
13a	Human Cannonball	Light grey	30	7.00	10.00	6.00
13b	Human Cannonball	Brown	30	7.00	10.00	6.00
14	Ringmaster	Light grey	44	7.00	10.00	6.00
15	Strongman	Honey brown	40	7.00	10.00	6.00

ENDANGERED NORTH AMERICAN ANIMALS

SEVENTH ISSUE

1998-2002

In late 1998, Red Rose Tea U.S.A. started to phase out the *Circus* models in preparation for their new *Endangered North American Animals* which was a set of 10 models included in Red Rose Tea boxes from December 1998. Also in the boxes was a leaflet offering collectors the opportunity of purchasing the last of the *Circus* models that they needed to complete their sets at $1.00 per model.

There are seven new designs in the *Endangered Animals* set. Three models have been used in previous promotions, but were recoloured and renamed i.e. "Spotted Owl" (previously the *English Whimsies* Barn Owl) "Bald Eagle" (previously the *Whimsie-land* British Wildlife Golden Eagle), "Polar Bear" (previously the Tom Smith Survival Polar Bear). Please note that the "Polar Bear" has a thicker white glaze applied over the original white glaze.

Backstamp: **A.** Embossed "Wade Eng" on Peregrine Falcon
B. Embossed "Wade England" on other models

No.	Name	Description	Size	U.S. $	Can. $	U.K. £
1	Bald Eagle / Golden Eagle (WL)	Honey brown	35 x 40	6.00	8.00	4.00
2	Florida Panther	Honey brown	35 x 40	6.00	8.00	4.00
3	Green Sea Turtle	Light green	30 x 44	6.00	8.00	4.00
4	Humpback Whale	Grey	20 x 53	6.00	8.00	4.00
5	Manatee	Blue-grey	25 x 53	6.00	8.00	4.00
6	Peregrine Falcon	Beige	25 x 45	6.00	8.00	4.00
7	Polar Bear (TS)	White	27 x 45	6.00	8.00	4.00
8	Spotted Owl / Barn Owl (EW)	Beige	35 x 20	6.00	8.00	4.00
9	Sturgeon	Blue	27 x 47	6.00	8.00	4.00
10	Timber Wolf	Grey	45 x 28	6.00	8.00	4.00

Note: The following initials indicate the origin of the models.
　　　　EW: *English Whimsies*
　　　　TS: Tom Smith
　　　　WL: Whimsie-Land

NOAH'S ARK
EIGHTH ISSUE
2002

In June 2002, Red Rose Tea U.S.A. issued a new series named "Noah's Ark," a set of 15 models, which was available in packages of Red Rose Regular, Decaffeinated and English Breakfast teas. The set includes Noah/Wife, a double-sided model, and a selection of animals. Also available via mail order was the opportunity to purchase a Wade Ceramics porcelain model of the Ark on which to display the complete set.

A variation exists in the shape of the base of "Noah and Wife." In Type 1 the base is oval, and in Type 2 the base is peanut shaped. There are also slight variations in the green glaze colours. Some models have a "Wade England" backstamp whilst others have "Wade Eng." Although an ongoing promotion, Red Rose Teas is not available in a large number of USA states.

Noah / Wife (oval base)

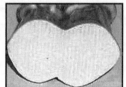

Noah / Wife
(peanut-shaped base)

Backstamp: A. Embossed "Wade England"
B. Embossed "Wade Eng"

No.	Name.	Description	Size	U.S. $	Can. $	U.K. £
1	Ark	Dark brown	120 x 280	25.00	50.00	30.00
2	Chicken, female, on nest	Green	30 x 30	4.00	6.00	4.50
3	Chicken, male, standing	Green	36 x 25	4.00	6.00	4.50
4	Elephant, female, trunk down	Grey	25 x 36	4.00	6.00	4.50
5	Elephant, male, trunk up	Grey	33 x 36	4.00	6.00	4.50
6	Goose, female, preening	Blue	33 x 38	4.00	6.00	4.50
7	Goose, male, feeding	Blue	30 x 35	4.00	6.00	4.50
8	Lion, female, lying	Honey	23 x 36	4.00	6.00	4.50
9	Lion, male, with mane	Honey	30 x 36	4.00	6.00	4.50
10a	Noah / Wife, Type 1	Green	41 x 25	6.00	9.00	4.50
10b	Noah / Wife, Type 2	Green	41 x 25	4.00	6.00	4.50
11	Rhinoceros, female, head down	Beige	28 x 35	4.00	6.00	4.50
12	Rhinoceros, male, head up	Beige	28 x 43	4.00	6.00	4.50
13	Sheep, female, head down	White	20 x 30	4.00	6.00	4.50
14	Sheep, male, head up	White	25 x 28	4.00	6.00	4.50
15	Zebra, female, lying	White	25 x 33	4.00	6.00	4.50
16	Zebra, male, standing	White	25 x 33	4.00	6.00	4.50

RICHLEIGH PROMOTIONS
THE CHILDREN OF THE WORLD

The first model in this series commissioned by Richard and Leigh Leford of Richleigh Promotions, was the "Japanese Girl," which was the only model produced in two colourways. The sixth model in this series was the Russian "Cossack Boy."

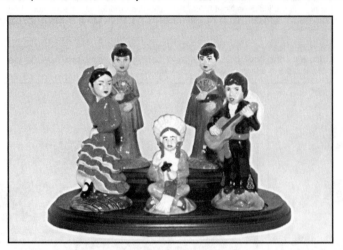 

Backstamp: **A.** Printed "Children of the World 1000 Ltd Edition Wade" [with name and number of model] and "RP" logo.
B. Printed "Children of the World 300 Ltd Edition Number Five The Eskimo Girl Wade" with "RP" logo
C. Printed "Children of the World, 300 Ltd. Edition, Number Six, The Cossack Boy" with "Wade" and "RP" logos

No.	Name	Date	Colourway	Issued/Price	Size	U.S. $	Can. $	U.K. £
1a	Japanese Girl	1997	Blue kimono; pink fan	1000/£33.00	105	60.00	70.00	35.00
1b	Japanese Girl	1997	Green kimono; blue fan	1000/£33.00	105	60.00	70.00	35.00
2	Indian Boy	1998	Beige-brown clothes	1000/£33.00	75	60.00	70.00	38.00
3	Spanish Girl	1998	Red dress; black hair, shoes	1000/£33.00	115	60.00	70.00	35.00
4	Mexican Boy	1998	Black suit; red sash	1000/£33.00	105	60.00	70.00	35.00
5	Eskimo Girl	1999	White suit with yellow stripes	300/£33.00	102	60.00	70.00	35.00
6	Cossack Boy	1999	Yellow shirt; green trousers; blue belt; grey hat, base	300/£33.00	95	60.00	70.00	35.00

ROBELL MEDIA PROMOTIONS LTD.

MR. MEN COLLECTION

The characters in this series are from storybooks by Roger Hargreaves. They were produced for the Mr. Men and Little Miss Club, and were marketed by Robell Media Promotions.

| Mr. Happy | Mr. Bump | Little Miss Giggles | Mr. Snow |

Backstamp: Black printed "Genuine Wade Porcelain Robell Produced exclusively for the Mr. Men & Little Miss Club Mr. Men and Little Miss TM & © 1997 Mrs. Roger Hargreaves" with "Mr. Happy and Little Miss" logo

No.	Name	Date	Colourways	Issued - Price	Size	U.S. $	Can. $	U.K. £
1	Mr. Happy	1997	Yellow; black eyes/mouth	2000 - £15.99	100	50.00	60.00	30.00
2	Little Miss Giggles	1998	Blue; red hair; yellow bows, nose	2000 - £15.99	95	50.00	60.00	30.00
3	Mr. Bump	1998	Blue; white bandages; green base	2000 - £15.99	95	50.00	60.00	30.00
4	Mr. Snow	1999	White; black hat; red/white scarf	2000 - £15.99	120	50.00	60.00	30.00

JAMES ROBERTSON & SONS
ROBERTSON'S JAM GOLLIES AND BANDSTAND
1963-1965

Golliwogs became the trademark of James Robertson & Sons after one of Mr. Robertson's sons visited the United States in the early 1900s. He purchased a golliwog doll for his children, and it was so loved by the family that they decided to use it as their trademark. In 1910 a golliwog first appeared on items from James Robertson Preserve Manufacturers Limited, such as labels and price lists.

Beginning in 1963 a Robertson's promotional campaign offered a series of eight golliwog musicians in exchange for ten paper golliwog labels per model and 6d in postage stamps. George Wade and Son Ltd. produced five models for a trial period only. At some time in 1965, Robertson's changed from using the Wade model to the cheaper Portuguese one.

None of the Golliwogs is marked with a Wade stamp or label, but it is relatively easy to spot a Wade model amongst the hundreds of Golliwogs seen at antique and collector shows. Only the Wade figures are standing on white bases. All the models have a raised "Robertson" mark on the front rim of the base, and all the *Gollies* are black, with blue coats and red trousers.

Wade records confirm that, out of the eight promotional models, it only produced five golliwog musicians: "Accordion Golliwog," "Clarinet Golliwog," "Bass Golliwog," "Saxophone Golliwog" and "Trumpet Golliwog." The three additional models, not confirmed by Wade and most likely produced by another manufacturer, are "Drum Golliwog," "Guitar Golliwog" and "Vocalist Golliwog."

Due to changing race relations laws in Great Britain during the late 1970s and early 1980s, the original name, *Golliwog*, was changed to *Golly Doll* or *Gollies*. The models below are listed by their original names.

Backstamp: **A.** Embossed "Robertson" (1-5)
 B. Red transfer print "Wade England" (6)

No.	Name	Description	Size	U.S. $	Can. $	U.K. £
1	Accordion Golliwog	Blue jacket; red pants; white/yellow accordion	65 x 25	240.00	360.00	150.00
2	Clarinet Golliwog	Blue jacket; red pants; black clarinet	65 x 25	240.00	360.00	150.00
3	Bass Golliwog	Blue jacket; red pants; white/yellow/brown bass	65 x 25	240.00	360.00	150.00
4	Saxophone Golliwog	Blue jacket; red pants; yellow saxophone	65 x 25	240.00	360.00	150.00
5	Trumpet Golliwog	Blue jacket; red pants; yellow trumpet	65 x 25	240.00	360.00	150.00
6	Bandstand	White	50 x 230	240.00	360.00	150.00

S & A COLLECTABLES LTD
JACK THE RIPPER
November 1999

This was the only model produced for S & A Collectables, it is of "Jack the Ripper," a notorious British serial killer who, during the reign of Queen Victoria murdered and mutilated five prostitutes in Whitechapel, London.

Backstamp: Printed "S & A Collectables Ltd Proudly Presents Jack The Ripper Produced in a Limited Edition of 1,000 Pieces Manufactured by Wade 1999"

No.	Name	Date	Colourway	Issue/Price	Size	U.S. $	Can. $	U.K. £
1	Jack the Ripper	1999	Black cloak, hat; red blood; grey base	1000/£45	122 x 120	75.00	90.00	45.00

ST. JOHN AMBULANCE BRIGADE (U.K.)

BERTIE BADGER

1989-2002

In 1987 the St. John Ambulance Brigade formed a section for children aged five to ten years, they are known as "Badgers" because of the black and white uniform. "Bertie Badger" was produced in a limited edition of 5,000 as a promotional item for the British St. John Ambulance Brigade in late 1989. It was given as a reward to child members of the brigade after they completed three years of service and training. Those models that are unmarked were produced from 1989 to 1994; those embossed with the Wade mark were produce from 1994 to 2001.

The "Bertie Badger Money Box" was produced exclusively for the St. John Ambulance Brigade. First produced in October 2001, at an issued price of £14.95, a thousand money boxes were produced in that year. This is an on-going line and is still available from the St. John Ambulance gift catalogue.

Bertie Badger

Bertie Badger Money Box

Backstamp: **A.** Unmarked
B. Embossed "Wade"

No.	Name	Date	Colourways	Issue	Size	U.S. $	Can. $	U.K. £
1	Bertie Badger	1989	Black/white; white coveralls	5000	100	240.00	300.00	150.00
2	Money Box	2001	Black/white; white coveralls	—	180	28.00	40.00	15.00

SALADA TEA CANADA

WHIMSEY-ON-WHY

1984

Six models from the *Whimsey-on-Why* sets 1, 2 and 3 were introduced as a short promotional offer by Salada Tea Canada between September and December 1984.

Backstamp: Embossed "Wade England"

No.	Name	Description	Size	U.S. $	Can. $	U.K. £
1	Pump Cottage	Brown thatch; white walls; yellow doors	28 x 39	15.00	22.00	10.00
2	Tobacconist's Shop	Brown roof; red doors	33 x 39	15.00	22.00	10.00
3	The Greengrocer's Shop	Grey roof; green windows, doors	35 x 35	15.00	22.00	10.00
4	The Antique Shop	Purple-brown roof; blue/yellow windows	35 x 37	25.00	37.00	18.00
5	The Post Office	Beige roof; yellow/blue windows	40 x 38	15.00	22.00	10.00
6	Whimsey Station	Red-brown; brown roof	35 x 39	25.00	35.00	20.00

SHARPS CHOCOLATE
HONEY-BROWN SMILING RABBIT

1970

The *Honey Brown Smiling Rabbit* was produced in 1970 as a premium with Sharps Chocolate Easter eggs. The box was shaped like a hollow log, and the rabbit was fixed beside an egg containing milk chocolate buttons. The original price was 7/9d.

Backstamp: Unmarked

No.	Description	Size	U.S. $	Can. $	U.K. £
1a	Honey-brown; large dark brown eyes	65 x 43	35.00	40.00	20.00
1b	Honey-brown; small brown eyes	65 x 43	35.00	40.00	20.00

HONEY-BROWN BO-PEEP

1971

The following year Wade produced the *Honey Brown Bo-Peep*, also as a premium with Sharps Chocolate Easter eggs. The model was fixed beside an egg containing milk chocolate buttons, and was packaged in a box decorated with a design of sheep and trees. The original price was 8/-.

Backstamp: Embossed "Wade England"

No.	Description	Size	U.S. $	Can. $	U.K. £
1a	Honey-brown	70 x 28	35.00	40.00	20.00
1b	Honey-brown; dark blue hair, apron, flowers	70 x 28	35.00	40.00	20.00

SIMONS ASSOCIATES, INC.

CIRCA 1975

Some time in the mid 1970s, Wade exported a set of 24 *English Whimsies* to Simons Associates, Inc., of Los Angeles, California. The models were packaged in a plastic bubble on a blue card. The front of the card has a colourful design of a tree, smiling sun, baby birds in a nest, butterfly, snail and toadstools. Also printed there is "Whimsies Miniatures Collection Solid English Porcelain," and each package is numbered in the top left corner. On the back is printed: "Collect all these Whimsies miniatures / little creatures from the farm, forest and jungle of solid porcelain," and on the top right hand corner, "Whimsies Wade of England Est. 1810," along with the Union Jack and the American flag.

The values are given for models intact on their cards as they are indistinguishable from Red Rose Tea or English Whimsies models outside the packet. Note that these models were not given the same issue numbers as *English Whimsies*, although they are identical to the originals.

Backstamp: A. Embossed "Wade England" (1-3, 5-8)
B. Embossed "Wade England" in a recessed base (4)

No.	Name	Description	Size	U.S. $	Can. $	U.K. £
1	Rabbit, open ears	Beige	30 x 30	8.00	10.00	5.00
2	Fawn	Brown; blue ears	30 x 30	8.00	10.00	5.00
3	Mongrel	Dark brown/light brown front	35 x 35	8.00	10.00	5.00
4	Squirrel	Grey; beige; yellow acorn	35 x 30	8.00	10.00	5.00
5	Elephant	Grey; with or without black eyes	55 x 50	14.00	16.00	8.00
6	Setter	Brown; grey-green base	35 x 50	8.00	10.00	5.00
7	Cat	Beige	40 x 17	22.00	28.00	14.00
8	Collie	Brown; grey-green base	35 x 35	12.00	16.00	8.00

Backstamp: **A.** Embossed "Wade England" (9-11, 14-16)
B. Embossed "Wade England" in a recessed base (12, 13)
C. Embossed "Wade" between front feet and "England" on back of model (10)

No.	Name	Description	Size	U.S. $	Can. $	U.K. £
9	Zebra	Light brown; green base	40 x 35	10.00	12.00	6.00
10	Bear Cub	Grey; beige face	30 x 40	7.00	8.00	4.00
11	Field Mouse	Honey; yellow corn; green on base	35 x 25	12.00	16.00	8.00
12	Owl	Dark brown; light brown chest, face	35 x 20	7.00	8.00	5.00
13	Kitten, seated	Dark/light brown; pink or red wool	30 x 30	7.00	8.00	5.00
14	Chimpanzee	Dark brown; light brown face, patches	35 x 35	7.00	8.00	5.00
15	Horse	Dark grey; green base	35 x 35	22.00	26.00	14.00
16	Duck	Blue/brown; yellow beak	30 x 40	9.00	12.00	7.00

Backstamp: **A.** Embossed "Wade England" (17-23)
B. Embossed "Wade England" in a recessed base (24)

No.	Name	Description	Size	U.S. $	Can. $	U.K. £
17	Spaniel	Honey; green on base	35 x 35	7.00	8.00	5.00
18	Giraffe	Beige	35 x 35	7.00	8.00	5.00
19	Lion	Light brown; dark brown head, mane	35 x 45	7.00	8.00	5.00
20	German Shepherd	Grey; tan face (formerly Alsatian)	30 x 40	7.00	8.00	5.00
21	Lamb	Light beige; green base	30 x 25	12.00	14.00	8.00
22	Pine Marten	Honey brown	30 x 30	7.00	8.00	5.00
23	Corgi	Honey; black nose	30 x 35	7.00	8.00	5.00
24	Hedgehog, Type 2	Dark brown; light brown face	23 x 40	7.00	8.00	5.00

STAFFORDSHIRE HOUSE GIFTS

FIRST WHIMSIES ENGLISH ANIMALS

SET TWO: CIRCA 1954-1958

These models were produced for "Staffordshire House" and were sold in a gift shop in Niagara Falls, Ontario, Canada. Each model is marked with a black, hand written "Made in England" on the base and has "Niagara Falls Canada" on the body of the model. The box for this set is different from the normal Whimsies boxed sets issued, the box has "Whimsies Porcelain Miniatures" on the front with a picture of "Dora the Donkey Soprano" from the *Drum Box* set. The inside of the box is a plain buff brown with silver lettering "Whimsies Porcelain Miniatures by Wade of England" there is also a black and gold label, which reads "A Staffordshire House Gift."

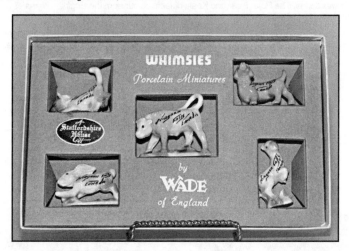

Backstamp: Black ink hand written "Made in England with Niagara Falls Canada"

No.	Name	Description	Size	U.S. $	Can. $	U.K. £
1	Bull	White with brown markings; green base; black lettering	45 x 55	110.00	140.00	70.00
2	Dachshund	Beige; black lettering	35 x 45	120.00	160.00	80.00
3	Hare	White with grey markings; green base; black lettering	30 x 45	50.00	65.00	35.00
4	Kitten	White with grey markings; blue bow; black lettering	30 x 40	125.00	165.00	80.00
5	Lamb	White with brown markings; green base; black lettering	42 x 25	80.00	105.00	50.00
—	5 pce set	Boxed	—	500.00	670.00	340.00

TOM SMITH AND COMPANY LTD.

1973-1999

The world famous Christmas cracker manufacturer, Tom Smith and Company Ltd., collaborated with George Wade and Son Ltd. over a number of years to produce a series of miniature animals exclusively for the Christmas and party cracker market. Each series of animals was used exclusively by Tom Smith for two years, after which time the design rights reverted back to Wade, then they could be reused for other premiums or included in the *English Whimsies* series. In August 1998 Tom Smith Crackers was sold to Napier Industries of Rickmansworth, Herts., UK and the factory closed in 1999.

The first models issued for Tom Smith and Company were eight figures previously used in the 1967-1973 Red Rose Tea Canada series. Next came a set of ten *Safari Park* models. All but two of the models —the "Lion" and the "Musk Ox"— were from either Red Rose Tea Canada or the *English Whimsies* series. The Polar Bear and Koala differ in colour from the *English Whimsies* models. Each is marked with "Wade England" embossed on the rim of the base.

Only the five models in the *Safari Park series Nos 2, 3, 4, 5, and 7* can be distinguished from those in the *English Whimsies* series; therefore, they have a higher collectors value. All models are listed in alphabetical order for ease of reference.

ANIMATE CRACKERS

1973-1975

Although a blue terrapin is illustrated on the outer box of the Tom Smith Animate Crackers, this colourway has not been seen.

Backstamp: Embossed "Wade England" on the rim or in a recessed base

No.	Name	Description	Size	U.S. $	Can. $	U.K. £
1	Alsatian	Dark grey/honey	30 x 40	5.00	6.00	3.00
2	Bluebird (recessed)	Light brown; blue wings	15 x 35	10.00	12.00	6.00
3	Bullfrog (recessed)	Light green	15 x 30	15.00	20.00	10.00
4	Butterfly (recessed)	Honey; grey tips; raised circles	10 x 45	10.00	15.00	7.00
5	Fantail Goldfish	Light green/yellow; blue base	30 x 35	10.00	12.00	6.00
6	Pine Marten	Honey	30 x 30	5.00	6.00	3.00
7	Terrapin (recessed)	Dark greenish-grey	10 x 40	10.00	14.00	7.00
8	Wild Boar	Beige; green base	30 x 40	9.00	10.00	5.00

ELEPHANT AND PIG

The elephant has a hole in the end of the trunk and the pig has a hole in the rump; these were intended holders for miniature sparkler fireworks.

Elephant

Pig

Backstamp: Unmarked

No.	Name	Date	Description	Size	U.S. $	Can. $	U.K. £
1	Elephant	c.1975	Charcoal grey (biscuit glaze)	27 x 35	50.00	75.00	35.00
2	Pig	c.1975	White (gloss)	25 x 50	50.00	75.00	35.00

SAFARI PARK

1976-1977

Backstamp: Embossed "Wade England"

No.	Name	Description	Size	U.S. $	Can. $	U.K. £
1	Kangaroo	Dark brown; light brown base	45 x 25	12.00	18.00	9.00
2	Koala	Black; brown stump	35 x 25	25.00	30.00	15.00
3	Langur, Type 1	Light brown; dark brown stump	35 x 30	5.00	8.00	4.00
4a	Lion, lying	Honey brown	30 x 45	15.00	22.00	11.00
4b	Lion, lying	Honey brown; green base	30 x 45	15.00	22.00	11.00
5	Musk Ox	Grey; brown horns	27 x 30	25.00	30.00	15.00
6	Orang-outan	Ginger	30 x 30	5.00	7.00	4.00
7	Polar Bear	Brown; black nose; grey/blue base	30 x 30	25.00	30.00	15.00
8	Raccoon	Brown; grey-green base	25 x 35	15.00	18.00	9.00
9	Tiger	Honey; green on base	35 x 25	15.00	18.00	9.00
10	Walrus	Brown; grey-base	30 x 30	10.00	12.00	6.00

CIRCUS ANIMATES CRACKERS

1978-1979

These ten models were set on drum bases, which are marked on their rims. These figures were reissued for Red Rose Tea U.S.A., with only a very slight variation in colour on some models. The "Lion," "Pony" and "Tiger," Type 1 are in the same glaze colour and are particularly hard to differentiate.

During the Red Rose Tea promotion a new mould was produced which resulted in two variations of the Tiger. Type 1 has a larger mouth; Type 2 has a smaller mouth, and added detail to the throat and chest resulting in a 'beard' effect. For Type 2 see Redco Foods U.S.A..

Circus Animates Crackers Box (1978-79)

Backstamp: Embossed "Wade England" on front and back rims

No.	Name	Description	Size	U.S. $	Can. $	U.K. £
1	Brown Bear	Red-brown	35 x 32	10.00	15.00	6.00
2	Chimpanzee Boy	Beige; blue teapot	43 x 18	10.00	15.00	6.00
3	Chimpanzee Girl	Beige; blue skirt	40 x 18	10.00	15.00	6.00
4	Elephant, Seated	Blue	30 x 30	10.00	15.00	6.00
5	Elephant, standing	Blue	30 x 30	10.00	15.00	6.00
6	Lion	Honey brown	37 x 22	10.00	15.00	6.00
7	Pony	Beige	43 x 20	10.00	15.00	6.00
8	Poodle	White; blue skirt	43 x 17	10.00	15.00	6.00
9	Sea Lion	Dark grey	43 x 30	10.00	15.00	6.00
10	Tiger, Type 1	Honey brown	42 x 20	10.00	15.00	6.00

BRITISH WILDLIFE

1980-1981

Backstamp: Embossed "Wade England"

No.	Name	Description	Size	U.S. $	Can. $	U.K. £
1	Badger	Dark grey	25 x 40	15.00	12.00	6.00
2	Dormouse	Honey; green base	30 x 35	15.00	12.00	6.00
3	Fox	Brown	35 x 40	15.00	12.00	6.00
4	Hare	Honey	50 x 30	15.00	12.00	6.00
5	Mole	Dark grey	25 x 40	15.00	12.00	6.00
6	Partridge	Beige; green base	30 x 20	15.00	12.00	6.00
7	Squirrel	Red-brown	40 x 40	15.00	12.00	6.00
8	Weasel	Beige; green base	35 x 40	15.00	12.00	6.00

FARMYARD ANIMALS

1982-1983

The "Goose" was previously used in the 1971-1979 Red Rose *Miniature Nurseries* series (the earlier model has a pink beak.)

Backstamp: Embossed "Wade England"

No.	Name	Description	Size	U.S. $	Can. $	U.K. £
1	Bull	Dark brown	30 x 50	15.00	12.00	6.00
2	Collie	Honey; brown base	25 x 50	15.00	12.00	6.00
3	Cow	Orange-brown	30 x 40	15.00	12.00	6.00
4	Duck, swimming	White; blue base	25 x 30	15.00	12.00	6.00
5a	Goat	Beige	40 x 40	15.00	12.00	6.00
5b	Goat	White; green base	40 x 40	15.00	12.00	6.00
6	Goose	Honey/brown; brown beak	35 x 40	15.00	12.00	6.00
7	Horse, cropped mane	Brown; green base	40 x 30	15.00	12.00	6.00
8	Pig	Pale pink	25 x 40	15.00	12.00	6.00

SURVIVAL ANIMALS

1984-1985

From 1984 onwards, all Tom Smith crackers models were produced in a one-colour glaze. The "Sea Lion" was previously used as the "Seal on Rock" in the 1967-1973 Red Rose *Miniature Animals* series; the earlier model is brown on a blue base. The "Bison" had been number 51 of the *English Whimsies* series, where it is honey brown and dark brown.

Backstamp: Embossed "Wade England"

No.	Name	Description	Size	U.S. $	Can. $	U.K. £
1	Armadillo (TS)	Dark grey	25 x 45	18.00	14.00	7.00
2	Bison (RRC, EW)	Dark brown	28 x 40	6.00	8.00	4.00
3	Eagle (TS)	Honey	35 x 23	18.00	14.00	7.00
4	Gorilla, seated (TS)	Brown	40 x 40	18.00	14.00	7.00
5	Polar Bear (TS)	White	27 x 45	18.00	14.00	7.00
6	Sea Lion (RRC)	Blue	38 x 30	18.00	14.00	7.00
7	Sea Turtle (TS)	Green-grey	25 x 45	18.00	14.00	7.00
8	Whale (Baleen) (TS)	Blue	25 x 50	18.00	14.00	7.00

Note: The following initials indicate the origin of the models.
    EW: *English Whimsies*
    RRC: Red Rose Canada
    TS: Tom Smith

NURSERY RHYME CRACKERS

Circa Mid-1980s

At some time in the mid-1980s, Tom Smith issued a box of "Nursery Rhyme" crackers. The box contained a set of six miniature nursery rhymes, the same models used in the Red Rose Tea Canada promotion of 1972-1979.

Backstamp: Embossed "Wade England" on rim

No.	Name	Description	Size	U.S. $	Can. $	U.K. £
1	Hickory Dickory	Red brown/honey brown	44 x 20	7.00	12.00	6.00
2	Humpty Dumpty	Honey; blue bow tie; brown wall	36 x 23	7.00	12.00	6.00
3	Little Bo-Peep	Beige; blue apron; green base	44 x 24	7.00	12.00	6.00
4	Old King Cole, Type 1	Gap; brown; blue hat, cloak	37 x 32	10.00	15.00	7.00
5	Old Woman Who Lived ina Shoe	Honey; red-brown roof	35 x 40	10.00	15.00	7.00
6	Wee Willie Winkie	Yellow hair; beige nightshirt	44 x 24	10.00	12.00	6.00

WILDLIFE

1986-1987

These models are reissued *English Whimsies* in all-over, one-colour glazes. Listed below are all the models that have been found in this series, although a number of British collectors have reported finding different figures in their crackers than were illustrated on the outer box (models 9 through 15). It is believed that surplus models from previous Red Rose Tea and Tom Smith promotions were used to fill the orders in time for Christmas sales.

Backstamp: Embossed "Wade England"

No.	Name	Description	Size	U.S. $	Can. $	U.K. £
1	Dolphin (EW)	Dark blue	30 x 40	18.00	25.00	8.00
2	Kangaroo (EW)	Beige	45 x 25	12.00	12.00	6.00
3	Koala (EW)	Honey	35 x 25	12.00	16.00	8.00
4	Leopard (EW)	Honey	17 x 45	5.00	7.00	3.00
5	Orang-outan (EW)	Dark brown	30 x 30	5.00	7.00	3.00
6	Penguin (EW)	White	45 x 17	18.00	25.00	8.00
7	Rhino (EW)	Grey	25 x 35	6.00	8.00	4.00
8	Wild Boar (RR/EW)	Beige	30 x 40	8.00	12.00	6.00

No.	Name	Description	Size	U.S. $	Can. $	U.K. £
9	Bison (RR/EW)	Brown	30 x 40	8.00	12.00	6.00
10	Collie (TSF)	Dark brown	25 x 50	15.00	20.00	10.00
11	Duck, swimming (TSF)	Dark blue	25 x 30	15.00	20.00	10.00
12a	Goat (TSF)	Beige	40 x 40	15.00	20.00	10.00
12b	Goat (TSF)	White; green base	40 x 40	15.00	12.00	6.00
13	Hare (TSB)	Brown	50 x 30	8.00	12.00	6.00
14	Squirrel (TSB)	Dark brown	40 x 40	15.00	12.00	6.00
15	Zebra (EW)	Blue-grey	40 x 35	5.00	6.00	3.00

Note: The following initials indicate the origin of the models:
EW: *English Whimsies*; RR: Red Rose Canada; TSB: Tom Smith *British Wildlife* set; TSF: Tom Smith *Farmyard* set

MISCELLANEOUS MODELS

1987-1996

Wade re-coloured surplus models from the *English Whimsies*, Red Rose Tea Whimsies, Whimsie-lands and former Tom Smith Crackers for the Tom Smith Group, who included them with other small gifts in their Bric-a-Brac, Catering, De Luxe, Luxury, Gallerie Noel, Table Decoration and Victorian Crackers. Only one or two models were used in each box of crackers and there is no reference to Wade on the outer box. Tom Smith do not keep records of these odd Wade models, and the only way to find them is to look closely at Tom Smith advertising leaflets and packaging where they can be seen amongst plastic toys and paper hats.

1987 ISSUE

Backstamp: Embossed "Wade England"

No.	Name	Description	Size	U.S. $	Can. $	U.K. £
1	Gorilla, seated (TSS)	Dark brown	40 x 40	6.00	8.00	4.00
2	Hare (TSB)	Beige	50 x 30	6.00	8.00	4.00
3	Hickory Dickory Dock (RRC)	Beige	44 x 20	6.00	8.00	4.00
4	Humpty Dumpty (RRC)	Brown	36 x 23	6.00	8.00	4.00
5	Little Bo-Peep (RRC)	Brown	44 x 24	12.00	16.00	8.00
6	Old King Cole (RRC)	Blue	37 x 32	18.00	24.00	12.00
7	Old Woman Who Lived in a Shoe (RRC)	Blue	35 x 40	18.00	24.00	12.00
8	Wee Willie Winkie (RRC)	Blue	44 x 24	18.00	24.00	12.00

Note: The following initials indicate the origin of the figures:
    EW: *English Whimsies*
    RR: Red Rose
    RRC: Red Rose Canada
    RRU: Red Rose U.S.A.
    TSB: Tom Smith *British Wildlife* set
    TSD: Tom Smith *Dogs* set
    TSS: Tom Smith *Survival* set

1989 ISSUE

Backstamp: Embossed "Wade England"

No.	Name	Description	Size	U.S. $	Can. $	U.K. £
1	Hickory Dickory Dock (RR, RRC)	Honey/dark brown	44 x 20	7.00	4.00	5.00
2	Kangaroo (EW, RRU)	Honey brown	45 x 25	8.00	12.00	5.00
3	Koala (EW)	Beige	35 x 25	7.00	10.00	5.00
4	Little Bo-Peep (RR)	Brown; blue apron	44 x 24	7.00	8.00	4.00
5	Wee Willie Winkie (RR)	Beige; yellow hair	44 x 24	10.00	5.00	7.00

1990 ISSUE

Backstamp: Embossed "Wade England"

No.	Name	Description	Size	U.S. $	Can. $	U.K. £
1	Hare (TSB)	Dark brown	50 x 30	8.00	12.00	6.00
2	Old King Cole (RR)	Brown; blue hat	37 x 32	10.00	5.00	7.00
3	Squirrel (TSB)	Blue	40 x 40	8.00	12.00	6.00

1991 ISSUE

Backstamp: Embossed "Wade England"

No.	Name	Description	Size	U.S. $	Can. $	U.K. £
1	Koala (EW)	Honey brown	35 x 25	12.00	16.00	8.00
2	Poodle (RR/TSD)	Dark orange/apricot	40 x 45	12.00	16.00	8.00

1992 ISSUE

Backstamp: Embossed "Wade England"

No.	Name	Description	Size	U.S. $	Can. $	U.K. £
1	Bluebird (RR/EW)	Blue	15 x 35	20.00	30.00	15.00
2	Bulldog (TSD)	Beige	35 x 35	12.00	14.00	7.00
3	Mongrel (RR/EW)	Blue	35 x 35	12.00	14.00	7.00

1996 ISSUE

Three *English Whimsies* models were used in assorted Tom Smith crackers. The "Duck" can be found in Tom Smith Catering, De Luxe and Luxury crackers, the "Camel" was used in the Gallerie Noel crackers, and the "Fieldmouse" was in Catering, De Luxe, Luxury and Table Decoration crackers.

Photograph not available
at press time

Backstamp: Unknown

No.	Name	Description	Size	U.S. $	Can. $	U.K. £
1	Camel (EW)	Light brown	35 x 35	6.00	8.00	4.00
2	Duck (EW)	Green	30 x 40	16.00	25.00	12.00
3	Duck, swimming (TS)	Beige	25 x 30	12.00	18.00	7.00
4	Field Mouse (EW)	Honey; yellow corn	35 x 25	9.00	12.00	6.00
5	Horse, cropped mane (TS)	Beige	40 x 30	12.00	18.00	7.00

VILLAGE OF BROADLANDS

1988

Due to high production costs, only five of these models were produced for Tom Smith and Company. A further set of five figures was planned, but never issued.

They come from the same moulds as the following *Whimsey-on-Why* models, but are in different colours:

Whimsey-on-Why	Village of Broadlands
Whimsy School	The Chapel
Whimsey Station	The Coach House Garage
Pump Cottage	The Thatched Cottage
The Sweet Shop	The Pink House
The Greengrocers Shop	The Village Store

Backstamp: Embossed "Wade England"

No.	Name	Description	Size	U.S. $	Can. $	U.K. £
1	The Chapel	Grey; green roof; brown door	38 x 51	40.00	50.00	25.00
2	The Coach House Garage	White; grey roof; black beams	35 x 39	40.00	50.00	25.00
3	The Pink House	Pink; grey roof	40 x 40	40.00	50.00	25.00
4	The Thatched Cottage	White; brown roof	28 x 39	40.00	50.00	25.00
5	The Village Store	Brown; brown roof	35 x 35	40.00	50.00	25.00

FAMILY PETS

1988-1989

Backstamp: Embossed "Wade England"

No.	Name	Description	Size	U.S. $	Can. $	U.K. £
1	Cockatoo	Green	35 x 30	6.00	9.00	4.00
2	Guinea Pig	Honey brown	20 x 30	16.00	20.00	10.00
3	Mouse, sleeping	White	15 x 25	20.00	30.00	12.00
4	Persian Kitten	Blue	25 x 33	6.00	9.00	4.00
5	Rabbit	Brown	30 x 25	6.00	9.00	4.00
6	Shetland Pony	Beige	25 x 30	6.00	8.00	4.00
7	Spaniel Puppy	Honey	25 x 30	6.00	8.00	4.00
8	Tropical Fish	Green	20 x 30	20.00	25.00	12.00

WORLD OF DOGS

1990-1991

Only two of these figures were new issues. The others were reissued *English Whimsies* and the first issue of Red Rose Tea Canada models in a new all-over, one-colour glaze.

Backstamp: Embossed "Wade England"

No.	Name	Description	Size	U.S. $	Can. $	U.K. £
1	Alsatian (RR/EW)	Dark brown	30 x 40	15.00	20.00	10.00
2	Bulldog	Beige	35 x 35	12.00	15.00	7.00
3	Corgi (RR/EW)	Honey	30 x 35	7.00	10.00	5.00
4	Husky (EW)	White	35 x 30	12.00	15.00	7.00
5	Mongrel (RR/EW)	Blue-grey	35 x 35	12.00	15.00	7.00
6	Poodle (RR)	Apricot	40 x 45	12.00	16.00	8.00
7	Spaniel (RR/EW)	Black	35 x 35	12.00	15.00	7.00
8	West Highland Terrier	White	30 x 30	12.00	15.00	7.00

Note: The following initials indicate the origin of the models:
EW: *English Whimsies*
RRT: Red Rose Tea Canada *Miniature Nurseries*

BIRDLIFE SERIES

1992-1993

All the models in the *Birdlife* series, except for the "Wren," had been previously issued, either as *English Whimsies*, as other Tom Smith cracker models or as *Whimsie-land* figures. The "Eagle" and the "Goose" were former Tom Smith models, but this time were produced in different coloured glazes than the originals.

Backstamp: Embossed "Wade England"

No.	Name	Description	Size	U.S. $	Can. $	U.K. £
1	Barn Owl (EW)	Grey-blue	35 x 25	15.00	20.00	10.00
2	Cockerel (WL)	Green	50 x 35	15.00	20.00	10.00
3	Duck (WL)	White	45 x 35	15.00	20.00	10.00
4	Goose (RRT/TS)	Honey	35 x 40	15.00	20.00	10.00
5	Eagle (TS *Survival*)	Beige	35 x 23	15.00	20.00	10.00
6	Partridge (WL)	Beige	35 x 35	15.00	20.00	10.00
7	Pelican (EW)	Brown	45 x 40	15.00	20.00	10.00
8	Wren	Beige	33 x 24	15.00	20.00	10.00

Note: The following initials indicate the origin of the models:
EW: *English Whimsies*
RRT: Red Rose Tea Canada *Miniature Nurseries*
TS: Tom Smith
WL: *Whimsie-land*

SNOWLIFE ANIMALS

1992-1994

All the models in this set, except the "Reindeer," had been previously issued as *English Whimsies*, Tom Smith cracker figures or in the *Whimsie-land* series. The models are produced in a different all-over, one-colour glaze from the originals. Due to a new mould being made, two types of Reindeer exist: Type 1 has a gap between the legs; Type 2 has no gap between the legs.

Reindeer Type 1
Gap between legs

Reindeer, Type 2
No gap between legs

Backstamp: A. Embossed "Wade Eng" (4a, 4b)
B. Embossed "Wade England" (1-3, 5-10)

No.	Name	Description	Size	U.S. $	Can. $	U.K. £
1	Fox (WL)	Red-brown	35 x 35	20.00	25.00	12.00
2	Penguin (EW)	Grey-blue	45 x 17	12.00	16.00	8.00
3	Polar Bear, head forward (EW)	White	27 x 45	12.00	16.00	8.00
4a	Reindeer, Type 1 (TS)	Gap between legs; beige	30 x 35	18.00	22.00	11.00
4b	Reindeer, Type 2 (TS)	No gap; beige	30 x 35	18.00	22.00	11.00
5	Seal Pup (EW)	Grey	17 x 30	12.00	22.00	11.00
6	Snow Goose (RR)	White	33 x 37	12.00	22.00	11.00
7	Snowshoe Hare (TS "Hare")	White	50 x 30	12.00	22.00	11.00
8	Snowy Owl (WL "Owl")	White	35 x 25	12.00	22.00	11.00
9	Walrus (EW)	Beige	30 x 30	12.00	22.00	11.00
10	Whale (Baleen TS)	Grey	22 x 52	12.00	22.00	11.00

Note: The following initials indicate the origin of the models:
EW: *English Whimsies*
RR: Red Rose
TS: Tom Smith
WL: *Whimsie-land*

TALES FROM THE NURSERY

1994-1996

Some of the models from the Red Rose Tea *Miniature Nurseries* were reissued for this set. Two new figures were added in 1994, "Ride a Cock Horse" and a newly modeled "Little Boy Blue." All the models are in an all-over, one-colour glaze. Although there are ten models in this set, the box contains only eight crackers, making some models more difficult to find than others.

Backstamp: Embossed "Wade England"

No.	Name	Description	Size	U.S. $	Can. $	U.K. £
1	Cat and the Fiddle	Light grey	47 x 33	6.00	9.00	4.00
2	Dr. Foster	Dark brown	43 x 26	6.00	9.00	4.00
3	Hickory Dickory Dock	Light brown	44 x 20	6.00	9.00	4.00
4	Humpty Dumpty	Pale blue	36 x 23	6.00	9.00	4.00
5	Little Bo-Peep	Wine	44 x 24	6.00	9.00	4.00
6	Little Boy Blue	Blue	41 x 25	6.00	9.00	4.00
7	Little Jack Horner	Honey	37 x 21	6.00	9.00	4.00
8	Queen of Hearts	Apricot	42 x 25	6.00	9.00	4.00
9	Ride a Cock Horse	Green	45 x 35	6.00	9.00	4.00
10	Tom Tom the Piper's Son	Honey	39 x 33	6.00	9.00	4.00

CAT COLLECTION

1996-1997

Eight of these cats are reissued from *English Whimsies*, the *Whimsie-land Series* and from Red Rose Tea's *Miniature Nurseries*. Some are in new colours, but others are similar to the Red Rose Tea U.S.A. issues. Two new cat models — one stalking and the other standing — were produced for this series. Although there are only eight crackers in a box, there are ten models in the set.

Collectors in the U.K. have reported a colour variation in two of the Tom Smith cat models: "Cat and the Fiddle" in a grey colourway, and "Puss in Boots" in a dark grey colourway.

Backstamp: Embossed "Wade England"

No.	Name	Description	Size	U.S. $	Can. $	U.K. £
1	Cat (EW)	Light brown/beige	40 x 17	9.00	12.00	5.00
2a	Cat and the Fiddle (RR)	Dark brown	46 x 33	9.00	12.00	5.00
2b	Cat and the Fiddle (RR)	Light grey	46 x 33	9.00	12.00	5.00
3	Cat, stalking	Apricot	23 x 43	10.00	15.00	6.00
4	Cat, standing	Light brown	35 x 34	10.00	15.00	6.00
5a	Kitten, lying (WL)	Dark blue	20 x 42	9.00	12.00	5.00
5b	Kitten, lying (WL)	Pale blue	20 x 42	9.00	12.00	5.00
6	Kitten, seated (EW)	Apricot	30 x 30	9.00	12.00	5.00
7	Leopard (EW)	Honey	17 x 45	5.00	7.00	3.00
8	Lion, standing (EW)	Honey	35 x 45	8.00	12.00	6.00
9a	Puss in Boots (RR)	Light grey	45 x 20	9.00	12.00	5.00
9b	Puss in Boots (RR)	Dark grey	45 x 20	9.00	12.00	5.00
10	Tiger (EW)	Honey	35 x 25	5.00	6.00	3.00

Note: The initials after the model indicates its origin.
EW: *English Whimsies*
RR: Red Rose *Miniature Nurseries*
WL: *Whimsie-land Series*

CHRISTMAS TIME CRACKERS

BEAR AMBITIONS

1996-1997

Tom Smith used the *Bear Ambitions* set, which was originally produced as a Wade giftware line, in its Christmas crackers. Four of the models are glazed in different colours from the originals, which were all honey brown. See also Bear Ambitions page 151 and Ripley Village Fete page 228.

Backstamp: **A.** Embossed "Wade England" (3)
B. Embossed "Wade Eng" (1, 2, 4, 5, 6)

No.	Name	Description	Size	U.S. $	Can. $	U.K. £
1	Admiral Sam	Dark brown	50	10.00	15.00	6.00
2	Alex the Aviator	Light brown	45	10.00	15.00	6.00
3	Artistic Edward	Light brown	40	10.00	15.00	6.00
4	Beatrice Ballerina	Honey	50	7.00	8.00	4.00
5	Locomotive Joe	Dark brown	50	10.00	15.00	6.00
6	Musical Marco	Honey	45	7.00	8.00	4.00

HEDGEROW and SEALIFE PARTY TIME CRACKERS

1998

There were two new Tom Smith Party Cracker Animal series produced for 1998-1999, *Hedgerow* and *Sealife*. Each set contained eight models, but the Tom Smith boxes contained only six crackers, which meant collectors would have to buy more than one box of crackers to complete a full set.

All the models had been used in previous promotions (some as many as four times). The models were produced in new all-over one-colour glazes except for the "Mole" and the "Badger," which are lighter colours than the originals. Models are listed in alphabetical order for ease of reference. The Tom Smith Company closed in 1999. These two sets were the last models produced for Tom Smith Crackers. The Tom Smith Company closed its doors for the last time in 1999.

Backstamp: Embossed "Wade England"

HEDGEROW - 1998

Although all the hedgerow animals are all previously issued models, they are all in new colours.

No.	Name	Description	Size	U.S. $	Can. $	U.K. £
1	Badger (TS)	Pale grey	25 x 40	9.00	10.00	5.00
2	Butterfly (RRC)	Blue	10 x 45	12.00	16.00	8.00
3	Hare (TS)	Light brown	50 x 30	9.00	8.00	4.00
4	Mole (TS)	Pale grey	25 x 40	9.00	8.00	4.00
5	Mouse (EW)	Apricot	40 x 25	8.00	11.00	6.00
6	Otter (RRC)	Dark brown	30 x 35	9.00	10.00	5.00
7	Rabbit (RRC)	Honey	30 x 30	8.00	11.00	6.00
8	Squirrel (RRC)	Apricot	35 x 30	9.00	8.00	4.00

Note: The following initials denote the series the model originated from.
　　　　EW: *English Whimsies*
　　　　KA: King Aquariums Ltd
　　　　RRC: Red Rose Tea Canada
　　　　TS: Tom Smith UK

SEALIFE - 1998

The "Whale" in this series is a brighter blue than the original 1984 "Survival Whale." For the honey colourway Whelk/Water Snail see King Aquarium, page 325.

No.	Name	Description	Size	U.S. $	Can. $	U.K. £
1	Angel Fish (EW)	Light green	35 x 40	9.00	14.00	5.00
2	Dolphin (EW)	Light grey	30 X 40	9.00	14.00	5.00
3	Seahorse (EW)	Apricot	50 x 17	9.00	14.00	5.00
4	Seal on Rock (RRC)	Dark brown	35 x 35	9.00	14.00	5.00
5	Turtle (EW)	Light green	15 x 50	9.00	14.00	5.00
6	Walrus (EW)	Honey	30 X 30	9.00	14.00	5.00
7	Whale (Baleen TS)	Bright blue	22 x 52	10.00	15.00	7.00
8	Whelk (Water Snail KA)	Bright blue	30 X 35	10.00	15.00	7.00

Note: The following initials denote the series the model originated from.
EW: *English Whimsies*
KA: King Aquariums Ltd
RRC: Red Rose Tea Canada
TS: Tom Smith UK

SPILLERS DOG FOODS LTD.

RETRIEVER

Commissioned by Spillers Dog Foods, this model could be obtained by sending in a certain number of tokens from packets of the dog food.

Backstamp: Embossed "Wade England"

No.	Name	Date	Colourway	Size	U.S. $	Can. $	U.K. £
1	Retriever	1991	Honey; green base	26 x 53	25.00	40.00	20.00

MARGARET STRICKLAND

POLACANTHUS MONEY BOX, THE ISLE OF WIGHT DINOSAUR

Margaret Strickland, a resident of the Isle of Wight, England, commissioned the *Polacanthus Money Box*. This model is an artists impression taken from the skeleton of a Polacanthus dinosaur, whose remains have only been found on the Isle of Wight.

Backstamp: Black transfer "Wade" in Isle of Wight outline, numbered

No.	Name	Date	Colourways	Issued	Size	U.S. $	Can. $	U.K. £
1	Money Box	1994	Honey/dark brown; green base	2000	79 x 205	80.00	110.00	50.00

THOMAS WAIDE & SONS LTD

1978

The Wade English Whimsies Horse (#29) was used in this packaging to mark the centenary of Thomas Waide & Sons Limited (1878-1978), printers and carton manufacturers, of Kirkstall Hill, Lees, U.K. The price given is for the model in the package.

Front

Back

Backstamp: Embossed "Wade England"

No.	Name	Description	Size	U.S. $	Can. $	U.K. £
1	Horse in Packet	Dark grey; green/beige base	38 x 30	40.00	50.00	25.00

TRAUFLER

A slip-cast Sheep in two colours and sizes and the Cockerel Salt Pot and the Hen Pepper Pot were produced by Wade for Traufler, a tableware manufacturer, to compliment its imported table wares, which featured sheep, shepherds and farmyard scenes. These models were also produced by another manufacturer and are also unmarked. Those figures not made by Wade have darker faces, more eyelashes and ears that are closer to their faces.

SHEEP

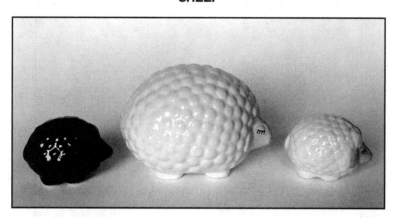

Backstamp: Unmarked

No.	Name	Date	Colourways	Size	U.S. $	Can. $	U.K. £
1a	Sheep, large	1992	Cream; pink face	85 x 145	30.00	45.00	22.00
1b	Sheep, large	1992	Black	85 x 145	30.00	45.00	22.00
2a	Sheep, small	1992	Cream; pink face	65 x 45	25.00	32.00	16.00
2b	Sheep, small	1992	Black	65 x 45	25.00	32.00	16.00

COCKEREL SALT POT AND HEN PEPPER POT

Backstamp: Unmarked

No.	Name	Date	Description	Size	U.S. $	Can. $	U.K. £
1a	Cockerel Salt	1992	White; red/black markings	110 x 55	25.00	32.00	16.00
1b	Cockerel Salt	1992	Yellow; pink comb; black markings	115 x 80	25.00	32.00	16.00
2a	Hen Pepper	1992	White; red/black markings	90 x 55	25.00	32.00	16.00
2b	Hen Pepper	1992	Yellow; pink comb; black markings	90 x 70	25.00	32.00	16.00

DAVID TROWER ENTERPRISES

POPEYE COLLECTION

1997-1998

Modeled by Ken Holmes and produced by Wade Ceramics for David Trower Enterprises.

Popeye, Wimpey, Brutus, Olive Oyl and Swee'Pea

Backstamp: A. Printed "Wade Popeye ™ & © 1997 King Features Synd Inc. Limited Edition of 2000 © David Trower Enterprises"
B. Printed "Wade Brutus ™ & © 1997 King Features Synd Inc. Limited Edition of 1500 © David Trower Enterprises"
C. Printed "Wade Olive Oyl and Swee'Pea ™ & © 1998 King Features Synd Inc. Limited Edition of 2000 © David Trower Enterprises"
D. Printed "Wimpy TM & © 1998 King Features Synd Inc Wade"

No.	Name	Date	Colourways	Issue - Price	Size	U.S. $	Can. $	U.K. £
1	Popeye	1997	Dark blue navy suit	2000 - £35.00	120	75.00	90.00	45.00
2	Brutus	1997	Orange T-shirt; blue trousers, hat	1500 - £36.00	129	75.00	90.00	45.00
3	Olive Oyl and Swee'Pea	1998	Olive Oyl: Red blouse; black skirt Swee'Pea: Red suite; white hat	2000 - £36.00	Unk.	75.00	90.00	45.00
4	Wimpy	1998	Dark blue jacket; orange trousers	1500 - £36.00	130	75.00	90.00	45.00

THE NURSERY RHYME COLLECTION

Humpty Dumpty, Goosey Gander

Little Bo-Peep

Little Jack Horner

Little Miss Muffett

Backstamp: Printed "Wade from the Nursery Rhyme Collection World Wide Limited Edition of 1,000 © 1998 Wade Ceramics Ltd © 1998 D.T.Ents" with name of model and year

No.	Name	Date	Description	Issue - Price	Size	U.S. $	Can. $	U.K. £
1	Humpty Dumpty	1998	Dark green/blue trousers, red hat	1000 - £32.00	115	75.00	110.00	55.00
2	Goosey Gander	1999	Black jacket; red waistcoat	1000 - £32.00	127	75.00	110.00	55.00
3	Little Bo-Peep	1999	White/blue dress; grey bonnet	1000 - £32.00	127	75.00	110.00	55.00
4	Little Jack Horner	2000	Dark blue suit; pale blue shirt	250 - £48.00	130	65.00	95.00	48.00
5	Little Miss Muffett	2000	Pink jacket; blue skirt	250 - £48.00	110	65.00	95.00	48.00
6	Cat and Fiddle	2001	Brown cat; tan fiddle	250 - £48.00	130	65.00	95.00	48.00

21ST CENTURY KEEPSAKES
MEMORIES COLLECTION

These models were based on string puppets in two 1950s BBC children's television programs; *Andy Pandy* and *Bill and Ben the Flowerpot Men*.

Andy Pandy (left) Looby Loo and Ted (right)   Bill and Ben and Little Weed

Backstamp: **A.** Printed "Limited Edition 1500 Wade England" with name of model and "21ST Century" logo (1, 2)
B. Printed "Bill & Ben Little Weed Limited Edition of 500 With Gold Edged Petals Wade England" with "21ST Century" logo (3)

No.	Name	Date	Colourways	Issued - Price	Size	U.S. $	Can. $	U.K. £
1	Andy Pandy	1998	Blue/white striped suit	1500 - £39.00	123	65.00	100.00	50.00
2	Looby Loo and Ted	1999	Ted: Brown; red bow; Looby Loo: White blouse; blue skirt	1500 - £39.00	100	65.00	100.00	50.00
3a	Bill and Ben/ Little Weed	1999	Bill/Ben: Red-brown flowerpots; Weed: Yellow	1500 - £39.00	115	65.00	100.00	50.00
3b	Bill and Ben/ Little Weed	1999	Bill/Ben: Red-brown flowerpots; Weed: Yellow, gold edged petal	500 - £39.00	115	80.00	120.00	60.00

UK INTERNATIONAL CERAMICS LTD.
THE FLINTSTONES COLLECTION

Backstamp: Printed "™The Flintstones™ Limited Edition of 1500 © 1996 H-B Prod. Inc © UKI Ceramics Ltd
Licensed by CPL [name of model]"

No.	Name	Date	Colourways	Issue - Price	Size	U.S. $	Can. $	U.K. £
1	Fred	1996	Orange/black coat; blue scarf	1500 - £34.00	120	80.00	110.00	55.00
2	Wilma	1996	White dress;	1500 - £34.00	125	80.00	110.00	55.00
3	Barney	1997	Brown coat	1500 - £34.00	105	80.00	110.00	55.00
4	Betty	1997	Pale blue dress	1500 - £34.00	115	80.00	110.00	55.00
5	Bamm Bamm	1998	Orange/black shorts	1000 - £34.00	100	80.00	110.00	55.00
6	Pebbles	1998	Green dress; blue pants	1000 - £34.00	100	80.00	110.00	55.00

FELIX THE CAT

Backstamp: Black printed "WADE TM™ 1997 FTC PROD. INC. Limited edition of 1500 ™ UKI CERAMICS LTD
Licensed by El Euro lizenzen, Munchen"

No.	Name	Date	Colourways	Issue - Price	Size	U.S. $	Can. $	U.K. £
1	Felix	1997	Black cat	1500 - £38.00	135	135.00	160.00	80.00

THE NODDY SET
STYLE TWO

"Noddy" and "Big Ears," were the first two models in this series. Unlike their 1950s predecessors, they are slip cast (hollow) and much larger. For Noddy and Big Ears, Style One, see page 60.

Backstamp: **A.** Black printed "Wade © UKI Cer. Ltd 1997 © D.W. 1949/90 Licenced by BBC WL Ltd [name of model]
Limited Edition 1500"
B. Printed "Wade Limited Edition 1,500 © 1998 EBL Ltd - A.R.R. © UKI Ceramics Ltd, 1998 [name of model]"

No.	Name	Date	Colourways	Issued - Price	Size	U.S. $	Can. $	U.K. £
1	Big Ears	1997	Dark blue coat; yellow/red sweater	1500 - £34.00	138	105.00	130.00	65.00
2	Noddy	1997	Red shirt; light blue shorts	1500 - £34.00	110	105.00	130.00	65.00
3	Mr. Plod	1999	Dark blue uniform	1500 - £42.50	140	105.00	130.00	65.00
4	Tessie Bear	1999	Pink/blue dress	1500 - £42.50	110	105.00	130.00	65.00

THE WADE CLASSICAL COLLECTION
DEER, POLAR BEAR AND MONKIES
1997

UK International Ceramics commissioned a set of three Art Deco style models which were originally intended to be a limited edition of 1,000 sets, but because of difficulties with copyright laws, only 260 sets were actually sold. The rest were withdrawn from sale and subsequently destroyed. The sets that were sold were issued with a numbered certificate of authenticity. The three models could be purchased by mail order only at a cost of £85.00 during January of 1998.

Deer

Polar Bear

Monkies

Backstamp: **A.** Printed "Wade Deer First in the Series of Wade Classical Collection Exclusive to UKI Ceramics Produced in a Limited Edition of 1,000 © Wade Ceramics Ltd ©UKI Ceramics Ltd"
B. Printed "Wade Polar Bear Second in the Series of Wade Classical Collection Exclusive to UKI Ceramics Produced in a Limited Edition of 1,000 © Wade Ceramics Ltd ©UKI Ceramics Ltd"
C. Printed "Wade Monkies Third in the Series of Wade Classical Collection Exclusive to UKI Ceramics Produced in a Limited Edition of 1,000 © Wade Ceramics Ltd ©UKI Ceramics Ltd"

No.	Name	Description	Size	U.S. $	Can. $	U.K. £
1	Deer	Off-white	133 x 101	160.00	200.00	100.00
2	Polar Bear	Grey	101 x 127	160.00	200.00	100.00
3	Monkies	Beige	114 x 88	160.00	200.00	100.00

TOM AND JERRY, Style Two

1998

The large size versions of *Tom and Jerry* standing on round bases were commissioned by UK International Ceramics in a limited edition of 1,500. The cost direct from UKI was £75.00 for the pair. For Tom and Jerry, Style One, see page 71.

Backstamp: **A.** Printed "Wade Tom from Tom & Jerry ❑ © 1997 Turner ENT. Co. A.R.R. Limited Edition of 1500
© UKI Ceramics LTD Licensed by CPL"
B. Printed "Wade Jerry from Tom & Jerry ❑ © 1997 Turner ENT. Co. A.R.R. Limited Edition of 1500
© UKI Ceramics LTD Licensed by CPL"

No.	Name	Description	Size	U.S. $	Can. $	U.K. £
1	Tom	Grey/white; pink inside ears; black eyebrows, eyes, nose, whiskers; white base	135	95.00	120.00	60.00
2	Jerry	Brown/beige; black eyebrows, eyes, nose, whiskers; white base	110	95.00	120.00	60.00

TAURUS THE BULL

1999

"Taurus The Bull" was the first model in an intended *Animal Collection* commissioned by UKI Ceramics. Produced in a limited edition of 350, the original cost direct from UKI was £38.50.

Backstamp: Printed "Wade Limited Edition of 150 ©Wade Ceramics Ltd. © UKI Ceramics Ltd. Taurus the Bull Produced Exclusively for UKI Ceramics Ltd in an Exclusive Worldwide Edition Tel: 01394386662 Fax: 01394 386742"

No.	Name	Description	Size	U.S. $	Can. $	U.K. £
1	Taurus the Bull	Cream bull, base; dark brown fill under stomach	140 x 180	105.00	130.00	65.00

THE CATKINS COLLECTION

1999-2001

The *Catkins* models were first displayed at UK Fairs in 1998-1999. In April 1999, UKI Ceramics introduced their new series of catkin models. Each model was issued in a limited edition of 750, at a cost of £28.00.

Clown Catkins (left) Out For A Duck (right) [1999]

Old Father Time (2000)

Policeman Catkins (2000)

England Olympic Catkins (2000)

Town Crier Catkins (2000)

Witch Catkins (2000)

Backstamp: A. Unknown
B. Printed "Exclusive Limited Edition of [number of pieces] Wade ©UKI Ceramics LTD ©Wade Ceramics LTD"

No.	Name	Date	Description	Issue - Price	Size	U.S. $	Can. $	U.K. £
1	Clown	1999	Yellow tunic; white hat, trousers; black collar, pompons	750 - £28.00	120	70.00	90.00	45.00
2	Out For a Duck	1999	White cricketing clothes	750 - £28.00	120	70.00	90.00	45.00
3	England Olympic	2000	Blue jersey, white trousers	100 - £50.00	130	100.00	120.00	60.00
4	Father Christmas	2000	Red/white suite	250 - £49.50	110	100.00	120.00	60.00
5a	Old Father Time	2000	White robes; gold watch chain	250 - £32.50	110	70.00	90.00	45.00
5b	Old Father Time	2000	Grey robes; gold watch chain	100 - £50.00	110	100.00	120.00	60.00
6	Policeman	2000	Dark blue uniform	200 - £45.00	120	100.00	120.00	60.00
7	Town Crier	2000	Red coat, hat; yellow trim	250 - £49.50	120	100.00	120.00	60.00
8	Witch	2000	Black cloak, hat; purple skirt	250 - £46.50	120	100.00	120.00	60.00

THE CATKINS COLLECTION (cont.)

CLOWN and GYPSY CATKINS

2001

The "Clown" and "Gypsy" were issued in nine different colourways, at an issue price of £45.00 each. There were 22 of each clown colourways and 45 of each Gypsy colourways.

Clown Catkins

Gypsy Catkins

Backstamp: Unknown

No.	Name	Description	Size	U.S. $	Can. $	U.K. £
1a	Clown	Yellow tunic; white trousers, hat; black ruff, bobbles	120	60.00	90.00	45.00
1b	Clown	Yellow tunic; red trousers; grey hat; black ruff, bobbles	120	60.00	90.00	45.00
1c	Clown	Yellow tunic; white trousers; gold hat; black ruff, bobbles	120	60.00	90.00	45.00
1d	Clown	Yellow tunic; white trousers; gold hat; black ruffle, pewter bobbles	120	60.00	90.00	45.00
1e	Clown	Blue tunic; white trousers; gold hat; black ruffle, pewter bobbles	120	60.00	90.00	45.00
1f	Clown	Yellow tunic; grey trousers, hat; black ruffle, bobbles	120	60.00	90.00	45.00
1g	Clown	Pink tunic; trousers, grey hat; black ruffle, bobbles	120	60.00	90.00	45.00
1h	Clown	Yellow tunic; white trousers; blue hat; black ruffle, bobbles	120	60.00	90.00	45.00
1i	Clown	Yellow tunic; white trousers; red hat; black ruffle, bobbles	120	60.00	90.00	45.00
2a	Gypsy	Grey shirt, maroon waistcoat; light blue trousers	120	60.00	90.00	45.00
2b	Gypsy	Pearl shirt; maroon waistcoat; bright blue trousers	120	60.00	90.00	45.00
2c	Gypsy	Pearl shirt; maroon waistcoat; dark blue trousers; black belt	120	60.00	90.00	45.00
2d	Gypsy	Pearl shirt; maroon waistcoat; dark blue trousers; gold belt	120	60.00	90.00	45.00
2e	Gypsy	Pearl shirt; maroon waistcoat; blue trousers	120	60.00	90.00	45.00
2f	Gypsy	Pearl shirt; dark blue waistcoat; purple trousers	120	60.00	90.00	45.00
2g	Gypsy	Silver shirt; maroon waistcoat; bright blue trousers	120	60.00	90.00	45.00
2h	Gypsy	Silver shirt; grey waistcoat; blue trousers	120	60.00	90.00	45.00
2i	Gypsy	Orange shirt; maroon waistcoat; bright blue trousers	120	60.00	90.00	45.00

WADEUSA.COM 2003

CHILDREN'S SONG FIGURINES

2003

This new Wade series named "Children's Song Figurines" was produced for Michael and Reva Matthew of wadeusa.com. The first model was named "When Elephants Fly," which is based on a song from the Walt Disney film *Dumbo*. It was produced in a limited edition of 225, and priced at $60.00. Twenty-five models, which were produced with gold wings, were used for prizes and promotions.

Backstamp: A. Printed "When Elephants Fly Children's Song Figurines June 2003 Limited Edition of 225 www.wadeusa.com"
B. Printed "When Elephants Fly Children's Song Figurines June 2003 Special Limited Edition of 25 www.wadeusa.com"

No.	Name	Description	Issued - Price	Size	U.S. $	Can. $	U.K. £
1a	When Elephants Fly	Grey; pink mouth; white wings, toe nails, base	225 - $60	80	60.00	90.00	45.00
1b	When Elephants Fly	Grey; pink mouth; gold wings; white toe nails, base	25 - Prizes	80		Rare	

WADE WATCH USA

2003

The "Pretty-in-Pink Budgerigar" Whimsie is from the C&S Direct Whimsie Budgie mould. Wade Watch in collaboration with C&S, produced a limited edition pink colourway of the budgie, the issue price was $10.50. See also C&S Collectables page 282.

Backstamp: Embossed "Wade C/S"

No.	Name	Description	Size	U.S. $	Can. $	U.K. £
1	Pretty-in-Pink Budgie	Pink	50	13.00	16.00	8.00

WARNER BROTHERS

MY DOG SKIP

2001

A solid Whimsie model of a Jack Russell terrier was produced for Warner Brothers, and was attached to their video film *My Dog Skip*. Fifty thousand models were produced and were available on the videos sold only in the U.K. Excess models were available from Wade at the Pennsylvania Wade Fest.

Backstamp: Embossed "Wade"

No.	Name	Description	Size	U.S. $	Can. $	U.K. £
1	My Dog Skip	White; brown ears, patches	40	12.00	16.00	8.00

ROBERT WILLIAMSON AND PETER ELSON
GINGERBREAD MAN AND GINGERBREAD CHILDREN
1995-1996

A hollow model of a giant gingerbread man was commissioned by Robert Williamson and Peter Elson. It was available for sale at the 2nd U.K. Fairs Wade Show in Birmingham. Following the success of the "Giant Gingerbread Man," a hollow model of the "Gingerbread Children" (a waving girl and boy) was produced in a limited edition of 2,000, (they were sold at the Dunstable Wade show in September 1996). The original cost of both models was £15.00 each.

Please note, the "Gingerbread Children" with a gold base were not produced by Wade.

Backstamp: Embossed "Wade"

No.	Name	Description	Size	U.S. $	Can. $	U.K. £
1	Gingerbread Man	Ginger brown	105 x 80	65.00	80.00	40.00
2	Gingerbread Children	Brown; dark green base	84 x 84	65.00	80.00	40.00

UNKNOWN COMPANY

Sometimes models are found in North America, the United Kingdom or even as far away as Australia which cannot be attributed to any company promotion, due to the fact that they were not found in their original packaging, or seen listed in company promotional advertising. Collectors from the U.K. could have transported models to North America, and models found in the U.K. could have been transported from North America.

KODIAK BEAR

Circa 1965

No one seems to be able to identify the series for which the "Kodiak Bear" was produced or why it was made. It may have been a prototype model produced for the first Red Rose Tea premiums, then rejected due to high production costs (its open arms required more fettling). As a result, the "Kodiak Bear" was not put into full production, and any models produced may have been used up in miscellaneous premiums. A second variation of the bear is slightly smaller in size and has a small gap between his legs.

Backstamp: A. Embossed "Wade England"
            B. Unmarked

No.	Description	Size	U.S. $	Can. $	U.K. £
1a	Beige brown; green base	35 x 25	65.00	90.00	40.00
1b	Brown; honey-brown face, chest, stomach	40 x 25	65.00	90.00	40.00
1c	Light brown; black nose; green base	40 x 25	65.00	90.00	40.00
1d	Red-brown	38 x 25	65.00	90.00	40.00

UNKNOWN COMPANY

3 FOR 49¢ WHIMSIES

CIRCA 1972

A number of red carded Whimsies have been discovered in Canada and the U.S.A. There has been no further information found as to who for or why these models were produced. It is probable that they were for a chain of North American Dime Stores. A Field Mouse on one of the red card models has a recessed base, as did some of the early 1967-1973 Canadian Red Rose Tea models. Others are from the 1971-1984 *English Whimsies* series, which would suggest that surplus stock was distributed to this company. A date of early 1970s is estimated for these models. The values given are for models intact on their cards, as some models are indistinguishable from Red Rose Tea or *English Whimsie* models outside the packet.

Backstamp: **A.** Embossed "Wade England" in recessed base
B. Embossed "Wade England" on rim
C. Embossed "Wade" between front feet and "England" on back of model (2)

No.	Name	Description	Size	U.S. $	Can. $	U.K. £
1	Alsatian	Grey; brown face	30 x 40	7.00	10.00	5.00
2	Bear Cub	Honey brown	34 x 20	7.00	10.00	5.00
3	Bison, large	Honey brown	34 x 46	32.00	40.00	20.00
4	Duck	Blue/brown; yellow beak	30 x 40	9.00	12.00	7.00
5	Field Mouse	Honey brown; yellow corn; green on base	35 x 25	11.00	16.00	8.00
6	Fox	Dark brown; fawn face	30 x 30	8.00	12.00	6.00
7	Giraffe	Beige	35 x 35	7.00	10.00	5.00
8	Kitten, seated	Dark/light brown; pink wool	30 x 30	7.00	10.00	5.00
9	Lion, standing	Light brown; dark brown mane	35 x 45	9.00	12.00	6.00
10	Mongrel	Dark brown back; light brown front	35 x 35	7.00	10.00	5.00
11	Setter	Brown; grey-green base	35 x 50	7.00	10.00	5.00
12	Terrapin	Beige; brown markings	10 x 40	12.00	16.00	9.00
13	Trout	Brown; red tail; grey-green base	30 x 30	7.00	10.00	5.00
14	Zebra	Black	40 x 35	65.00	95.00	50.00

UNKNOWN COMPANY
MISCELLANEOUS WHIMSIE MODELS

These models, in all-over one colour glazes, are promotional models and most likely Redco Foods (Red Rose Tea U.S.A.) or Tom Smith (Miscellaneous) Cracker Models.

Backstamp: Embossed "Wade England" on rim

No.	Name	Description	Size	U.S. $	Can. $	U.K. £
1	Collie (TS)	Beige	25 x 50	12.00	15.00	10.00
2	Duck, standing (EW)	Beige	30 x 40	12.00	15.00	10.00
3	Duck, swimming (TS)	White	25 x 30	12.00	15.00	10.00
4a	Elephant (EW)	Dark grey	35 x 28	12.00	15.00	10.00
4b	Elephant (EW)	Pale grey	35 x 28	12.00	15.00	10.00
5	Little Jack Horner (RRC/TS)	Blue	40 x 20	12.00	15.00	10.00
6	Old Woman Who Lived in a Shoe	Honey	40 x 40	12.00	15.00	10.00
7a	Persian Kitten (TS)	Apricot	25 x 33	12.00	15.00	10.00
7b	Persian Kitten (TS)	Dark brown	25 x 33	12.00	15.00	10.00
7c	Persian Kitten (TS)	Honey	25 x 33	12.00	15.00	10.00
8	Rabbit, open ears (RR/EW)	Grey body; white face; black eyes; pink nose	30 x 30	12.00	15.00	10.00

Note: The black kitten is suspect, as Wade rarely reglaze models black. In the known black models that were reglazed by Wade, the original design (fur/stripes) on the model can still be seen beneath the black glaze, as in the *English Whimsie* black "Zebra" and black "Poodle" models. Some models have been deliberately painted black by persons unknown to mislead collectors; these suspect models have a heavy coat of paint applied over the original Wade glaze.

The following initials indicate the origin of the model.
EW: *English Whimsies*
RRC: Red Rose Tea Canada
TS: Tom Smith

UNKNOWN COMPANY
MISCELLANEOUS WHIMSIE MODELS
COLOUR VARIATIONS

The reason for these colour variations is unknown. They may have been sample colourways not accepted by the commissioner and used in miscellaneous promotions in the U.K. and U.S.A. to fill orders.

Elephant (RRC)

Hedgehog (RRC)

Rabbit, Type 2, Ears open (EW)

Cat (EW), Humpty Dumpty (RRC), Persian Kitten (TS), Kitten (EW)

Backstamp: Embossed "Wade England"

No.	Name	Colourways	Size	U.S. $	Can. $	U.K. £
1	Bo Peep (RRC)	Olive green	44 x 24	12.00	15.00	10.00
2	Cat (EW)	Light blue	40 x 17	12.00	15.00	10.00
3	Duck (WL)	Dark brown	45 x 35	12.00	15.00	10.00
4a	Eagle (TS)	Olive green	35 x 23	12.00	15.00	10.00
4b	Eagle (TS)	Tan	25 x 23	12.00	15.00	10.00
5	Elephant (EW)	Cream	35 x 28	12.00	15.00	10.00
6	Hedgehog (EW)	Grey	23 x 40	12.00	15.00	10.00
7	Humpty Dumpty (RRC)	Dark brown	36 x 23	12.00	15.00	10.00
8	Kitten (EW)	Grey	30 x 30	12.00	15.00	10.00
9a	Persian Kitten (TS)	Apricot	25 x 33	12.00	15.00	10.00
9b	Persian Kitten (TS)	Dark brown	25 x 33	12.00	15.00	10.00
9c	Persian Kitten (TS)	Honey	25 x 33	12.00	15.00	10.00
10	Pine Martin (EW)	Grey	30 x 30	12.00	15.00	10.00
11	Rabbit, Type 2 (EW)	White	25 x 30	12.00	15.00	10.00
12	Trout (EW)	Grey	30 x 30	12.00	15.00	10.00

INDEX

416